W9-CZT-682

A Guidebook for Teaching ALGEBRA

QA
159
.G85
1984

A Guidebook for Teaching
ALGEBRA

Terry A. Goodman

John Bernard

Martin P. Cohen

Joanne E. Meldon

Allyn and Bacon, Inc.   Boston • London • Sydney • Toronto

GOSHEN COLLEGE LIBRARY
GOSHEN, INDIANA

This book is part of A GUIDEBOOK FOR TEACHING Series

Copyright © 1984 by Allyn and Bacon, Inc., 7 Wells Avenue, Newton, Massachusetts 02159.

All rights reserved. No part of the material protected by this copyright notice, except the Reproduction Pages contained within, may be reproduced or utilized in any form or by any means, electronic or mechanical, including photocopying, recording, or by any information storage and retrieval system, without written permission from the copyright owner.

The Reproduction pages may be reproduced for use with this book, provided such reproductions bear copyright notice, but may not be reproduced in any other form for any other purpose without permission from the copyright owner.

Library of Congress Cataloging in Publication Data
Main entry under title:

A guidebook for teaching algebra.

   (Guidebook for teaching series)
   Includes bibliographical references.
   1. Algebra—Study and teaching. I. Goodman, Terry A.
II. Series.
QA159.G85   1984   512.9'07   83-27151
ISBN 0-205-08117-7

Printed in the United States of America

10 9 8 7 6 5 4 3 2 1   89 88 87 86 85 84

About the Authors

Terry A. Goodman received his Ph.D. from the University of Texas at Austin. He has held the positions of Associate Professor of Mathematics at Central Missouri State University and high school mathematics teacher in Waco, Texas. He is active in both the National Council of Teachers of Mathematics and the School and Mathematics Association and is the author of numerous articles dealing with problem solving, microcomputer applications, estimation, and statistics.

John Bernard also received his Ph.D. from the University of Texas at Austin. He has twenty years' experience teaching at the secondary and college levels including the position of Professor of Mathematics Education at the University of Georgia. He has conducted research and authored publications dealing with equation solving and the understanding of algebraic symbolism.

Martin P. Cohen has taught high school mathematics in the Houston Independent School District and has served as Associate Professor at the University of Pittsburgh. He earned his Ph.D. at the University of Texas at Austin. Dr. Cohen is a member of the Board of Directors of the School Science and Mathematics Association and has authored numerous articles on algebra and problem solving.

Joanne E. Meldon, a teacher of high school mathematics for nineteen years, received her M.A. at the University of Pittsburgh. She is co-author of courses of study, including Algebra I and Algebra II, adopted by the Pittsburgh Board of Education.

Gene Stanford, *Consulting Editor for the Guidebook for Teaching Series*, received his Ph.D. and his M.A. from the University of Colorado. Dr. Stanford has served as Associate Professor of Education and Director of Teacher Education Programs at Utica College of Syracuse University and is a member of the National Council of Teachers of English and the International Council on Education for Teaching. Dr. Stanford is the author and co-author of several books, among them, *A Guidebook for Teaching Composition, A Guidebook for Teaching Creative Writing, A Guidebook for Teaching about the English Language,* and *Human Interaction in Education,* all published by Allyn and Bacon, Inc.

Contents

Preface

We believe that teaching mathematics is both an important and difficult task. We hope that this book will help algebra teachers to accomplish this task more completely. We have attempted to provide a general framework useful for organizing a reasonable instructional program in algebra. We wanted to go beyond a general discussion, however, to include a large collection of specific strategies, activities, and resources that the algebra teacher can use directly in the classroom. In addition, there are over one hundred Reproduction Pages that provide skill reinforcement and discovery.

For each major topic, then, in this book we present a general approach for instruction together with specific activities and resources that can be used on a daily basis in the classroom.

The topics in this book correspond to those generally found in what would be identified as a first-year algebra course. We have not attempted to present a "best" way to teach the topics. Rather, we suggest how to organize an algebra course, how to relate one topic to another, how to provide for individual differences, and how to provide for understanding, skill development, and problem solving. We are sure that some of our "biases" emerge—like most teachers we have our personal viewpoint. We believe that students best learn when they are actively involved in the learning process. The reader will find, therefore, that most of our suggested activities are designed to provide for student involvement. In addition, we feel that problem solving is one of the most basic of "basic skills." Thus, this book focuses strongly on helping students learn to apply algebra concepts and skills. We do not apologize for these and other preferences. We think there is enough variety in this book for the individual classroom teacher to choose those materials and activities most compatible with his or her own approach to instruction.

Generally, for each topic this book provides:

1. An introduction to the concepts in that chapter.

2. A list of specific objectives for the students.

3. Teaching strategies, sequences, student activities (group and individual), instructional materials, and worksheets.

4. A series of challenge problems.

5. A sample evaluation related to the student objectives.

6. An annotated list of resources, including books, journals, films, etc.

Most of the approaches and activities found in this book have been used successfully with our own classes, so we are confident that many other teachers will find them useful. We certainly encourage you to send comments to us concerning this book. You may want to use the Feedback Form found at the end of the book. We truly appreciate your comments and suggestions.

We want to acknowledge a number of people who provided help and support in the preparation of this book. Many of our colleagues provided helpful suggestions and we thank them for their input. We want to thank our families—Teresa Goodman, Faye Cohen, Anita Bernard, and Richard Meldon—for their support and encouragement. Special thanks must also go to Anita for her help with the Answers to Selected Reproduction Pages and the resource lists. Finally, we appreciate so much the help of Becky White who typed and helped us organize our final manuscript.

Terry Goodman
John Bernard
Martin Cohen
Joanne Meldon

1

Planning to Teach Algebra

INTRODUCTION

Where does one begin in planning to teach algebra? The first task may be to decide on content. For many people, algebra means formulae, symbols, and definitions. In one recent survey, when asked to associate one word with algebra, the majority of people replied "*x*." Certainly, as mathematics teachers, we see algebra as more than the study of *x* and we hope to help our students develop a broader and deeper understanding of this area of mathematics. Teachers want to emphasize relationships, generalizations, applications, and indeed, thinking. This is a difficult, yet important, task.

To develop the content found in this book, it is assumed that students have had one basic mathematics course. Such a course concentrates on developing understanding and skill in the use of whole numbers, fractions, decimals, and percent. Of course, such skills should be reviewed during the early part of an algebra course, but not in such detail or at such a slow pace as new learning would require.

In a first course in algebra, students will be introduced to new terminology, principles, techniques, and strategies. Most students will also work with applications of equations to the solutions of specific types of verbal problems (coin, motion, mixture, etc.) and gain some experience in graphing with quadratic equations and radicals. All of these, too, will be prerequisites for the topics in an advanced algebra course.

The goals for students in an algebra course will certainly vary from teacher to teacher. However, we suggest the following rather broad objectives:

1. To review and extend basic skills and concepts developed previously

2. To develop a broader understanding of the real numbers by way of extension from the integers and the rational numbers as well as emphasis on unifying concepts such as function

3. To develop a broader understanding of the applications and relevance of mathematics to the real world by studying specific functions and mathematical models

1

4. To improve understanding and efficiency with specific mathematical systems of relations through graphing and other special techniques

Of course, these broad goals will be useful only as they can be related to specific concepts and skills within the algebra content. In the following chapters, objectives will be suggested for each concept and skill considered.

With respect to the third goal listed above, one rather important emphasis will be on the ways that algebra can be used in areas other than mathematics. Certainly, the concepts and skills considered here are prerequisite for study in other mathematics courses, such as advanced algebra, mathematics for business and social studies, statistics, calculus, and linear algebra. However, the usefulness of algebra can also be illustrated in other fields, such as business, economics, medicine, and the sciences.

This emphasis is important not only because of the many applications of these algebraic concepts, but also because of its service as a strong positive influence on the motivation of the students. Even though some algebra students will be self-motivated, real-world applications of the algebra content can help them to broaden their views of algebra as well as increase their interest.

Also, by considering the ways these concepts and skills can be applied, we may more effectively answer some of the current criticism that much of school mathematics is not relevant. Certainly, one of the "basics" in mathematics is the ability to apply mathematics in relevant, real-world settings (solve problems). In the remainder of this book we will attempt to keep this a central theme.

LEARNING ALGEBRA

The content in algebra can be separated into three basic parts:

1. Terminology and notation

2. Concepts

3. Processes (techniques and strategies)

One difficulty in any mathematics course is the large amount of new terminology and notation. The terminology and notation in algebra are necessary for communication among students, teacher, and textbook. This "language" allows us to know what things are called and what each symbol means. A student cannot be expected to develop this kind of information himself. Students will not be able to "discover" the definition of a quadratic function. Certainly the notation for rational numbers or polynomial functions is not obvious: we must agree on the notation to facilitate communication.

This notational information does not easily lend itself to insight or relations to other ideas. As such, this kind of learning is quite susceptible to forgetting and interference. Presentation, recall, and feedback should be an ongoing activity in such learning.

The word "concept" has taken on so many different meanings that it has come close to having no meaning at all. In this book, however, a concept involves developing meaning for terminology and notation. Perhaps an example will best illustrate this kind of learning. A student may know that a quadratic function is a function of the form $f(x) = ax^2 + bx + c$

where *a*, *b*, *c* are real numbers. However, this concept of a quadratic function and its meaning may be rather shallow. Meaning for quadratic functions comes through understanding properties of these functions (roots, graphs, etc.), similarities and differences with other kinds of functions, and applications of quadratic functions (symmetry, maxima, minima). Thus concepts involve understanding in terms of generalizations, comparisons, transformations, relationships, and properties.

Certainly, concept learning cannot be accomplished through pure memorization. It appears that learning the necessary notation and terminology is prerequisite to understanding concepts. It is important to emphasize that concept learning is much different from learning notation and terminology.

A third kind of learning in mathematics involves processes. By processes, we mean techniques and strategies. Techniques often involve such skills as simplifying fractions and algebraic expressions. While these are rather elementary skills, they should be directed toward developing the more difficult notion of algebraic equivalence. These skills can also be extended to relational and functional equivalences as in solving equations through a sequence of equivalent equations. Solve the following equation for *x* and note how often you use these elementary skills, as well as the more complicated equivalences and relations.

$$3x^2 + 8x - 2 = 0$$

Although these techniques may seem to students to be mere manipulations, we know that they are related to concepts and not simply practiced as "moving of symbols."

Strategies are directional ideas which develop with problem-solving skills and the use of certain techniques. We are not talking about solving problems simply by imitation (i.e., the teacher does three examples on the board and then the students solve ten more just like those shown). Imitation may be *part* of problem solving and does require some strategy. Problem solving, however, involves dealing with situations where the solution is not immediately obvious. Strategies can probably best be developed through demonstration and discussion of the solutions of sample problems accompanied by practice and observation on the part of the learner.

You have encouraged your students to develop this kind of learning when you made such suggestions as "Look for a pattern," "Have you worked a similar problem before?" or "Can you work a more simple problem?" Strategies enable students not only to solve the problems they find in class, but, hopefully, to apply what they know in unique and unfamiliar settings. Again, note that terminology, notation, concepts, and techniques are all necessary in solving problems. A useful strategy is also needed, but these other skills and ideas must be remembered and put together. Consider the notation and terminology that is needed in solving the following problems. What concepts must you understand? What techniques and strategies do you use?

1. You want to make a cube with a diagonal of 2 meters. How long should the side of the cube be?

2. If a man can cut a log into 3 pieces in 15 minutes, how long would it take him to cut a similar log into 4 pieces?

3. A missile fired from a launching pad followed a path whose equation is $y = x - (3.125 \cdot 10^{-6})x^2$. Determine:
   a. the maximum altitude attained by the missile
   b. the distance from the launching pad to the point of impact

ORGANIZING FOR INSTRUCTION

The first consideration in organizing for instruction is the learner. What characteristics of the learner should we take into account in the classroom? What do we know about how people learn mathematics? Are there some principles we can follow?

First, we must recognize that students often have difficulty learning more abstract concepts. Specifically, many algebra concepts involve a great deal of symbolism and we know that symbolic (abstract) representations of concepts are difficult for many students. In this book, we will emphasize physical and pictorial representations (models) of concepts.

Many ideas found in an algebra course do not lend themselves to concrete representations, but physical models can be used quite well with topics such as square roots, factoring, and equations.

While we are somewhat limited in terms of physical models, pictorial representations can be and should be used often with algebra students. Since so much of what we consider in this course is in terms of functions and equations, graphs and properties of functions illustrated by graphs should be extensively used. In the chapters that follow, many of the suggested activities will involve physical and/or pictorial models.

The major advantage in initiating learning with these less abstract models is that they enable students to be more active in learning. Physical and pictorial models allow students to generate their own meanings for concepts. At the same time we can relate the content to these less abstract models by building new concepts from those previously learned. In algebra, some major threads of content are equations, number systems, functions, and graphing. We return to these ideas again and again, each time helping the students relate new ideas to these unifying strands.

Another way a teacher can assist students in developing conceptual understanding and processing information is by asking "key" questions. Hence, samples of questions and answers, many from actual classroom experiences, will be provided for topics in this book.

Example

Topic: Inverse of Functions

Question: Is there a function that is equal to its inverse?

Discussion Response: The identity function defined by $f(x) = x$ is one such function that is equal to its inverse. Also $f(x) = \dfrac{x}{x-1}$, $x \neq 1$ is another example.

(The student may even be led to discover that any whose graph is symmetric to the line $y = x$ is a function that is equal to its inverse.)

We feel that these questions and answers are valuable resource materials for teachers. They are intended to stimulate classroom discussions and/or provide thought-provoking homework problems.

Finally, we should also emphasize multiembodiment of concepts. Basically this means that a student should encounter a concept in a variety of contexts and through a variety of examples. If a student's experiences with a concept are too narrow, then his concept will not be complete or may be weak. For example, at the elementary level, we want children to deal with the concept of one-half of a discrete set, as a ratio, congruent and noncongruent halves, and perhaps as an ordered pair of integers. All of these contexts are needed to provide the full meaning for one-half. In algebra, the concept of equation can be dealt with in many settings—as formulae, number problems, types of equations, in terms of graphs, and through applications. If a student's concept is broad, then it is more stable and useful for him or her.

In the following chapters, we will suggest many approaches for teaching the content in algebra. These include exposition (lecture), discovery, demonstration experiment, and mathematics laboratory. It is not the purpose here to discuss the merits of these various approaches, although some emphasis will be given later to mathematics laboratory activities, especially problem-solving laboratories. The specific approach a teacher uses in the classroom is not most important. What is important is whether or not the approach helps the students to learn. We feel that the suggestions previously made in this section can help to make these various approaches more successful. The specific activities found later in the book are not designed to fit any one instructional approach. In fact, it is hoped that you will find these activities useful regardless of your particular preference for classroom organization.

EVALUATION IN ALGEBRA

One other factor should be considered and that is the level of understanding implied by one's specific objectives. We need to determine prior to instruction what level of understanding we want students to demonstrate with respect to a particular concept. In the objectives in this book, we will refer to the following four levels.

1. *Computation*—recall and recognition of basic facts, definitions, properties, and skills
   Example:
   Factor the following: $2x^2 + 3x - 2 = 0$

2. *Comprehension*—use of generalizations, transformations, relations, theorems, and properties
   Example:
   If the two solutions for a quadratic equation are $x = \frac{1}{2}$ and $x = \frac{1}{4}$, then how would you express the quadratic as the product of two binomials?

3. *Applications*—routine applications of concepts and skills (students have encountered similar problems)
   Example:
   A rectangular box with square base and open top is to be made from 12 m^2 of cardboard. What is the maximum possible volume of such a box?

4. *Analysis*—nonroutine applications of concepts, skills, and techniques
   Example:
   A speeder going 75 miles per hour passes a state tropper parked by the side of the road. The trooper gives chase; within $1\frac{1}{2}$ minutes he has reached a speed of 90 mph and has gone 0.15 miles. If he continues at this speed, how long will it take him to overtake the speeder?

Notice that the level of our objectives will influence not only our test questions but the materials we use and the approach in the classroom. In each of the following chapters, we will include sample test questions (of course, the classroom questions may also be used as test questions). These will be related to previously stated objectives for the content being considered. We will also point out how the various levels of objectives can be approached in the actual instructional sequence. We hope that this will allow individual teachers to present the concepts, skills, and techniques found in algebra at many different levels of understanding.

USING THIS GUIDEBOOK

Each chapter in this *Guidebook* focuses on a specific fundamental topic in algebra. Each chapter begins with an overview of the content to be considered. This overview will include discussion of a general framework for teaching the content as well as potential difficulties for the students.

A list of objectives will be provided for each chapter. This will be followed by specific learning experiences related to the chapter objectives. These learning experiences will include student activities, teacher presentations, and key questions. These learning experiences will often refer to activities found in the Reproduction Pages. These pages will be reproducible and will be designed to provide for student activities. Reproduction Pages 1–36 will provide review sheets for the various chapters. These will take the form of "Daily Dozen Quizzes" which will provide students with practice of basic computations and skills.

Following the learning experiences in each chapter will be a set of ten Challenge Problems. These can be used for enrichment as well as reinforcement of problem-solving skills and strategies. Each chapter also includes a sample chapter evaluation and resources that a teacher might find useful in teaching the topics discussed in the chapter.

Some additional features of this *Guidebook* will make it even more useful. First, each chapter will include some calculator and/or microcomputer activities. There is also one chapter devoted entirely to the important topic of problem solving, primarily word problems. Certainly, this chapter can be used with the Challenge Problems at the end of the other chapters.

This book is intended to be a useful resource for the algebra teacher. We encourage you to use it to support, supplement, and extend your instruction. We have attempted to emphasize a basic framework for teaching algebra as well as to provide specific, practical activities and resources that can be used in a variety of instructional settings.

We hope this *Guidebook* will aid you in meeting the challenge of teaching algebra.

RESOURCES

Learning and Mathematics

Bruner, J. S., *Toward a Theory of Instruction.* Cambridge, MA: The Belnap Press of Harvard University, 1966.

Gagné, R. M., *The Conditions of Learning* (3rd Ed.). New York: Holt, Rinehart, and Winston, Inc., 1977.

Gagné, R. M., and Briggs, L. J., *Principles of Instructional Design.* New York: Holt, Rinehart, and Winston, Inc., 1974.

National Council of Teachers of Mathematics, *An Agenda for Action: Recommendations for School Mathematics of the 1980s.* Reston, VA: NCTM, 1980. Official viewpoint of NCTM that presents recommendations for programs of the 1980s.

National Council of Teachers of Mathematics, *Research in Mathematics Education.* Reston, VA: NCTM, 1980. Considers research findings, particularly findings related to learning of skills, concepts, and problem solving.

Wittrock, M. C., A generative model of mathematics learning. *Journal for Research in Mathematics Education,* 1974, *5*, 181-196.

Organizing for Mathematics (Algebra) Instruction

Aichele, D. B., and Reys, R. E., *Readings in Secondary School Mathematics.* Boston: Prindle, Weber, and Schmidt, Inc., 1971. Presents selected readings intended to provide a broader and deeper understanding of the current state of mathematics education.

Kastner, B., *Applications of Secondary School Mathematics.* Reston, VA: NCTM, 1978. Helps teachers answer the recurring question "What's it good for?" with responses the student will find interesting and important.

National Council of Teachers of Mathematics, *Applications in School Mathematics.* Reston, VA: NCTM, 1979. Practical applications of mathematics in fields such as environment, finance, music, and statistics.

National Council of Teachers of Mathematics, *Growth of Mathematical Ideas, Grade K–12.* Reston, VA: NCTM, 1959. A highlighting of the essential elements of those basic mathematical understandings which should be continually developed and extended throughout the entire mathematics curriculum. An excellent chapter on relations and functions.

National Council of Teachers of Mathematics, *The Mathematics Teacher.* Reston, VA: NCTM. A journal published monthly (September through May) for junior and senior high and two-year college teachers. Includes articles of algebra content and instruction with special sections on sharing teaching ideas and activities.

National Council of Teachers of Mathematics, *Organizing for Mathematics Instruction.* Reston, VA: NCTM, 1977. Discusses alternative teaching approaches such as individualization, survival groups, simulations, open schools, and others; emphasizes how to organize for such approaches and gives specific illustrative examples.

National Council of Teachers of Mathematics, *The Teaching of Secondary School Mathematics.* Reston, VA: NCTM, 1970. Forces shaping today's mathematics programs are described; teaching for special outcomes is discussed; then examples are given to demonstrate classroom applications, with emphasis on teacher planning.

National Society for the Study of Education, *Mathematics Education.* Chicago: University of Chicago Press, 1970. A broad look at mathematics education including a chapter on algebraic systems, number systems, functions, applications of mathematics, and evaluation.

National Society for the Study of Education, *Theories of Learning and Instruction.* Chicago: University of Chicago Press, 1964. Discusses theories of learning and instruction with emphasis on issues, trends, and problems of the classroom.

School Science and Mathematics Association, Inc., *School Science and Mathematics.* Bowling Green, OH: SSMA. A journal published monthly (October through June). Contains articles on algebra content and instruction.

Problem Solving

National Council of Teachers of Mathematics, *Problem Solving in School Mathematics.* Reston, VA: NCTM, 1980. Contains ideas, problems, examples, and illustrations related to problem solving.

Newell, A., and Simon, H. A., *Human Problem Solving.* Englewood Cliffs, NJ: Prentice-Hall, 1972. Consideration of problem solving from an information-processing viewpoint.

Polya, G., *How to Solve It.* Princeton, NJ: Princeton University Press, 1945, 1973. Using specific examples, Polya emphasizes a method for solving a large variety of problems.

Wicklegren, W. A., *How to Solve Problems.* San Francisco: W. H. Freeman, 1974. Elements of a theory of problems and problem solving. Includes many problems and exercises.

Evaluation

Creative Publications, *Didactics and Mathematics.* Palo Alto, CA: Creative Publications, 1978.

Research Council for Diagnostic and Prescriptive Mathematics, *An Annotated Bibliography of Periodical Articles Relating to the Diagnostic and Prescriptive Instruction of Mathematics.* Bowling Green, OH: RCDPM, 1979.

Suydam, M. N., *Evaluation in the Mathematics Classroom: From What and Why to How and Where.* Columbus, OH: ERIC, 1974. Quick reference guide to evaluation for the classroom teacher; includes scope of testing purposes and procedures, how to plan and write tests, and bibliography.

Wilson, J. W., Evaluation in mathematics education. *Handbook on Formative and Summative Evaluation of Student Learning.* New York: McGraw-Hill, 1971. Discusses levels of learning in relation to specific mathematical objectives. Includes discussion of testing and other forms of evaluation.

2

Number Systems

Generally, there are two major emphases found in the early stages of beginning algebra:

1. A review of basic prerequisite concepts and skills from arithmetic
2. A thorough introduction to the language of algebra

These two emphases are most often embodied in a study of number systems. Thus, in this chapter we will focus on this very important foundation area.

This chapter begins with a review of basic operations with particular emphasis on order of operations. Since these topics are review, the teacher should be especially careful to make the activities new and interesting so that students will not see this as "the same old stuff." One approach will be to use formulae to review basic operations. These can be embodied in interesting problems and puzzles.

After a review of basic operations, the algebraic (field) properties can be introduced. Consideration of the commutative, associative, distributive, and identity properties will help students formalize their generalizations about the whole numbers. We can also help students to realize that there are not whole number solutions to equations such as:

a. $x + 4 = 3$

b. $3x = 2$

c. $x^2 = 3$

This will lead to an investigation of other number systems, i.e., integers, rationals, and irrationals.

The concept of absolute value and the number line will prove quite useful when introducing these other number systems. As each number system is developed, new algebraic

9

properties can be generalized (inverses, zero-multiplication properties, cancellation properties, etc.). Equation solving can be introduced and reviewed here also.

Finally, this section will be culminated with a study of the real-number system and the field properties. The development just described is important as a foundation for the remainder of the algebra course. We do not want to overwhelm students with language and symbolism, but instead structure a framework that will help them to organize concepts they encounter later.

Some teachers may not want to cover all the number systems discussed in this chapter. Hence, this chapter may be used at various points in the curriculum.

OBJECTIVES

As a result of the learning experiences in this chapter, the student should be able to:

1. Evaluate expressions using the four basic operations for whole numbers

2. Use the rules for order of operations to evaluate expressions

3. Find the unknown quantity in a formula

4. Identify the algebraic (field) properties for whole numbers

5. Use absolute value, the number line, and geometry to illustrate integer, rational, and irrational numbers

6. Perform basic operations for integral, rational, and irrational numbers

7. Compare number systems with respect to the algebraic properties satisfied in each

8. Use the algebraic (field) properties to simplify real-number expressions

---

LEARNING EXPERIENCES

Topic 1: Basic Operations

1. *Teacher Presentation.* Many students will need a review of basic operations with whole numbers. To make this review more palatable for the students, we suggest that the teacher make this review part of some enrichment activities. In this section, we will include activities involving geometry and statistics. Other areas could be used to aid in this review—number theory, probability, etc. Using some of these other topics will not only help reinforce basic operation skills, but will involve reviewing order of operations and the language of algebra (formula, equation, variable, etc.).

    Begin by asking the following:

    Suppose you have 100 feet of fence. You are going to make a rectangular garden. What is the largest garden (in area) you could make with your fence?

    Student-Teacher Discussion: Many students will require a review of perimeter and area. Some may insist that it makes no difference how you make the garden. Present fig. 2.1 as an example.

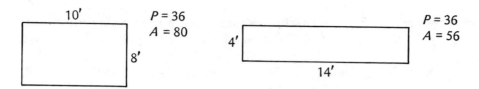

Figure 2.1

Students will need to recall the formulae $P = 2L + 2W$ and $A = L \cdot W$ for a rectangle having the dimensions L and W.

2. *Activity.* Have students complete the following chart to help them answer the preceding question.

L	W	$P = 2L + 2W = 100$	$A = L \cdot W$
40	10	100	400
35	15		
30	20		
25	25		
20	30		
15	35		
10	40		

Students should decide that the largest garden will be made by having length = width = 25 feet. Some students may need to review how to evaluate $P = 2L + 2W$. Of course, this is what we want, since it brings about a review of order of operations.

3. *Teacher Presentation.* Have students consider the following chart.

Day	Wind Speed
1	0
2	10
3	20
4	20
5	0

Average wind speed (for the 5 days) = _____

Discuss with students how to find the average (mean). Emphasize the order involved.

4. *Activity.* Review other "well-known" formulae emphasizing the order of operations. Examples should include:

a. $A = \frac{1}{2} bh$

b. $S = 2\pi r^2 + 2\pi rh$ (surface area of cylinder)

c. $P = 2L + 2W = 2(L + W)$

d. $d = rt$

e. $F = \frac{9}{5} C + 32$

Ask the class to compute

$$2 + 5 \cdot 8 - 4 \div 2$$

Students will provide a multitude of answers. Write them on the board. Circle the one answer which is universally accepted, i.e., 40. You may use the mnemonic device "*My Dear Aunt Sally*," but make sure that the students understand what it means:

"Multiply or divide (whichever comes first) from LEFT to RIGHT, before you add or subtract from left to right."

Perhaps the most important fact to get across is that *exponents* are king—they must be removed first before one applies the order of operations rule.

Have students complete Reproduction Page 37, finding the unknown quantity in a formula. This can be approached by considering multiplication and division at one level and addition and subtraction at another.

Topic 2: Algebraic Properties of Whole Numbers

1. *Activity.* Have students complete the following table.

Number Pattern	Example	Is It a Property?
a, b are whole numbers		
1. $a + b$ is a whole number	$3 + 5 = 8$	yes
2. $a + b = b + a$	$5 + 9 = 9 + 5$	
3. $a + (b + c) = (a + b) + c$	$7 + (3 + 6) = (7 + 3) = 6$	
4. $a + 0 = 0 + a = a$	$5 + 0 = 0 + 5 = 5$	
5. $a \cdot b$ is a whole number	$5 \cdot 6 = 30$	
6. $a \cdot b = b \cdot a$	$5 \cdot 6 = 6 \cdot 5$	
7. $a \cdot (b \cdot c) = (a \cdot b) \cdot c$	$3 \cdot (4 \cdot 5) = (3 \cdot 4) \cdot 5$	
8. $a \cdot 1 = 1 \cdot a = a$	$5 \cdot 1 = 1 \cdot 5 = 5$	
9. $a(b + c) = a \cdot b + a \cdot c$	$5(6 + 3) = 5 \cdot 6 + 5 \cdot 3$	
10. $a + (b \cdot c) = (a + b) \cdot (a + c)$	$4 + (3 \cdot 2) = (4 + 3) \cdot (4 + 2)$	no

2. *Teacher Presentation.* Review the above properties by grouping them:
   a. 1 and 5   —   Closure properties
   b. 2 and 6   —   Commutative properties
   c. 3 and 7   —   Associative properties
   d. 4 and 8   —   Identity properties
   e. 9   —   Distributive property

Discussion question: Where are these properties used?

Discussion: Help students to focus on these uses:

a. As an aid in multiplication (distributive law)

$$7(24) = 7(20 + 4)$$
$$= 140 + 28$$
$$= 168$$

b. As an aid in addition (associative and commutative properties)

$$3 \cdot 10 + 9 = 39$$

Have students complete Reproduction Page 38.

Topic 3: Other Number Systems

1. *Teacher Presentation.* Have the students consider finding whole numbers to solve the following.
   a. $x + 4 = 2$
   b. $2x = 3$
   c. $x^2 = 5$

   There are no whole number solutions. We need some "new" numbers. Use the number line to illustrate negative numbers as "opposites" of whole numbers. Emphasize that –3 is the opposite of 3 in that these numbers are the same distance from 0 on a number line, but in opposite directions.

   Absolute value can also be used to emphasize the "distance" idea. Have students complete Reproduction Page 39.

2. *Activity.* Have students deal with operations on integers by considering the following embodiments.

Addition—gain and loss football bank account	*Multiplication*—repeated addition patterns
Subtraction—gain and loss thermometer	*Division*—patterns how related to multiplication

   The number line can be a particularly useful model, with several adaptations. For example, when considering subtraction, the thermometer as a special number line is effective. Have students consider the following:
   A. What is the difference between a temperature of 7° and 29°?
      (On a thermometer, how far is it from 7° to 29°?)
      Mathematical sentence: $29 - 7 =$ _____
      Note: We could simply count from 7° to 29° to find the "difference."
   B. What is the difference between a temperature of –6° and 15°?
      Mathematical sentence: $15 - (-6) =$ _____
      Note: Here, counting from –6° to 15° appears to be very useful. We conclude that $15 - (-6) = $ __21__ .
   C. Other examples can be dealt with in a similar manner. Have students work the following examples using the "difference" model.
      a. $-12 - 6 =$ (Interpret as the distance from 6° to –12°.)
      b. $3 - (-4) =$
      c. $8 - (-7) =$
      d. $-3 - (-5) =$
      e. $2 - 9 =$
      f. $-8 - 6 =$
      g. $-9 - (-1) =$
      h. $15 - (-2) =$

   There are also many models that can be used to represent integers. These are referenced in the Resource section at the end of this chapter. One excellent physical model involves the use of different-colored chips. For an example of this approach see Kohn, Judith B., A physical model for operations with integers. *Mathematics Teacher*, December 1978.

3. *Teacher Presentation.* Students should now be ready to generate the rule for subtraction of integers, namely,

$$a - b = a + (-b)$$

Many students would be encouraged to "discover" this rule while dealing with previous activities. Using similar activities, help students to see $a - b = -(b - a)$ and $-(a) = -1 \cdot a$.

4. *Activity.* Have students complete Reproduction Page 40. This activity is designed to help them with multiplication of integers, especially the more difficult cases of the product of a positive and a negative and the product of two negative integers.

5. *Teacher Presentation.* Students should be encouraged to investigate which properties of the whole numbers are also satisfied by the integers. They should be encouraged to find that the closure, commutative, associative, identity, and distributive properties still hold. Have the student consider:

$$2 + \underline{\hspace{1.5cm}} = 0$$
$$3 + \underline{\hspace{1.5cm}} = 0$$
$$-4 + \underline{\hspace{1.5cm}} = 0$$

The students should see that we can "solve" these problems by using integers. We are now able to solve some of the equations that we could not solve before when we were restricted to whole numbers.

Example:

$x + 3 = 2$ Solve for x.

Solution 1:

$$-1 + 3 = 2$$

Solution 2:

$$(x + 1) + 2 = 2$$
$$x + 1 = 2 - 2$$
$$x + 1 = 0$$
$$x = 0 - 1$$
$$x = -1$$

6. *Activity.* Students should be familiar with positive fractions and their operations. Have students do the following so that they can extend their concept to the set of rational numbers. It will also be important to consider:

$$-\frac{7}{3} = \frac{-7}{3} = \frac{7}{-3}$$

Have the students write each of the following as a fraction:

Example: $2 = \frac{2}{1}$

a. 3

b. −5

c. 0

d. $7\frac{1}{2}$

e. $-2\frac{1}{3}$

7. *Teacher Presentation.* Using the results of the preceding activity, students can generalize that all whole numbers can be written in the form $\frac{a}{b}$ where a and b are whole numbers. Likewise, all integers can be written in the form $\frac{a}{b}$. Illustrate for the students how negative fractions can be located on a number line. We now have a new set of numbers—the rationals. It may be necessary to review equivalent fractions. Students can now consider equivalence classes of rationals. The number line can be especially useful. Also, several resources at the end of the chapter will be useful here.

8. *Activity.* Have the students answer the following.
   a. Which properties that we have studied are satisfied by the rational numbers?
   b. $6 \cdot$ _____ $= 1$ _____ $= ?$

   $\frac{2}{3} \cdot$ _____ $= 1$ _____ $= ?$

   $-3 \cdot$ _____ $= 1$ _____ $= ?$

   Given any rational number, say a, it is always possible to find another rational number, b, so that $a \cdot b = 1$?
   c. $2x = 3$ Find x.

9. *Activity.* Have students do the following:
   a. On a geoboard or on dot paper, make a square that has an area of 4 square units. (See fig. 2.2 for example.)

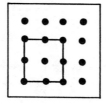

Figure 2.2

   How long is one side of the square? _____
   How are the area and length of the side related? _____
   b. On a geoboard, make a square that has an area of 2 square units. (See fig. 2.3 for example.)

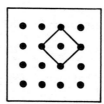

Figure 2.3

10. *Teacher Presentation.* Use the preceding activity to motivate discussion of irrational numbers. Help the students conclude that if s is the length of a side of the square in the example, then $s^2 = 2$ (the area). We need a number so that the number multiplied by itself gives 2. Ask the students if there is such a rational number. Show students how this number can be found on a number line (as a length). Using the idea of a square, ask students to investigate other irrational numbers.

$$s^2 = 5 \qquad s = \sqrt{5}$$
$$s^2 = 8 \qquad s = \sqrt{8}$$

11. *Activity.* Have students complete Reproduction Page 41. This page will provide more insight into irrational numbers as well as summarize the properties of the *real number system.*

12. *Activity.* Have students complete Reproduction Page 42. This can be used as an enrichment activity.

13. *Activity.* Students should be encouraged to use what they have learned about number systems to simplify algebraic expressions. In the beginning, they should be asked to state what property justifies a particular step.
Example:
Simplify

$3(a + 2) + (2a - 6)$

$3(a + 2) + (2a - 6) = (3a + 6) + (2a - 6)$	Distributive property
$= (3a + 2a) + (6 - 6)$	Associative and commutative properties of addition
$= (3a + 2a) + 0$	Additive inverse
$= (3 + 2)a + 0$	Distributive property
$= 5a$	Additive identity

The exercises can be varied.
Simplify

$3x + 7 - 4 + 6 - 2x$

$3x + 7 - 4 + 6 - 2x = (3x - 2x) + (7 - 4 + 6)$	_____
$= (3x + {-2x}) + (7 - 4 + 6)$	_____
$= $ _____	Distributive property
$= x + 9$	_____

CHALLENGE PROBLEMS

1. What percent of $\frac{1}{2}$ is $\frac{1}{3}$?

2. The state income tax was increased from 2% to 2.2%. What was the percent increase?

3. Under what conditions is $a < a^2$?

4. Find two numbers evenly spaced between $\frac{3}{4}$ and $\frac{7}{8}$.

$$\frac{3}{4} \; {-} \; {-} \; \frac{7}{8}$$

5. Using only four 3s and the four arithmetic operations, write expressions for the numbers 1–10.

$$\frac{(3+3)}{(3+3)} = 1 \qquad 3 \cdot 3 - \frac{3}{3} = 8$$

6. For the whole numbers $\{0, 1, 2, 3, 4, \ldots\}$ define $x \odot y$ as follows:

$x \odot y = 0$ if x, y, or both are even
$x \odot y = 1$ if both x and y are odd

Is $\odot$ a binary operation? Is $\odot$ commutative, associative?

7. Find the value of the "continued fraction."

$$\cfrac{1}{2+1+\cfrac{1}{2+\cfrac{1}{1+\frac{1}{2}}}} = \underline{\hspace{2cm}}$$

Irrational numbers can also be written as continued fractions. For example:

$$\sqrt{8} = 2 + 1 + \cfrac{1}{4+\cfrac{1}{1+\cfrac{1}{4+\cfrac{1}{1+\frac{1}{4}+\ldots}}}}$$

Let students take successive approximations of $\sqrt{8}$.

8. If r is a positive rational approximation to $\sqrt{2}$, explain why $\dfrac{r+2}{r+1}$ is *always* a better approximation.

9. If $a * b = \dfrac{a+b}{a-b}$, find $8 * (8 * 8)$.

10. Let $\textcircled{L} = LCM$ and $\textcircled{G} = GCF$.
   Consider the set of factors of $12 - \{1, 2, 3, 4, 6, 12\}$.
   Are $\textcircled{L}$ and $\textcircled{G}$ closed on the set?
   Are $\textcircled{L}$ and $\textcircled{G}$ commutative, associative?
   Are there identities, inverses?

EVALUATION

1. Find the value of each:

   a. $6 \cdot (14 + 5)$

   b. $-3 \cdot (6 + [-5])$

   c. $|9 + (-10)|$

   d. $\dfrac{-2}{3} \div \dfrac{3}{4}$

   e. $18 \cdot \left(-\dfrac{3}{5}\right)$

2. Find the area and perimeter of each rectangle:
   a. $l = 3$; $w = 2$ $A =$ _____ $P =$ _____

   b. $l = 2\frac{1}{2}$; $w = 1\frac{1}{4}$ $A =$ _____ $P =$ _____

   c. $l = 10$; $w = \frac{3}{4}$ $A =$ _____ $P =$ _____

3. Simplify each:
   a. $8x + 4x$

   b. $\frac{1}{2} \cdot (12 + 6)$

   c. $(-3a)(-2a)$

4. Name the property illustrated by each:
   a. $5 \cdot (30 + 6) = (5 \cdot 30) + (5 \cdot 6)$ _____
   b. $xy + 2zx = xy + 2xz$ _____
   c. $9 + 0 = 9$ _____
   d. $\left(\frac{1}{2} + \frac{1}{2}\right) \cdot 10 = 10$ _____

5. Answer the following true or false. If false, tell why.
   a. $|3 \cdot (-2)| = |3| \cdot |2|$ _____
   b. $|3| + |-6| = |3| + |-6|$ _____
   c. The associative property holds
      for subtraction   _____

6. Show the following on a number line.
   a. $7 + (-6)$ ⟵———————————⟶
   b. $4 \cdot (-2)$ ⟵———————————⟶

7. Suppose you know $3^2 + 5^2 = c^2$.
         Then, $c =$ _____

8. Write a subtraction sentence for each:
   a. The difference between -3 and 6.   _____
   b. What must be added to -4 to get 9?   _____

9. A picture frame is $2 + x$ units long and 4 units wide. Then
   a. Area = _____
   b. If $x = 5$, then area = _____

10.

53		23
	8	38
-7		

Fill in the spaces so that the sum of all rows, columns, and diagonals is the same.

RESOURCES

Below is a selected list of resources for teaching number systems. Addresses of publishers can be found in the alphabetical list in Appendix A.

Bitter, Gary G., and Mikesell, Jerald L., *Activities Handbook for Teaching with the Hand-Held Calculator*. Newton, MA: Allyn and Bacon, Inc., 1980. Familiarizes teachers with basic methods for using the calculator as a teaching tool.

Clark, Alice, and Leitch, Carol, *Amusements Developing Algebra Skills, Volume 1*. Pacific Grove, CA: Midwest Publications, 1983. Provides an ideal combination of extensive algebra practice exercises embedded in cross number puzzles, line designs, decodes, picture graphs, optical illusions, and others.

Crouse, Richard D., and Sloyer, Clifford W., *Mathematical Questions from the Classroom*. Newton, MA: Allyn and Bacon, Inc., 1983. A collection of questions and suggested answers for secondary school mathematics students.

Modern Algebra Film Series. San Francisco, CA: Modern Learning Aids, 1983. Films on addition and subtraction of rational numbers, multiplication and division of rational numbers, and natural numbers, integers, and rational numbers.

National Council of Teachers of Mathematics, *Developing Computational Skills*. (40th Yearbook). Reston, VA: NCTM, 1978. This yearbook looks at computational skills using whole numbers, integers, fractions, and decimals.

National Council of Teachers of Mathematics, *Experiences in Mathematical Discovery*. Reston, VA: NCTM, 1971. Considers rational numbers and positive and negative numbers.

National Council of Teachers of Mathematics, *The Growth of Mathematical Ideas, Grades K-12*. (24th Yearbook). Reston, VA: NCTM, 1959.

National Council of Teachers of Mathematics, *The Mathematics Teacher*. Reston, VA: NCTM. This monthly journal is published nine times a year and includes useful suggestions for teaching various topics in the secondary school curriculum.

National Council of Teachers of Mathematics, *The Teaching of Secondary School Mathematics*. (33rd Yearbook). Reston, VA: NCTM, 1970. This yearbook contains sections about preparing plans for teaching algebra (among others).

Plan, Algebra 1. Oak Lawn, IL: Plan Products, 1983. Provides the complete introductory algebra curriculum advocated by the School Mathematics Study Group. The teacher's kit includes placement tests, achievement tests, and duplicating masters.

Rassmussen, Peter, *Key to Algebra*. Hayward, CA: Activity Resources Co., 1974. A set of small pamphlets that provide practice in basic algebraic skills.

3

Solving Equations and Inequalities In One Variable

CONTENT OVERVIEW

Solving equations is at the heart of elementary algebra. It is a basic skill around which much of the course can be organized. The theme reoccurs with each conceptual advance—as with integers, irrational numbers, exponents, polynomials, functions, and complex numbers. Also, at each stage, equations (and inequalities) are invaluable problem-solving tools: they provide the means for expressing or recording the relationships uncovered through mathematical analysis of a given situation. More generally, they are the elements of mathematical models whose solutions provide corresponding solutions to the situations from which they were translated.

To help students develop some sophistication with these important skills, we take a problem-solving approach, discussing various strategies and, ultimately a general plan for solving equations. A mechanism of *theme with variation* is used throughout. Basic ideas and techniques are motivated and discussed with examples in teacher presentations. Students are then led to discover variations on the basic theme through class discussions and sets of exercises. New features are introduced gradually so that, by comparison with the familiar, students will be able to identify a subproblem, working toward the familiar as a subgoal. We hope this will provide a stimulating atmosphere in which students will continue to develop an appreciation of mathematics.

OBJECTIVES

As a result of the learning experiences in this chapter, the student should be able to:

1. Evaluate algebraic expressions, given values for the variables

2. Simplify algebraic expressions containing variables and grouping symbols

3. Identify equations and inequalities in contrast to other mathematical sentences

---

4. Identify the solution set for an elementary open sentence from among several choices and to give reasons why the others do not qualify

5. Solve linear equations with one unknown

6. Solve basic formulae for a specified variable, provided the formula is linear in that variable

7. Describe solution strategies for solving equations and formulae whether there is a single occurrence of the unknown or if unknowns appear on both sides

8. Solve basic inequalities by either
   a. using the corresponding boundary equation, or
   b. by transformations with "balance operations"

9. Solve double and absolute value inequalities

LEARNING EXPERIENCES

Topic 1: Algebraic Expressions

Some activities are provided for working with algebraic or numerical expressions. The order-of-operations analysis is important and will be used for developing the "undoing" strategy for solving equations. The discussion of the domain of a variable is more or less optional and designed to establish a basis for a general understanding of the truth set for an open sentence.

ORDER OF OPERATIONS
Through mathematical tradition, rules have evolved for performing a complex series of operations. For expressions involving a mixture of addition, subtraction, multiplication, division, or exponentiation, but no grouping symbols:

1. First compute the powers of the exponents as they occur from left to right

2. Next, perform the multiplications and/or divisions as they occur from left to right, and

3. Finally, do the additions and/or subtractions, again from left to right
   Thus,

$$100 \div 5^2 \cdot 4 - 3 + 7$$

is equal to twenty; the tags ($\smile°$) below indicate the order in which the operations are to be performed.

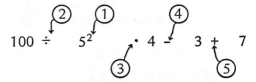

Note: For some expressions, because of certain algebraic properties, the operations can be executed in an order different from that implied by these rules and still give the same answer. For example, $2 \cdot 3 + 4^2$ gives the same result (22) whether evaluated by the rules,

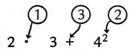

or as follows:

$$2 \cdot 3 + 4^2$$

Such equivalences are properly discussed in algebra; the ultimate criteria being that such changes systematically produce the same results as the basic order-of-operations rules. Too, this order of operations is for evaluation purposes. (For solving equations we will sometimes be interested in the reverse order.)

I. *Activity.* Many of the activities suggested in Chapter 2 will be useful here. You will want to use more variable expressions.

GROUP SYMBOLS
The following table presents the grouping symbols in common use.

	Symbol	Descriptive Term	Sample Usage
1.	( )	parentheses	$(x + 2)(x - 2)^2$
2.	[ ]	brackets	$3[4 + 2x]$
3.	{ }	braces	$\{3 - 2\} \cdot 4$
4.	_____	vinculum (bar)	$\dfrac{2x}{x + 1}$

Proper usage dictates that braces, brackets, and parentheses be used in matched sets such that, for example, each left bracket "[" must be followed by a uniquely corresponding right bracket "]." Nesting, where one set of parentheses, braces, or brackets appears inside another, however, is acceptable as in:

$3(x + 2(x - 4(x + 1)))$

Reading and interpreting nested quantities can be aided if different types of symbols are used. For the above expression we could use:

$3\{x + 2[x - 4(x + 1)]\}$

The vinculum is most often used, as illustrated above, to simultaneously indicate grouped quantities and their quotient. Using parentheses, $(2x) \div (x + 1)$ would be the equivalent of $\dfrac{2x}{x + 1}$. Grouping symbols may be used to sequence operations in orders different from those dictated by the basic order-of-operations rules. To illustrate, instead of:

$$2 + 3 \cdot 4 = 14$$

we have:

$$(2 + 3) \cdot 4 = 20$$

with markings ① over the first step and ② over the second step

by the following agreements.

A. Perform operations within grouping symbols first

B. In nesting, begin in the innermost grouping and work outward

C. Within grouping symbols, perform the operations as sequenced by the basic rules

2. *Activity.* Insert parentheses (if needed) so that the final result is always 10.

Teacher	Students
1. $2 \cdot 3 + 2$	1. $100 \div 2 \cdot 6 - 2$
2. $10 + 10 \cdot 10 \div 10 - 10$	2. $1 + 5^2 + 4 \div 4$

EVALUATING VARIABLE EXPRESSIONS

If an expression involves a variable x, computation may proceed as usual once the variable is replaced by an appropriate numerical value. Mathematically this replacement process is called *substitution*.

Example:
Evaluate: $x^2 - 2x$ for $x = 3$
Solution: First substitute 3 for each x
$$(3)^2 - 2(3)$$

Note: Each x was actually replaced by "(3)." The parentheses may be necessary to give the proper interpretation. This is the case with "$2x$"; 2(3) has the proper meaning whereas 23 does not. Perform the calculations:

$$(3)^2 - 2(3) =$$
$$9 - 6 =$$
$$3$$

Agreements for substitution:

1. All occurrences of a specific variable must be replaced by the same value

2. If two or more different variables appear in a certain expression they may, but need not, be replaced by different values (still adhering to the first agreement)
   Example:
   Evaluate: $ab + ac$ for $a = 2$, $b = 3$, and $c = 3$
   Solution: $(2)(3) + (2)(3)$ by substitution
   $$6 + 6 =$$
   $$12$$

3. *Activity.* Have students evaluate (discuss and compare answers) each of the following using the given values.
   a. Evaluate $a(b + c)$ for $a = 2$, $b = 3$, and $c = 3$
   b. Evaluate $x^2 - x$ for $x = 7$

    c. Evaluate $0 \cdot x + 2$ for $x = 5$
    d.* Evaluate 2 for $x = 5$

DOMAIN OF A VARIABLE

Instead of considering only a single value for a variable as in the preceding evaluations, we often are interested in substitutions with many different values. Collectively these replacements form the domain of the variable. Hence, the domain of a variable is the set of all possible replacements for that variable. If, for example, 1, 2, and 3 are the only possible replacements for x, then $\{1,2,3\}$ is the domain of x. To convey this strictly in symbols, we write**

$$x \in \{1,2,3\}$$

Where "$\in$" means "is an element of."

4. *Teacher Presentation.* State the problem: Evaluate $3x^2 + 1$ for $x \in \{1,2,3\}$. Suggest using a table like the following to organize the work.

Value of Substitution

x	in $3x^2 + 1$	Computation	Value
1	$3(1)^2 + 1$	$3(1) + 1 = 3 + 1$	4
2	$3(2)^2 + 1$	$3(4) + 1 = 12 + 1$	13
3	$3(3)^2 + 1$	$3(9) + 1 = 27 + 1$	28

The computation could be performed elsewhere and left out of the table.

AGREEMENT CONCERNING DOMAINS

In algebra the domain of a variable is either stated explicitly or assumed to be the set of all real numbers, with certain exceptions.

    One important exception that could be mentioned at this time stems from the restriction against dividing by zero.

    To illustrate, the real number 5 must be excluded from the domain of:

$$\frac{x}{x-5}$$

because $\dfrac{(5)}{(5)-5} = \dfrac{5}{0}$ indicates division by zero.

Since 5 is the only such value we can indicate the domain of x by:

$$x \in \{x : x \neq 5\}$$

5. *Activity.* Have students determine domains for each of the following.
    a. $3x^2 + 1$
    b. $4 + \dfrac{3}{1-x}$

---

*This last exercise might seem rather unusual. The teacher should indicate that the $0 \cdot x + 2$ found in number 3 is equivalent. Thus, "shouldn't we get the same answer?"

**Note: Some authors prefer $D(x)$ or $Dom (x) = \{1,2,3\}$.

c. $\dfrac{1}{x^2 + 1}$

SIMPLIFYING EXPRESSIONS

In the course of other work (solving equations, for example) it often is convenient to replace all or part of an algebraic expression by a less complicated looking expression. The following table shows some examples.

	Original Expression	Simplified Version
1.	$(3x + 2) - 2$	$3x$
2.	$(8x - 9) - 8x$	-9
3.	$4x + (5 + 3x)$	$7x + 5$
4.	$3x - 2(x - 2)$	$x + 4$

The only requirement is that, for each and every value in the domain of the variable(s), the simplified version must yield the same number as the original. Some instances are given below for the last example in the preceding table.

Value of x	Value of $x + 4$ Simplified Version	Value of $3x - 2(x - 2)$ Original Version
0	4	4
-2	2	2
$\dfrac{1}{2}$	$4\dfrac{1}{2}$	$4\dfrac{1}{2}$

Of course trying just a few values is no guarantee that the expressions are equivalent. A more reliable approach is to use properties, definitions, axioms, and theorems such as the associative, commutative, and distributive properties. We use these in an expression-reason format to show the equivalence for the third example.

Expression	Reason	Comments
$4x + (5 + 3x)$	Given	Attracting the
$4x + (3x + 5)$	Commutative property of addition	x-terms
$(4x + 3x) + 5$	Associative property of addition	Collecting or combining
$(4 + 3)x + 5$	Distributive property	the x-terms
$7x + 5$	Addition fact	

This proves that $7x + 5$, the simplified version, is equivalent to the original and hence can be used to replace $4x + (5 + 3x)$.

6. *Activity.* Have students show the equivalence of $x + 4$ and $3x - 2(x - 2)$ using the above approach. Note: they will need the definition of subtraction, $a - b = a + (-b)$.

7. *Teacher Presentation.* Since the first and second examples are typical in equation solving, we approach these in a general way, dealing with

$$(A + B) - B = A$$

and

$$(B - A) - B = -A$$

respectively.

Expression	Reason
$(A + B) - B$	Given
$(A + B) + -B$	Definition of subtraction
$A + CB + (-B)$	Associative property of addition
$A + O$	Inverse property of addition
A	Identity property of addition

Thus, we can simply write A instead of $(A + B) - B$. The flow of associations below (arrows) show how this property can be used to simplify $(3x + 2) - 2$

$$(3x + 2) - 2 = 3x$$
$$\downarrow \quad \downarrow \quad \downarrow \quad \uparrow$$
$$(A + B) - B \longrightarrow A$$

Notice, too, that this property makes sense. We are starting with A, adding on B, and then taking B away. Shouldn't we be back to A where we started in the first place?

8. *Activity.* Follow the above approach, first proving the property $(B - A) - B = -A$ and then applying it to simplify $(8x - 9) - 8x$. The following table includes the two preceding properties and four other properties that are useful simplification procedures for solving equations. Each is accompanied by an illustrative example.

Property	Example
1. $(A + B) - B = A$	$(3x + 2) - 2 = 3x$
2. $(A - B) + B = A$	$(3x - 2) + 2 = 3x$
3. $(B + A) - B = A$	$(3x + 2) - 3x = 2$
4. $(B - A) - B = -A$	$(3x - 2) - 3x = -2$
5. $\dfrac{BA}{B} = A;\ (B \neq 0)$	$\dfrac{3x}{3} = x$
6. $B\left(\dfrac{A}{B}\right) = A;\ (B \neq 0)$	$3\left(\dfrac{x}{3}\right) = x$

9. *Activity.* Select 2 or 3 of the above properties. Make up a ditto containing the proofs of these properties. Have the students supply the missing steps and/or reasons.

10. *Activity.* Have students simplify the expressions on Reproduction Page 43. When they can, have them use the simplification properties above.

Topic 2: Mathematical Sentences

Equations and inequalities are properly viewed as special kinds of sentences. Other modes of expression are perfectly acceptable even though we use standard mathematical symbols. Discussions and activities are to help students learn the meaning and proper use of the symbols and to introduce them to solution sets for open sentences.

BASIC SYMBOLISM

The essentials are given in this section. The next section provides an enrichment.

1. *Teacher Presentation.* Present and discuss the following table illustrating the meaning and use of each symbol.

	Symbol	Meaning	Illustrated Use
1.	$=$	is equal to	$\frac{2}{4} = \frac{1}{2}$ or $x = 2$
2.	$<$	is less than	$4 < 5$
3.	$\leqslant$	is less than or equal to	$5 \leqslant 5$
4.	$>$	is greater than	$2x > 6$
5.	$\geqslant$	is greater than or equal to	$x \geqslant x^2 - 2$

Discussion points: These symbols express some very important mathematical relations which often are used to analyze and solve real problems. The symbols might be considered abbreviations for the corresponding phrases listed under *meaning,* but other equivalent verbal phrases should also be allowed.

Mnemonic Devices: Some students make reversal errors using "$<$" for "is greater than" or "$>$" for "is less than." For such students it may help to mention one of the following:

A. "$<$" and "$>$" can be viewed as arrowheads pointing, respectively, to smaller or larger values as on a horizontal number line

B. The point each of "$<$" and "$>$" is attached to the smaller value and the "arms" open (in astonishment) to the larger of the two

C. "$<$" is like "$\subset$" and if $A \subset B$, in a sense, A is "smaller" than B

D. The top part of the compound relations "$\leqslant$" and "$\geqslant$" indicates the appropriate order relation while the "_" is "half of an equal sign"

2. *Teacher Presentation.* Use the leading question "What is an equation?" to bring out some of the following ideas. Equations are sentences stating that two things are equal. These sentences may be expressed in words or mathematical symbols and relate either numbers, sets, or other types of things. At this time we are interested only in these statements which use the equal sign (=) to express the equivalence of two algebraic/numerical expressions; for example,

$$2x + 1 = 5$$

Thus, our equations will have the general form

$$\underbrace{\hspace{3cm}}_{\text{Left Member}} = \underbrace{\hspace{3cm}}_{\substack{\text{Equal Sign} \\ \text{(Verb)}}} \underbrace{\hspace{3cm}}_{\text{Right Member}}$$

The equal sign is the verb. The left and right members may be composed of numerals, variables, signs of operation, grouping symbols, or other mathematics symbols. To illustrate,

$$2\pi r, \quad 2x+, \quad \text{and} \quad 2)x + 1($$

would not be acceptable, whereas

$$r^2, \quad 5, \quad 2x + 1, \quad \frac{x-1}{x+1}, \quad 10, \quad \text{and} \quad 2(x+1)$$

are acceptable algebraic/numerical expressions.

3. *Activity.* Using only the expressions,

$$\pi r^2, \quad 5, \quad 2x + 1, \quad \frac{x-1}{x+1}, \quad 10, \quad \text{and} \quad 2(x+1)$$

have students generate some equations.

4. *Teacher Presentation.* Consider the leading question "What is an inequality?" Use similarity and contrast to guide the discussion. Inequalities have the general form

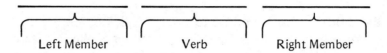

As with equations, the two members must be well-formed expressions representing numbers. Instead of the equal sign, one of the symbols $<$, $\leq$, $>$, or $\geq$ should appear as the verb. Note, once again, the statement need not be true. Techniques for solving inequalities have been devised for determining their solution sets. For the compound sentences with $\leq$ and $\geq$, any value which satisfies either of the conditions is included among the solutions.

5. *Activity.* Have students construct some possible inequalities that can be made using only the expressions:

$$5, \quad 2x + 1, \quad \text{and} \quad \pi r^2$$

6. *Activity.* Have students judge and discuss the items on Reproduction Page 44. This may be considered a supplementary or enrichment activity mixing equations and inequalities with nonexamples. The last few items might introduce students to unfamiliar, but acceptable, mathematical symbols.

OPEN SENTENCES AND SOLUTION SETS

7. *Teacher Presentation.* Have students determine the truth or falsity of mathematical sentences like those in the following table.

Mathematical Sentence	True or False?
$2 + 3 \leq 3 + 2$	True
$3 + 3 = 4$	False
$4 + 5 > 5 + 4$	False
$6 + 2 = 2(3 + 1)$	True

There are no variables in the equations and inequalities above so the truth or falsity of the sentences can definitely be decided. When variables are present, the situation is more complex since the truth or falsity might change for different values of the variable. The following table shows such an example.

x	x^2	$2x$	$x^2 = 2x$
0	0	0	True
1	1	2	False
2	4	4	True
3	9	6	False

Thus, the sentence $x^2 = 2x$ is true if x is 0 or 2, but false when x is 1 or 3. The truth or falsity depends on the value of the variable. When first presented with such a sentence then, we say it is an *open* question as to when the sentence is true and when it is not. This provides intuition for the concept of an open sentence.

8. *Activity.* Pose the problem of solving:

$$3n + 5 \leqslant 25 - n$$

where the domain of n is limited to {0,1,2,3,4,5,6,7,8,9}. Distribute the task of checking for solutions by having different students check different values from the domain. Assemble the acceptable values to form the solution set. Discuss solution strategies and possible adjustments for infinite domains including decimal and negative numbers, or for more complicated sentences. This should be informal in nature, pointing toward the strategies and techniques that "experts" use.

Topic 3: Solving Equations

This section takes a problem-solving approach developing first a working backward or "undoing" strategy, followed by other elements of a general method. Teachers should alert students to certain surface features, some indicating progress toward solution, others presenting obstacles that need to be overcome. The usual balance operations are included. This development should provide a basis for the later discussion of inequalities.

THE "UNDOING" STRATEGY

1. *Teacher Presentation.* Given an equation like $3 \cdot x + 5 = 17$, one could use trial and error methods to find the solution set. The ancient Egyptians had such a method called the "Rule of False Position." We, however, would like to be more systematic, building on things we already know. Substituting 4 in the left member, we have

$$\overset{①}{3 \cdot} \quad \overset{②}{(4) +} \quad 5$$

where the tags indicate the order of operations as prescribed by the basic rules for evaluation. Carrying these out we have first $12 + 5$, then 17, verifying that 4 is indeed the solution.

Once again, the important step for developing a solution strategy is to note the sequence of operations and their result. First, whether 4 or any other value for x is being used, we multiply by 3. Then, to that answer, we add 5, hoping to get 17. This is shown explicitly in fig. 3.1.

The solution strategy evolves from realizing the reversibility of this action sequence. That is, we can work backwards from the 17 to the starting value x (the solution) by simply *undoing* what has been done. Let's see how it works.

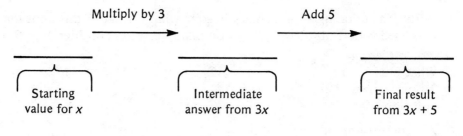

Figure 3.1

The last thing done is the first undone. How can we undo "adding 5"? Answer: "By subtracting 5." This moves us back from 17 to the intermediate value 12, as shown in fig. 3.2.

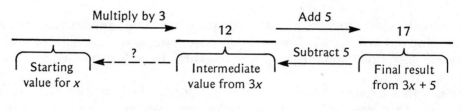

Figure 3.2

We are now part way and know that $3x = 12$. To get back the rest of the way we need to undo "multiplying by 3." To do this, we "divide by 3." Thus, 4 is revealed as the starting value for x and hence the solution of the equation, illustrated in fig. 3.3.

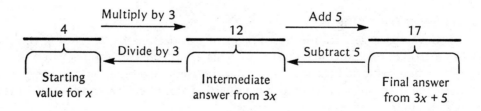

Figure 3.3

Note: The undoing approach uses the order of operations and the knowledge that addition and subtraction, multiplication and division are inverse operations. Throughout the study of mathematics, operations and their inverses continue to be learned (e.g., powers and roots, logarithms and antilogs, integration and differentiation). Whenever a problem can be analyzed into a sequence of such operations leading to a known result, this inversion or "undoing" strategy can be applied. Thus, even though it does not always work and other strategies need also be learned, it is important enough to warrant practice.

2. *Activity.* The undoing approach is still somewhat formal. A different method which may be used is that of "Cover-Up." For example, again consider $3x + 5 = 17$.

Cover-Up Method
a. What plus 5 = 17?   (12)
b. 3 times what = 12?   (4)
   Solution: 4

   Another example: $\dfrac{2x - 4}{6} = 5$

Cover-Up Method
a. What divided by 6 equals 5?   (30)
b. What minus 4 equals 30?   (34)
c. What times 2 equals 34?   (17)
   Solution: 17

It should be noted that this method will get "messy" if fractions appear early in the process.

3. *Activity.* Have students practice using the "undoing" approach for the exercises on Reproduction Page 45. For some of these, discuss the order of operations, the inverse operations, and the process of reversing the actions applied to x.

The last four exercises may need special attention. For number 11, the addition of 5 and x should be commuted before beginning the undoing process. For number 12, we suggest the following changes:

$$9 - x = 4 \xrightarrow{\text{to}} 9 + (-1) \cdot x = 4 \xrightarrow{\text{to}} -1 \cdot x + 9 = 4$$

For number 13, apply symmetry and a sequence like that of number 12. Finally, number 14 provides a solution set with more than one root and an opportunity to discuss the complications of undoing the squaring process.

UNKNOWN ONLY ON ONE SIDE
This section develops a general method for solving equations by extending the "undoing" strategy and introducing additional strategies. This approach also applies when the unknown appears in both members and balance operations are used. Algebraic operations (associativity, commutativity, and so on) will be emphasized with a statement-reason format in teacher-led discussions as they are used to solve equations.

4. *Teacher Presentation.* Consider the equation:

$$44 = 3x + 2.$$

Using the symmetric property of equality, we can now proceed to solve $3x + 2 = 44$ with our "undoing" strategy and still get the solution for the equation as stated in its original form.

As we solve equations, not only will we want to make changes like the one above, but we will want to keep making changes, one right after another until a solution is found. Thus, we will need an orderly, compact scheme for showing our work. The statement-reason format below is often used.

Statement	Reason
1. $44 = 3x + 2$	1. Given
2. $3x + 2 = 44$	2. Symmetric Property of Equality
3. $3x = 42$	3. Subtracting 2
4. $x = 14$	4. Dividing by 3

Checking, we have:

$$44 \text{ vs. } 3(14) + 2$$
$$\text{vs. } 42 + 2$$
$$\text{vs. } 44$$

Thus, {14} is the solution set for $44 = 3x + 2$.

Looking back at the complete solution, what was the effect of using the symmetric property? Expected answer from students: to get the unknown on the left instead of the right. So, with occurrences of the unknown only on one side, if necessary we can put them on the left by simply switching sides.

Note: Hereafter, the demonstration equations will use the left side for the unknown. However, student activities will use either side. Also, the teacher may want to make some agreements for when students need to give reasons and on how much detail should be included in the solution and in checking.

5. *Teaching Presentation:* Isolating the Unknown

Think about *undoing* and solving each of the four equations below.

a. $7 + x = 8$ 	b. $4 - x = 1$

c. $x + (7 + 3) = 14$ 	d. $\dfrac{x - 3}{9} = 7$

Even though there is only one occurrence of the unknown in each equation, only d. can be solved strictly by undoing the actions applied to x. In a. 7 is the starting value and x is added (this is the action) to get eight. In b., the starting value is 4; x is subtracted to give 1. In c. the first operation is adding 7 plus 3, not even involving x. For this reason we would like to show some processes that can give us an undoing type of equation. When we combine these with undoing, the more general strategy is called *isolating the unknown.* Later, when solving more complex equations, solvers should switch to this strategy as soon as the number of occurrences of the unknown has been reduced to one.

The case for a. is easy.

Statement	Reason
1. $7 + x = 8$	1. Given
2. $x + 7 = 8$	2. Commutative property of addition
3. $x = 1$	3. Subtracting 7

Once the addition is commuted, the action is being applied to x.

Problem b. is the most difficult of the examples. We will use the following two principles:

Definition of Subtraction $a - b = a + (-b)$
Property of (-1) $-b = -1b$

Statement	Reason
1. $4 - x = 1$	1. Given
2. $4 + (-x) = 1$	2. Definition of subtraction
3. $4 + (-1x) = 1$	3. $-b = -1 \cdot b$
4. $-1 \cdot x + 4 = 1$	4. Commutative property of addition
5. $-1 \cdot x = -3$	5. Subtracting 4
6. $x = 3$	6. Dividing by -1

6. *Activity.* Have students complete the isolation exercises on Reproduction Page 46. Be sure to use the term isolation during discussions any time there is only one occurrence of the unknown.

7. *Teacher Presentation:* Attraction and collection.
Consider the equations below.
a. $2x + (3x + 7) = 17$
b. $3x + 4(x + 1) = 25$
Isolation cannot be applied directly because each has more than a single occurrence of the unknown. If possible, while preserving the solution set, we would like to reduce the number of such occurrences to one so that we can use the isolation techniques.

Example a: $2x + (3x + 7) = 17$

According to the statement, $2x + (3x + 7)$ is a numeral representing the number 17. Since the properties just reviewed permit us to make changes in this numeral while still representing the same number, this is what we will do as we try to reduce the number of occurrences of the unknown. Applying the associative property for addition:

$$2x + (3x + 7) \longrightarrow (2x + 3x) + 7$$

We can *attract* the x terms bringing them closer together to get

$$(2x + 3x) + 7 = 17$$

Using the distributive property, we get

$$5x + 7 = 17,$$

which we can now solve as before.

Example b: $3x + 4(x + 1) = 25$

The multiplication of 4 times the quantity in parentheses presents an obstacle to attraction and collection. We overcome this by using the distributive property.

Statements	Reason	Strategy
$3x + 4(x + 1) = 25$	Given	
$3x + (4x + 4) = 25$	Distributive property	Remove ( )
$(3x + 4x) + 4 = 25$	Associative property	Attraction
$7x + 4 = 25$	Distributive property	Collection
$7x = 21$	Subtracting 4	Isolation
$x = 3$	Dividing by 7	

Check and express the solution set.

Discussion Points: Attraction, collection, and isolation are elements of a general method for solving equations, whether they have unknowns on one or both sides. This method can be used even in more advanced courses such as working with trigonometry or logarithms. Removing parentheses is one of several ways to deal with obstacles. Other techniques are introduced as the need arises (e.g., clearing fractions and factoring).

8. *Activity.* Have students use the basic method of removing parentheses, attraction, collection, and isolation while solving the equations on Reproduction Page 47.

9. *Activity.* Using the solutions to the exercises on Reproduction Page 46, have students name the properties or processes useful for attraction, collection, and isolation.

UNKNOWNS ON BOTH SIDES

We again use the basic method of attraction, collection, and isolation viewing the state of having unknowns only on one side as a subgoal. In cases where occurrences of the unknown are on both sides, the balance operations provide a means for bringing these together (attraction). Thus, *attraction* is extended across the equal sign.

10. *Teacher Presentation:* Balance operations.

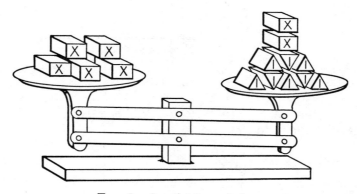

Two-Pan Parallel Beam Balance

Figure 3.4

The device shown in fig. 3.4 is called a beam balance. If weights are placed on each of the pans such that the beam comes to rest in a level position with the pans at the same height, we say the system is balanced. More important, this also means that the weights are equal. Thus, such a device can be used to model equations, the left pan holding the amount for the left number and the right pan holding the amount for the right side of the equation. Equality, as indicated by the equal sign in the equation, corresponds to balancing the system. The picture shows a model for

$$5x = 9 + 2x$$

where the triangular bars are one unit each and the square bars are x's.

$x = \underline{\qquad ? \qquad}$
Equation Form

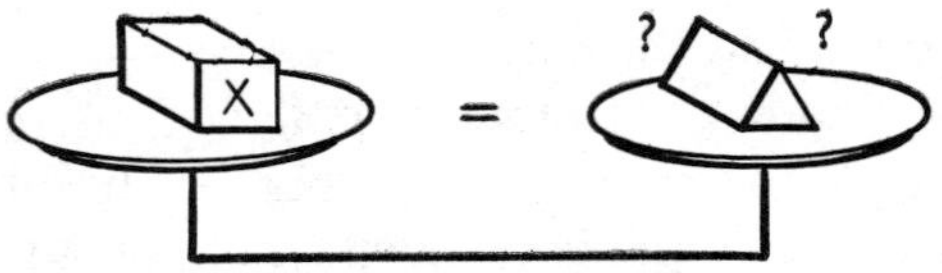

Balance Model

Figure 3.5

Our job is to find out how many triangular bars are needed to balance one bar labeled *x*. This would look like fig. 3.5, with just one *x*, on the left pan, and the correct number of units on the other side. Looking back to the model for $5x = 9 + 2x$, one difference comes from having *x*'s on both sides instead of only on the left. One remedy for this is to remove the *x*'s that are on the right. Unfortunately, this upsets the balance. There is something we can do to restore the balance. It would be appropriate to also "take away" two *x*'s from the left side, giving the situation in fig. 3.6.

$3x = 9$
Equation Form

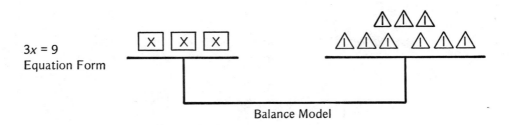

Balance Model

Figure 3.6

This "taking the same amount from both sides" is a useful tool for solving equations. Have students generalize the following:

SUBTRACTION PROPERTY OF EQUALITY
    If $a = b$, then $a - c = b - c$.

As we continue to solve the equation, we see in fig. 3.7 that both sides can conveniently be separated into three equal parts. From the obvious correspondence we have the solution in fig. 3.8.

$3x = 9$
Equation Form

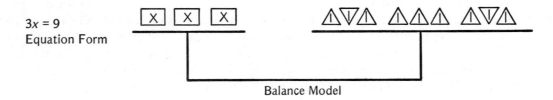

Balance Model

Figure 3.7

Students should be helped to generalize the division property of equality.

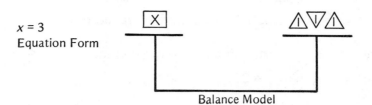

$x = 3$
Equation Form

Balance Model

Figure 3.8

DIVISION PROPERTY OF EQUALITY

If $a = b$, then $\dfrac{a}{c} = \dfrac{b}{c}$ provided $c \neq 0$.

Point out to the students that having *3 times x*, with division being the inverse of multiplication, is why we divided both sides by 3.

We review our solution of $5x = 9 + 2x$, showing how to present the solution algebraically, without the balance. Students should be encouraged to relate the two approaches.

Statement	Reason	Comments
1. $5x = 9 + 2x$	1. Given	
2. $5x - 2x = (9 + 2x) - 2x$	2. Subtraction property of equality	"Get x's on one side," a combination of both attraction and collection
3. $3x = 9$	3. Left side: Distributive property Right side: Simplify using $(A + B) - B = A$	
4. $\dfrac{3x}{3} = \dfrac{9}{3}$	4. Division property of equality	Isolation, "undoing" multiplication by 3
5. $x = 3$	5. Left side: Simplify using $BA/B = A$	

Equation Form   Balance Model

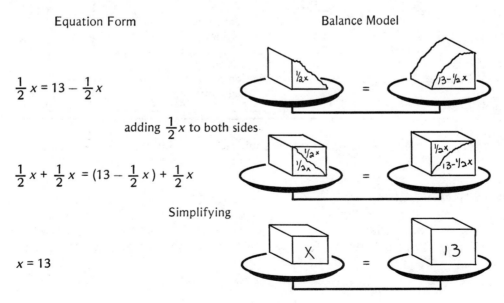

$\dfrac{1}{2}x = 13 - \dfrac{1}{2}x$

adding $\dfrac{1}{2}x$ to both sides

$\dfrac{1}{2}x + \dfrac{1}{2}x = (13 - \dfrac{1}{2}x) + \dfrac{1}{2}x$

Simplifying

$x = 13$

Figure 3.9

Fig. 3.9 shows how adding the same amount to both sides can be used to solve an equation.

Finally, we can multiply each side of an equation in order to solve it. This is a useful tool for solving equations like $\frac{x}{3} = 2$.

11. *Activity.* Have students solve $\frac{x}{3} = 2$ by using the balance model. You may want to encourage them to make an appropriate drawing.

In summary, then, we have the following properties of equality that should be emphasized for students.
   a. If $a = b$, then $a - c = b - c$ Subtraction
   b. If $a = b$, then $\frac{a}{c} = \frac{b}{c}$; $c \neq 0$ Division
   c. If $a = b$, then $a + c = b + c$ Addition
   d. If $a = b$, then $a \cdot c = b \cdot c$ Multiplication*
       (or $c \cdot a = c \cdot b$)

12. *Activity.* We suggest a combined teacher-led discussion and demonstration, solving equations such as
   a. $6x = 2(5 + x)$ b. $15x = 7 - 2(x - 4)$
   c. $8 - 3x = 9x + 2$ d. $2(5x + 8) = 3x - 2(7 - x)$

13. *Activity.* Have students complete dittos with questions similar to the following where they are asked to fill in the blanks.

Statement	*Reason*	*Strategy*
1. $2(5x + 8) = 3x - 2(7 - x)$	Given	
2. $10x + 16 = 3x - 14 + 2x$	_____	
3. $10x + 16 = -14 + 5x$	_____	
4. _____	Subtraction property of equality	
5. $5x + 16 = -14$	Simplifying	
6. $(5x + 16) - 16 = (-14) - 16$	_____	
7. $5x = -30$	Simplifying	
8. _____	Division property of equality	
9. $x = -6$	_____	

14. *Activity.* Have students practice their solving skills with the exercises on Reproduction Page 48.

WORKING WITH FORMULAS
15. *Teacher Presentation.* Formulae are equations used to express relationships between two or more variables. They usually are stated in such a way as to relate one type of quantity to the others. Review some examples with your students such as:
   a. $A = \frac{1}{2}bh$

---

*Caution students that multiplying both sides by zero will change the solution set as in $x = x + 1$ versus $0 \cdot x = 0 \cdot (x + 1)$.

b. $P = 2(l + w)$

c. $d = rt$

Introduce this section with this example: How far would a car travel at 30 mph for 2 hours? Students should be encouraged to see that this problem requires only computation. We want them to see how the equation-solving techniques they have been using can help them in other types of problems involving formulae.

Give them this example: What is the height of a 75 square inch triangle having a 10 inch base? Solve this problem on the overhead with the students' participation.

$$A = \frac{1}{2}bh$$

$$75 = \frac{1}{2}(10)h$$

$$5h = 75$$

$$h = 15$$

Encourage students to see how we substituted 75 and 10 for A and b respectively before starting the solution process. Do the following on the overhead to illustrate an important alternative method; expressing h in terms of A and b, then substituting and computing.

$$A = \frac{1}{2}bh$$

$$\frac{1}{2}bh = A$$
$$bh = 2A$$
$$h = \frac{2A}{b} \ (b \neq 0)$$
⎫ first solve for h

$$h = \frac{2(75)}{10}$$
$$h = 15$$
⎫ substitute and compute

Have students complete Reproduction Page 49.

CHECKING PROCEDURES

This section provides motivation for the usual checking procedures, namely, testing roots in the original equation. It also presents a follow-up procedure which might be used to pinpoint an error, should one occur. We urge teachers to encourage students to check their solutions. For new learners especially, we recommend a "looking back" approach, not only checking computation at each step, but also reviewing strategies.

16. *Teacher Presentation.* Solving equations often involves several steps and many calculations. Thus, it is not unreasonable to wonder if all of these were done without error. It could be that the value revealed at the end is not really a root of the original equation. Certainly, when in doubt, it is best to check. Present the following example to the class.

$$2x + 3(x - 1) = 4x + 1$$

The proposed solution is $x = 4$

For the left side we have

$$2(4) + 3(4 - 1)$$
$$8 + 3(3)$$
$$8 + 9$$
$$17$$

For the right side we have

$$4(4) + 1$$
$$16 + 1$$
$$17$$

Barring any new errors, we now know that 4 is a solution for the equation. We will want to encourage students to go back and find where they made an error (if their solution does not check).

17. *Activity.* Have students identify the errors in the so-called "solutions" on Reproduction Page 50.

18. *Activity.* Have students take turns, one generating an erroneous solution and the other finding the error. Also, have students find their own errors on homework problems.

Topic 4: Solving Inequalities

Here we move directly from symbolically expressed inequalities to the solving skills. Comments of a more general nature along with related activities can be found in Topic 2, Mathematical Sentences.

1. *Teacher Presentation.* Introduce inequalities by completing the following chart with the class.

Sample Inequality	Value of x		
	$x = 1$	$x = 2$	$x = 3$
$3x + 2 < 8$	$5 < 8$	$8 < 8$	$11 < 8$
	true	false	false
$3x + 2 > 8$	$5 > 8$	$8 > 8$	$11 > 8$
	false	false	true
$3x + 2 \geqslant 5x - 2$	$5 \geqslant 3$	$8 \geqslant 8$	$11 \geqslant 13$
	true	true	false
$3x + 2 \leqslant 5x - 2$	$5 \leqslant 3$	$8 \leqslant 8$	$11 \leqslant 13$
	false	true	true

Our main concern is finding truth values for open inequalities. In the cases of $\leqslant$ and $\geqslant$ a truth value only needs to satisfy one part of the relation.

Emphasize the following:

LAW OF TRICHOTOMY
For any two designated numbers a and b, one and only one of the following must be true:

a. $a < b$

b. $a = b$

c. $a > b$

REVERSIBILITY PRINCIPLE

a. $b > a$ if and only if $a < b$

b. $b \geqslant a$ if and only if $a \leqslant b$

Applied to $8 \leqslant 3x + 2$ the reversibility principle gives us

$3x + 2 \geqslant 8$.

Thus, this gives us a way to "switch sides" so that when only one side contains the unknown, those instances can be on the left.

GRAPHS OF SOLUTION SETS FOR BASIC INEQUALITIES

2. *Teacher Presentation.* Review for students how to illustrate numbers on a number line. Have students give solutions for $x > -2$. The students will probably give integer values such as $-1, 0, 1, 2, 3$, etc. Point out that some numbers are missing—rationals such as $-\frac{1}{2}, \frac{1}{2}, -\frac{1}{4}, \frac{1}{4}$ and irrationals such as $\sqrt{2}$. Have students indicate the solution set on a number line as follows:

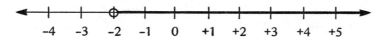

Point out that this method allows us to "show" the solution set even though we could not list all the solutions.

Have students compare what they have just done with the solution of $x > -2$. Continue this presentation by considering other examples.

3. *Activity.* Have students make graphs for the sample inequalities on Reproduction Page 51.

EQUALITY AS A BOUNDARY

4. *Teacher Presentation.*

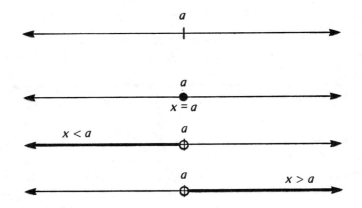

Refer to the above number lines one at a time. Point out to the students how the dot on *a* separates the "is less than" condition from the "is greater than" condition. The equality acts as a boundary separating the other two. Even in more complicated problems, this boundary idea still will occur. Since we already know how to solve equations, we can couple this separation idea with our equation-solving skills in order to solve inequalities.

Have the students consider inequalities such as

a. $6x + 2 < 14$
b. $8 - 3x > -13$
c. $22 \leqslant 4 - 2(x + 1)$
d. $14 - 3(x + 2) \geqslant 3x + 5$

Use the second one as an example. Suppose that there is some value of *x* which will make

$$8 - 3x = -13$$

and that this value separates the other two possibilities. We leave the inequality for now and solve the equation.

$8 - 3x = -13$	Given
$-3x = -21$	Subtract 8 from both sides
$x = 7$	Divide both sides by -3

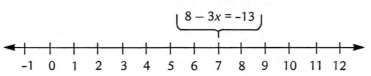

We now see that at $x = 7$ on the number line, $8 - 3x = -13$. Now all we need to do is to find out whether the "is greater than" condition of our inequality is to the left or to the right of 7. Since *all* of the numbers to a given side act the same, we can find out by arbitrarily choosing test numbers, for example, $x = 0$ to the left of 7 and $x = 9$ to the right.

For $x = 0$	For $x = 9$
$8 - 3(0) > -13$	$8 - 3(9) > -13$
$8 - 0 > -13$	$8 - 27 > -13$
$8 > -13$	$-19 > -13$
True	False

Our test shows that the "is greater than" condition is true to the left of 7. Therefore, the solution set for $8 - 3x > -13$ is given by

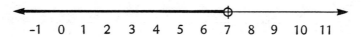

Point out to the students that:

A. They may want to try a few more values to feel more confident with this method. The key is to recognize that all values to one side of the equality act the same.

B. The original inequality was $>$ while the answer was to the left of the equality. Students should not generalize that the direction of the answer and the original inequality will be the same.

4. *Activity.* Have students find solutions to the other examples given above using this method.

BALANCE OPERATIONS FOR INEQUALITY

5. *Teacher Presentation.* Instead of switching to an equation, solving the equation, and then testing the original inequality as we did in the preceding section, we can encourage students to solve inequalities directly as we did for equations. We want them to see that with slight adjustments, the addition, subtraction, multiplication, and division properties can be used with inequalities.

6. *Teacher Presentation.* Have students consider what happens when the same number is added to both sides of an inequality. Use the diagrams below to help.

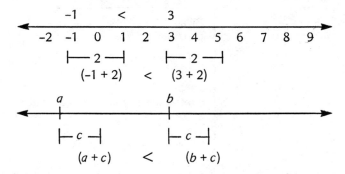

Help students decide that, in general, if $a < b$, then $(a + c) < (b + c)$. Of course, you will want to consider the other cases $(>, \geqslant, \leqslant)$. Have students solve $x - 3 < 7$ using this property.

7. *Activity.* Have students illustrate the subtractive property of inequality on a number line.

If $a < b$, then $(a - c) < (b - c)$

8. *Teacher Presentation.* Special care needs to be taken with multiplication. Use the following examples to illustrate this to the students.

a. Negative Multiplier   b. Zero Multiplier   c. Positive Multiplier

a. Negative Multiplier	b. Zero Multiplier	c. Positive Multiplier
$2 < 3$	$2 < 3$	$2 < 3$
Mult. by -1	Mult. by 0	Mult. by 7
$-2 > -3$	$0 = 0$	$14 < 21$

Emphasize that the results depend on the kind of multiplier used. Figure 3.10 is intended to give some insight as to how the order switches when a negative multiplier is used. Remember how multiplying by negative 1 gives the opposite of a number. Then, as the diagram shows, the order relation is switched also.

If $a < b$ then $-a > -b$

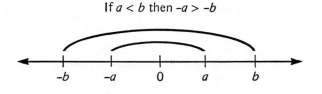

Figure 3.10

The division property is similar, but more simple because we do not divide by zero.

9. *Activity.* Have students complete the following examples to verify the division property.

a.	12 < 36	b.	–20 < 8	c.	–27 < –9
	Divide by –3		Divide by 4		Divide by –1
	_____		_____		_____

10. *Teacher Presentation.* Present the following on the overhead to help students see how these properties can be used to solve inequalities.

Statement	Reason	Comment
$4(x + 1) < 25 - 3x$ $4x + 4 < 25 - 3x$	Given Distributive property	} Remove ( )
$(4x + 4) + 3x < (25 - 3x) + 3x$ $(4x + 3x) + 4 < 25$	Additive property of inequality Simplify	} Attraction
$7x + 4 < 25$ $(7x + 4) - 4 < (25 - 4)$	Simplify Subtractive property of inequality	} Collection
$7x < 21$ $\dfrac{7x}{7} < \dfrac{21}{7}$ $x < 3$	Simplify Division property of inequality Simplify	} Isolation

11. *Activity.* Have students solve $8 - 3x > -13$ to check their use of a negative divisor.

12. *Activity.* Have students practice solving inequalities for the exercises on Reproduction Page 52.

DOUBLE AND ABSOLUTE VALUE INEQUALITIES
Here we introduce the students to double inequalities such as

$-3 < x \leqslant 2$

Solving techniques for inequalities are extended for direct work on this variety of inequality. Applications are made to solving absolute value inequalities like

$|x - 2| \leqslant 3$ and
$|x - 2| > 3$.

13. *Teacher Presentation.* Present the following compound sentence to the students.

   $x > 3$ and $x < 9$

Ask students for numbers that make both parts of this statement true. Graph these solutions on a number line. Emphasize that the word "and" means that a value for x must satisfy both inequalities for the entire statement to be true. Referring to the graph

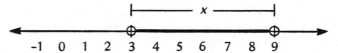

emphasize that the solution is "x is between 3 and 9." Introduce the notation $3 < x < 9$ and point out that it is equivalent to $x > 3$ and $x < 9$. Therefore, "$< x <$" means "is between."

Present the following table to the students to help them see the variations here.

Double Inequality	Meaning
$3 < x < 9$ or $9 > x > 3$	x is between 3 and 9
$0 \leqslant x \leqslant 1$ or $1 \geqslant x \geqslant 0$	x is between 0 and 1, inclusively
$-1 \leqslant x \leqslant 1$ or $1 > x \leqslant -1$	x is between -1 and 1, including -1
$-3 < (x-2) \leqslant 3$ or $3 \geqslant (x-2) > -3$	$(x-2)$ is between -3 and 3, including 3

14. *Activity.* Have students complete the practice and discovery exercises on Reproduction Page 53.

15. *Teacher Presentation.* Present the following to the students for solution:

$$19 \leqslant 3x - 2 < 25$$

Help the students develop a systematic approach by working simultaneously with all three members of the double inequality.

Encourage the students to analyze the expression $3x - 2$ to see that x is first being multiplied by 3 and then that answer is reduced by 2. Thinking of undoing these actions, we want to add back the 2 and then divide by 3. Show the following to the students.

Statement	Comment
$19 \leqslant 3x - 2 < 25$	Given
$19 + 2 \leqslant (3x - 2) + 2 < 25 + 2$	Add 2 to each member
$21 \leqslant 3x < 27$	
$\dfrac{21}{3} \leqslant \dfrac{3x}{3} < \dfrac{27}{3}$	Divide each member by 3
$7 \leqslant x < 9$	

If students have questions about the legitimacy of this approach, show them that $7 \leqslant x < 9$ is equivalent to $19 \leqslant 3x - 2 < 25$.

7, 8, and $8\frac{2}{3}$ are easily seen to be solutions for $7 \leqslant x < 9$. Have students confirm by substitution the following:

$$3(7) - 2 = 21 - 2 = 19$$
$$3(8) - 2 = 24 - 2 = 22$$
$$3\left(8\frac{2}{3}\right) - = 26 - 2 = 24$$

This shows that each is also a solution for the original inequality. You might also

GOSHEN COLLEGE LIBRARY
GOSHEN, INDIANA

want to have students check to see that nonsolutions of $7 \leqslant x < 9$ are nonsolutions for $19 \leqslant 3x - 2 < 25$.

16. *Activity.* Have the students, as a group, discuss solutions to

a. $19 \leqslant 2 - 3x < 25$ and   b. $2 - 5x < 5 - 2x < 11 - 5x$

The first is intended to provide a demonstration of the switching of order relations for negative multipliers or divisors. The second should show that the method can be used in special cases when x's occur in the outer members.

17. *Activity.* Have students practice the solution process by doing the exercises on Reproduction Page 54.

18. *Teacher Presentation.* Have students examine the solution sets for each problem in fig. 3.11.

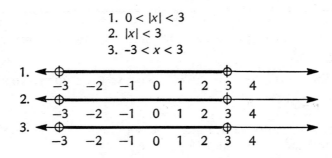

1. $0 < |x| < 3$
2. $|x| < 3$
3. $-3 < x < 3$

Figure 3.11

The students will see that they are all the same. Point out to the students that these statements are equivalent (have the same solution sets). Emphasize examples 2 and 3 to obtain the following:

$|N| < A$
means $-A < N < A$ $A > 0$

This gives us a way to solve absolute-value inequalities. Present the following to the class:

$|2x - 25| < 3$

Have the students think of $(2x - 25)$ as one number whose absolute value is less than 3. Have students complete the following:

_____ $< 2x - 25 <$ _____

Have the students complete the solution to obtain

$22 < 2x < 28$
$11 < x < 14$

19. *Activity.* Have students practice these ideas with the following exercises.
    a. $|2x - 7| \leqslant 9$
    b. $|7 - 2x| \leqslant 9$

20. *Teacher Presentation.* Review the solution process for inequalities such as $|2x - 7| \leqslant 9$. Ask the students how they think we might approach those like $|2x - 7| > 9$. Help them recall that the solution set for $|2x - 7| \leqslant 9$ is

The solution for $|2x - 7| > 9$, then, is the *complement* (everything else).

Point out that since this is made up of two parts, $x < -1$ and $x > 8$, it can be described by the compound *or*-statement:

$x < -1$ or $x > 8$.

Help the students recall that an or-statement is false only when both parts are false. Thus, for example, 2 is not a solution since

$2 < -1$ or $2 > 8$

has both parts false. On the other hand, –2 and 9 are both solutions

$-2 < -1$ or $-2 > 8$ $\qquad$ $9 < -1$ or $9 > 8$

the left being true in the first and the right side being true in the second.

The students should be encouraged to generalize the following:

$|N| > A$ means
$N < -A$ or $N > A$

Illustrate the use of this idea in the following.

Statement	Comment
$|2x - 7| > 9$	Given
$2x - 7 < -9$ or $2x - 7 > 9$	Equivalent statement
$2x < -2 \qquad$ or $\quad 2x > 16$	Simplify both single inequalities
$x < -1 \qquad\quad$ or $\quad x > 8$	Simplify each
	The solution set for an or-statement is the union of those for the separate clauses.

21. *Activity.* Have students complete and discuss the practice items on Reproduction Page 55.

CHALLENGE PROBLEMS

1. $x + \dfrac{1}{x} = 3\dfrac{1}{3}$. Solve for x.

2. If x is a real number and $|x - 4| + |x - 3| < a$ where $a > 0$, then the range of a is _____.

3. If $7x - [8x + 4(x + 2)] = -(1 + x)$, then $x =$ _____.

4. $\dfrac{1}{2 - \dfrac{x}{1 - x}} = \dfrac{1}{2}$. Solve for x.

5. If $2x + 3 = 5$ and $ax - 3 = 7$, then $a =$ _____.

6. If $\left| \dfrac{1}{x} - 5 \right| < 1$, find the range of x.

7. The sides of a rectangle are $x + 3$ and $2x - 5$. If the perimeter is 20, what are the lengths of the sides?

8. If $|x - a| = |x - b|$, and if $a \neq b$, find the value of x in terms of a and b.

9. To number the pages in a math book the printer used 2989 digits. How many pages are in the book?

10. How many problems must a student get right to score 100 on a 120-question test if the teacher gives one point for each correct answer but subtracts $\dfrac{1}{4}$ point for each wrong answer? (An answer left blank is the same as an incorrect answer.)

EVALUATION

Evaluating algebraic expressions.

For each item, using the given values for the variables, determine the numerical value for the given expression.

1. $2(x + 5)$; $x = 7$
2. $x(9 - 3y)$; $x = (-1)$, $y = 4$
3. $ab + ac$; $a = 3, b = 6, c = 4$
4. $5\left(\dfrac{F - 32}{9}\right)$; $F = 32$

Simplify each of the following algebraic expressions, removing grouping symbols and combining like terms.

1. $2(x + 5) + 3x$
2. $4x - 2(x + 1)$
3. $2x + 3y - (3x - 2y)$
4. $2(x + 2(x - 2))$

Identifying equations and inequalities.

For each of the following, indicate whether it is an equation (write E), an inequality (write I), or neither (write N).

1. _____ $3x + 2 \leqslant 5$
2. _____ $x \in \{x \mid x = 2\}$
3. _____ $x^2 + 2x = 3$
4. _____ $3x \leqslant 2 \leqslant 5x$

Identifying solution sets for open sentences.

For each open sentence in Column I, choose the corresponding solution set in Column II.

Column I	Column II

Column I

1. _____ $x + 4x = 12$

2. _____ $x + 2 \leqslant 15$

3. _____ $4x - 2(x + 1) = 4 - x$

4. _____ $2(x + 5) = 3x$

5. _____ $-6 \leqslant x \leqslant 2$

Column II

A. (number line from −6 to 2)

B. $\{10\}$

C. $\{-6, 2\}$

D. $\{2\}$

E. $\{-6\}$

F. (number line from 0 to +13)

G. None of the above

Solving linear equations.

Solve.

1. $3(x + 1) = 24$

2. $\dfrac{x - 3}{8} = 2$

3. $x + 2(x - 1) = 10$

4. $4 - 3(x + 2) = 10$

5. $x + 7 = 3(x - 1)$

6. $3(x + 2) = 7 - 4(3 - x)$

7. $\dfrac{x + 2}{5} = 3(x + 2)$

8. $5 - 3(x - 4) = 2(x - 4)$

Solving formulas.

Given the formula, solve for the indicated variable.

1. $a = lw$; for w

2. $P = 2(l + w)$; for w

3. $E = \dfrac{1}{2}mv^2$; for m

4. $F = \dfrac{9}{5}C + 32$; for C

5. $A = p + prt$; for p

6. $T = 2(lw + lh + wh)$; for w

Solution strategies.

1. For which *one* of the following is it necessary to remove parentheses before combining like terms?
   a. $2x + 5 = x - (3 + 2)$ b. $5x = x - 3(x + 2)$
   c. $3(x + 2) + 2(x + 2) = 17$ d. $(2x - 3x) + 5 = 17$
   e. All of the above

2. Which *one* of the following *cannot* be solved by simply undoing the order of operations?

   a. $3(x + 2) = 7$ b. $\dfrac{x - 3}{2} = 5$

   c. $2(x + 2) + 5 = 13$ d. $2(x + 2 + 5) = 13$
   e. $2x + 4x + 10 = 13$

Solving inequalities.

Solve for the unknown and graph the solution set.

1. $2x + 1 \leqslant 19$

2. $\dfrac{x - 1}{3} > 7$

3. $x + 2(x - 1) < 4x + 3$

4. $8 - 2x \geqslant 18$

Solving double inequalities and absolute value inequalities.

Solve and graph the solution set.

1. $0 \leqslant 2x - 9 < 99$ 2. $3 \geqslant 3 - x > 6$

3. $|x - 2| \leqslant 7$ 4. $|8 - x| \geqslant 2$

5. $|2x - 3| < 11$ 6. $3 \leqslant |x| < 5$

RESOURCES

Below is a selected list of resources for teaching the solution of linear equations and inequalities in two variables. Addresses of publishers can be found in Appendix A.

Applications in Mathematics (A.I.M.): Equations and Formulas. Glenview, IL: Scott, Foresman, 1983. Includes a set of duplicating masters and overhead visuals for teaching equations to lower-level students. Minimal reading required.

Clark, Alice, and Leitch, Carol, *Amusements in Developing Algebra Skills, Volume 1.* Pacific Grove, CA: Midwest Publications, 1983. Provides an ideal combination of extensive algebra practice exercises, embedded in cross number puzzles, line designs, decodes, picture graphs, optical illusions, and others. Includes fifty-two duplicating masters.

Inequalities. Chicago, IL: LaPine Scientific Company, 1983. Includes four filmstrips (forty frames each) on the graphing of inequalities in one and two variables.

Introduction to Algebraic Equations. Chicago, IL: LaPine Scientific Company, 1983. Includes two captioned filmstrips presenting a systematic approach to solving equations by considering inverse operations, equivalent equations, and the four basic arithmetic operations.

The Math Group, *Journey into Algebra.* Clinton, IA: EDUCAT Publishers, 1983. A set of clever puzzles and other activities for learning and practicing the skills of algebra.

National Council of Teachers of Mathematics,

The Mathematics Teacher. Reston, VA: NCTM. This monthly journal is published nine times a year and includes useful suggestions for teaching various topics in the secondary school mathematics curriculum.

National Council of Teachers of Mathematics, *The Teaching of Secondary School Mathematics* (33rd Yearbook). Reston, VA: NCTM, 1970. This yearbook contains sections about preparing plans for teaching algebra (among others).

Plan, Algebra 1. Oak Lawn, IL: Plan Products, 1983. Provides the complete introductory algebra curriculum advocated by the School Mathematics Study Group. The teacher's kit includes placement tests, achievement tests, and duplicating masters.

Plastigraph. Bronx, NY: Academic Industries, Inc. A board with prenumbered x and y-axes—coated with a durable plastic to ensure a long life.

Rectangular Coordinates Stamp. Chicago, IL: LaPine Scientific Company, 1983. A rubber stamp measuring 3 X 3 inches; available in 100 blocks or 16 blocks per square inch. Ideal when a rectangular coordinate system is needed for tests or assignments.

The Skills Group, *Equations, Module Five.* New York: Harper and Row, 1983. Slides, filmstrip, and tape cassette dealing with solving equations in algebra.

Solving Equations 1. Chicago, IL: LaPine Scientific Company, 1983. Includes four filmstrips for solving equations.

4

Solving Equations and Inequalities In Two Variables

CONTENT OVERVIEW

The systems of simultaneous linear equations of concern in elementary algebra are limited to only two equations in two unknowns. The three commonly used methods for solving such systems are (1) the graphical method, (2) the method of substitution, and (3) the method of linear combination. Solving pairs of linear inequalities will be limited here to the graphical method. Students should be able to compare and contrast these methods along the dimensions of practicality and efficiency.

Although many elementary algebra textbooks are not sequenced as such, it will be our goal to demonstrate that solving equations in two variables is a natural extension of solving equations in one variable. The principles and procedures discussed in the preceding chapter will be applied by the student to the solution of two equations in two unknowns (variables). Students will be provided with a preview of the graphs of linear functions (Chapter 7) and with a review of the algebraic field properties (Chapter 2) and their role in the solution of simultaneous linear equations. Applications or word problems are examined in Chapter 8.

OBJECTIVES

As a result of the learning experiences in this chapter, the student should be able to:

1. Graph a line(s) given its equation on a coordinate plane

2. Graph a linear inequality on a coordinate axis

3. Solve pairs of linear equations by graphing

4. Determine whether a pair of linear equations is inconsistent or dependent or independent

5. Solve pairs of linear inequalities by graphing

51

6. Find the solution of two equations in two variables by substitution

7. Find the solution of two equations in two variables by the use of linear combinations

LEARNING EXPERIENCES

Topic 1: Graphing Lines and Half-Planes

1. *Teacher Presentation.* Introduce the idea of ordered pairs, lines, and half-planes by referring to the section of land in fig. 4.1 called Equation City. Here the streets run north and south and the avenues run east and west. Ask students to meet you at the corner of 2nd and 3rd. There are two possible locations, A and B. Define the intersection as (street number, avenue number). After discussing this enigma with the students, write the intersection so that the first "move" runs east-west and the second, north-south. Emphasize the importance of order. Therefore Location P is represented as (1, 3): indicating the corner of 1st Street and 3rd Avenue and the students should all meet you at point A!

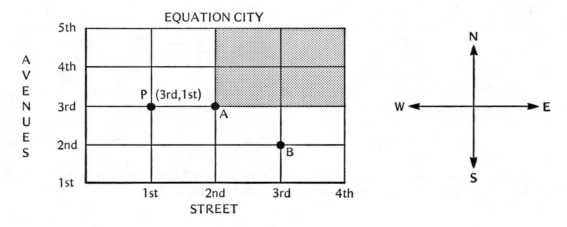

Figure 4.1

2. *Activity.* Ask students for other intersections in Equation City. Let students draw lines passing through two intersections. Finally have students shade the area north of 3rd Avenue and east of 2nd Street. Ask students to define other subsections in a similar manner. You may wish to define planes and half-planes.

3. *Teacher Presentation.* The solution of an equation in one variable (e.g., $2x + 5 = 9$) was that value of the variable (e.g., $x = 2$) which made the equation true. In a similar manner, the solution(s) of an equation in two variables are those values of the variables which make the equation true.
Example:
Let $y = 2x - 1$

a. If $x = 0$, then $y = 2x - 1 = 2(0) - 1 = -1$,
    Thus $(0, -1)$ is a solution.
b. If $x = 1$, then $y = 2x - 1 = 2(1) - 1 = 1$,
    Thus $(1, 1)$ is a solution.

4. *Activity*. Give the students several equations and have them list some solution (ordered) pairs determined by each equation. Emphasize the importance of order.

   Examples:
   a. $y = 2x$ $(0, 0), (1, 2), (-3, 6), \ldots$

   b. $F = \dfrac{9}{5} C + 32$ $(0, 32), (100, 212), (-40, -40), \ldots$

   c. $y = 3$ $(0, 3), (1, 3), (-2, 3), \ldots$

5. *Activity*. Have the students plot each set of ordered pairs on a coordinate plane. By connecting the points, it should be clear that the graph of an equation is the geometric representation of its solutions. Repeat this exercise with the examples found on Reproduction Page 56. Students may want to use a calculator.

6. *Teacher Presentation*. Although two points are sufficient for graphing a linear equation, emphasize the fact that a third point is useful as a checking device.

7. *Teacher Presentation*. Briefly review the concept of inequalities in one variable. Just as the solution of an inequality in one variable (e.g., $2x + 4 \leqslant 10$) are those values of the variable for which the equation is true (e.g., $x = \ldots -3, -2, -1, 0, 1, 2, 3$), the solution of an inequality in two variables consists of those solution pairs which make the inequality true. (The graph of an inequality in one variable may be represented as a ray or a half-line on a number line.)

   Examples:
   a. $y \leqslant 3x - 2$ $(0,-2), (0,-3), (5,10), \ldots$
   b. $y > x + 4$ $(0,5), (-4,6), (5,10), \ldots$
   c. $x > y + 3$ $(0,-4), (5,1), (5,0), \ldots$

8. *Activity*. Have students graph $y = 3x - 2$ and $y = x + 4$ as well as solution pairs of $y \leqslant 3x - 2$ and $y > x + 4$, respectively. Define half-planes in terms of the solution pairs of an inequality in two variables.

Topic 2: Solving Systems by Graphing

1. *Activity*. Have students graph the following pairs of equations:
   a. $6x - 2y = 12$
      $4x + 2y = 18$
   b. $2x - 3y = 4$
      $2x - 3y = 7$
   c. $5x - 10y = 5$
      $3x - 6y = 3$

   The graphs should reveal two intersecting lines for the first pair, two parallel lines for the second pair, and two coinciding lines for the third pair. Now ask the class the following questions:

   A. Do the coordinates of each point on the graph of $6x - 2y = 12$ satisfy this equation? Is the same true for the graphs of the other equations?

B. How many points do the graphs of the first pair of equations have in common? The graphs of the second pair? The graphs of the third pair?

C. What are the coordinates of the common point for the graphs of the first pair of equations? Do these satisfy both equations?

D. What is different about the three pairs of equations? Why do their graphs appear as they do? At this point, the terms independent, dependent, and inconsistent might be introduced. On the other hand, you might wish to define these terms after solving equations by linear combinations has been discussed.

2. *Teacher Presentation.* Students should now be helped to make some generalizations. For example, equations of the form $ax + by = c$ and $ax + by = d$ have no common solution if $c \neq d$. They are called inconsistent equations. Ask students to write the general form of a pair of linear equations that are dependent; that have a common solution. You may wish to briefly introduce the concept of slope (Chapter 7).

3. *Activity.* Given the common point (2,3), have students construct and graph a pair or system of simultaneous linear equations (e.g., $x + y = 5$ and $2x - y = 1$). Have students compare their equations and graphs with each other. Now define equivalent systems of equations.

   Discussion Question: What is the difference between equivalent systems of equations and equivalent equations?

   Discussion: Equivalent equations (see Chapter 3) are equations that have the same solution; for example $3x + 5 = 11$ is equivalent to $3x = 6$ or $x = 2$.

   Equivalent systems of equations are systems of equations that have the same solution; for example:

   $$\left. \begin{array}{l} x + y = 5 \\ 2x - y = 1 \end{array} \right\} \text{ is equivalent to } \begin{array}{l} x = 2 \\ y = 3 \end{array}$$

   It is important to note, however, that even though equivalent systems of equations have the same solution, the equations forming the equivalent systems need not be equivalent.

   Have students complete Reproduction page 57.

4. *Teacher Presentation.* Briefly review the terms and properties associated with solving inequalities in one variable (e.g., order, half-plane). Have students graph $y \geqslant x + 1$ and $2x + y < 3$ on the same coordinate axis. Ask students if all solution pairs which satisfy both inequalities simultaneously can be listed. The students should be convinced that the solution of two simultaneous linear inequalities must be presented graphically. You may want to refer to the activity with Equation City. For enrichment, linear programming could be discussed.

5. *Activity.* Have students complete Reproduction Page 58. Emphasize the use of a test point in checking your solution.

Topic 3: Solving by Substitution

1. *Teacher Presentation.* Although the graphic method is interesting and illustrative, it is not, in general, an accurate way of determining the solution of a system of equations. To introduce the need for a more systematic method for solving two equations in two variables, ask the class to solve this system graphically:

$$4x + 8y = 1$$
$$x - y = 1$$

The solution $\left(\frac{3}{4}, -\frac{1}{4}\right)$ is difficult to determine from the graph of the equations. They will probably say $(1,0)$ is the solution! Have the students check their answer and find out that it is incorrect.

2. *Activity*. Ask students to solve the following system of equations:

$$y = -2x$$
$$y = 3x - 4$$

As before, graphing does not provide an accurate answer. Students may try to guess common coordinates by evaluating the equations at different points. It is hoped that the "obvious" manner of presentation and the fact that whatever value of y satisfying the first equation must also satisfy the second will lead students to solve for x in $-2x = 3x - 4$. Point out to the students that this, in fact, is a method of substitution.

3. *Teacher Presentation*. Present students with a detailed step-by-step solution to:

$$4x - 3y = 2$$
$$2x + y = -4$$

Emphasize that the substitution method is most easily applied when the coefficients of one of the variables in one of the equations is 1 or –1. Therefore, in the second (bottom) equation, y should be isolated $[y = -2x - 4]$.

STEPS FOR SOLVING A SYSTEM BY THE SUBSTITUTION METHOD

$4x - 3y = 2$
$\quad y = (-2x - 4)$

a. Solve one of the equations for one of the variables in terms of the other and enclose in ( ).

$4x - 3\,(y) = 2$
$4x - 3(-2x - 4) = 2$
$4x + 6x + 12 = 2$
$\qquad 10x = -10$

b. Now substitute this value for y in the other equation.

c. Perform the indicated operations and collect terms.

$x = -1$
$y = -2(-1) - 4 = -2$
$\qquad$ or
$4(-2) - 3y = 2$

d. Solve for x.

e. Substitute the value of x into the expression enclosed in ( ) in step a. and solve for the other variable.

Thus,
$-3y = 6$ or $y = -2$
Hence the solution is $(-1, -2)$.

The student should be made aware of how the field properties allow for the operations to be used in passing from one step to another. Point out that other sequences could be used, but this one is most convenient.

4. *Teacher Presentation*. Have students solve

$$y = 2x + 1$$
$$y = 2x - 1$$

by substitution. In general, if $Ax + B = Cx + D$, then consider $\dfrac{D - B}{C - A}$. If the denominator is zero and the numerator is not zero, then the lines will be parallel; if both the numerator and denominator are zero, then the lines will coincide. Otherwise, the lines will have a unique solution.

Examples:

$$\text{a.} \quad 2x + 3y = 9 \xrightarrow{} y = -\frac{2}{3}x + 3$$

$$8x + 12y = 1 \xrightarrow{} y = -\frac{8}{12}x + \frac{1}{12}$$

where the circled labels are $\textcircled{A}$ $\textcircled{B}$ over the first equation's right side and $\textcircled{C}$ $\textcircled{D}$ over the second.

Hence

$$\frac{D-B}{C-A} = \frac{\frac{1}{12} - 3}{-\frac{8}{12} - \left(-\frac{2}{3}\right)} = \frac{-2\frac{11}{12}}{0}$$

Thus, the lines are parallel.

$$\text{b.} \quad y - 6 = 3x \xrightarrow{} y = 3x + 6$$
$$y - 3x = 6 \xrightarrow{} y = 3x + 6$$

Hence

$$\frac{D-B}{C-A} = \frac{6-6}{3-3} = \frac{0}{0}$$

Thus, the lines coincide.

Students should be asked to graph these examples for verification. For enrichment, students could be asked to show why these rules work.

Topic 4: Solving by Linear Combinations

1. *Teacher Presentation.* Ask students to solve the following system of equations by substitution:

$$\begin{cases} 2x - y = 9 \\ x + y = 6 \dots y = 6 - x \end{cases}$$

This will yield $2x - (6 - x) = 9*$ which the students can solve for x. Point out that if we add the equations (using the addition property of equality), we will have:

$$2x - y + x + y = 9 + 6$$

or

$$2x + x = 9 + 6$$

or

$$2x + x - 6 = 9$$

or

$$2x + (-6 + x) = 9$$

or

$2x - (6 - x) = 9*$ (the same result when substitution was used)

Hence we can add (or subtract) equations when it is convenient to do so.

2. *Activity.* Have students solve the following equations using this method. Encourage students to substitute the solution into the original equations to check their work.

a. $\begin{cases} 3x - y = 5 \\ x + y = 7 \end{cases}$ b. $\begin{cases} 3y + 2x = 11 \\ 2y + 2x = 8 \end{cases}$

c. $\begin{cases} x + y = 6 \\ x + y = 12 \end{cases}$ d. $\begin{cases} 2x + y = 8 \\ x + 3y = 14 \end{cases}$

If students have difficulty with c., have them graph it on a coordinate plane. As for d., students will be unable to eliminate the x or y variable using the add or subtract method. Now ask the students to graph $x + 3y = 14$ and $6x + 6y = 24$ on the same coordinate plane. Remind students that multiplying both members of an equation by a nonzero constant produces an equation whose graph is identical to that of the original equation. In other words, $ax + by = c$ is equivalent to $kax + kby = k$ ($k \neq 0$). Hopefully, students will be able to use this information to solve d.

3. *Teacher Presentation.* Write the following equations on the board.
   a. $3x + y = 5$
   b. $x - y = 7$

Ask students to perform the following operations on these equations:
   a. Add the two equations.
   b. Subtract the second equation from the first.
   c. Multiply both sides of the second equation by three.

4. *Activity.* Put the following problems on the board.

a. $\begin{cases} 3x + 27 = 14 \\ 2x + y = 3 \end{cases}$ b. $\begin{cases} 4a - 3b = 1 \\ a - b = 6 \end{cases}$

c. $\begin{cases} 3x + 4y = 7 \\ 2x + 3y = -5 \end{cases}$ d. $\begin{cases} 2p + 6q = 20 \\ 7p - 8q = 12 \end{cases}$

Ask the students to determine a number(s) by which they can multiply one or both of the equations in the system in order to eliminate a particular variable. Have students complete Reproduction Page 59.

5. *Activity (Enrichment).* Have students attempt to solve the following system.

$$\begin{cases} x + y + z = 6 \\ x - y + z = 4 \end{cases}$$

You might wish to discuss that the intersection of two planes is one line, one plane (coinciding), or $\emptyset$ (given planes are parallel). What is the intersection of three planes? As an extension, you may present three equations in three unknowns.

6. *Activity (Enrichment).* Have students solve the following systems.

a. $\begin{cases} x + 2y = 3 \\ 4x + 5y = 6 \end{cases}$ b. $\begin{cases} 2x + 5y = 8 \\ 11x + 14y = 17 \end{cases}$

c. $\begin{cases} 10x + 9y = 8 \\ 7x + 6y = 5 \end{cases}$ d. $\begin{cases} 6x + 11y = 16 \\ 21x + 26y = 31 \end{cases}$

The students will notice that the solution of each system is $(-1, 2)$. What is the generalization? It is true that $(-1, 2)$ is the solution set of all pairs of equations where the coefficients and righthand members are members of any arithmetic sequence. Are there similar results for other kinds of sequences?

CHALLENGE PROBLEMS

1. If $x : y = 8 : 5$ and $x - y = 6$, find (x, y).

2. If the graphs of $2y + x + 3 = 0$ and $3y + ax + 2 = 0$ are to meet at right angles, the value of $a =$ _____ .

3. The set of points satisfying the pair of inequalities $y > 2x$ and $y > 4 - x$ is contained entirely in quadrants:
   a. I and II
   b. II and III
   c. I and III
   d. III and IV
   e. I and IV

4. Find the minimum value of $\sqrt{x^2 + y^2}$ if $5x + 12y = 60$.

5. Find the ordered pair (x, y) which satisfies

   $$y = 5x - 15$$

   but *does not* satisfy

   $$\frac{y}{x - 3} = 5$$

6. Find the ordered pair of numbers (x, y) for which

   $$123x + 321y = 345$$
   $$321x + 123y = 543$$

   Hint: Add the two equations.

7. If the ratio $2x - y$ to $x + y$ is $\frac{2}{3}$, what is the ratio x to y?

8. Solve the following system for x and y.

   $$ax + by = c$$
   $$\frac{x}{a} + \frac{b}{y} = c$$

9. $a = 11 - b$
   $2a = 22 - 2b$

   $$3(a + b) = \text{_____}$$

10. $\left(\frac{4}{s} - \frac{s}{4} \right)^2 = 0$, then $s^2 =$ _____ .

EVALUATION

Graph the following pairs of simultaneous linear equations and describe the solution as independent, dependent, or inconsistent.

1. $x - 2y = 6$
   $2x + 3y = 5$

2. $x - y = 8$
   $2x - 2y = 8$

3. $4x - 6 = y$
   $2y - 3 = 4x$

4. $y = 5x$
   $x = 2$

5. $3x + 3y = 3$
   $x + y = 1$

6. $y = 3x + 4$
   $x + 2y = 6$

Solve by substitution or linear combination.

1. $x - y = 8$
   $x + y = 43$

2. $x - 2y = 6$
   $2x + 3y = 5$

3. $x = 4y - 5$
   $y = 4x - 5$

4. $x + 3y = 4$
   $2x + y = 5$

Solve graphically and check with a test point.

1. $3x + 4y \geq 12$
   $6x - 2y > 4$

2. $y \geq x$
   $2x - 3y < 3$

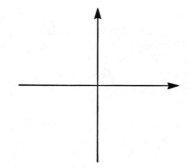

Given the equation $x + 2y = 5$, write another equation that makes a pair of simultaneous equations:

1. that are independent _____

2. that are dependent _____

3. that are inconsistent _____

RESOURCES

Below is a selected list of resources for teaching the simultaneous solution of linear equations and inequalities. Addresses of publishers can be found in Appendix A.

Beckenbach, Edwin, and Bellman, Richard, *An Introduction to Inequalities*. New York: Random House, 1975. This book provides additional information on inequalities (not found in texts).

Bitter, Gary G., and Mikesell, Jerald L., *Activities Handbook for Teaching with the Hand-Held Calculator*. Newton: Allyn and Bacon, 1980. Familiarizes teachers with basic methods for using the calculator as a teaching tool.

Clark, Alice, and Leitch, Carol, *Amusements in Developing Algebra Skills, Volume 1*. Pacific Grove, CA: Midwest Publications, 1983. Provides an ideal combination of extensive algebra practice exercises embedded in cross number puzzles, line designs, decodes, picture graphs, optical illusions, and others.

Crouse, Richard J., and Sloyer, Clifford W., *Mathematical Questions from the Classroom*. Newton, MA: Allyn and Bacon, 1983. A collection of questions and suggested answers for secondary school mathematics students.

Inequalities. Chicago: LaPine Scientific Company, 1983. Includes four filmstrips (forty frames each) on the graphing of inequalities in one and two variables.

Linear Equations: Graphic and Algebraic Approaches. Chicago: LaPine Scientific Company, 1983. Includes two captioned filmstrips for assisting students in solving a system of two linear equations by plotting them on a coordinate grid.

Modern Algebra Film Series. San Francisco: Modern Learning Aids, 1983. Of particular interest is the film titled *Solving Simultaneous Linear Equations.*

National Council of Teachers of Mathematics, *The Mathematics Teacher.* Reston, VA: NCTM. This monthly journal is published nine times a year and includes useful suggestions for teaching various topics in the secondary school mathematics curriculum.

National Council of Teachers of Mathematics, *The Growth of Mathematical Ideas, Grades K–12* (24th Yearbook). Reston, VA: NCTM, 1959.

National Council of Teachers of Mathematics, *The Teaching of Secondary School Mathematics* (33rd Yearbook). Reston, VA: NCTM, 1970. This yearbook contains sections about preparing plans for teaching algebra (among others).

Plan, Algebra 1. Oak Lawn, IL: Plan Products, 1983. Provides the complete introductory algebra curriculum advocated by the School Mathematics Study Group. The teacher's kit includes placement tests, achievement tests, and duplicating masters.

Rassmussen, Peter, *Key to Algebra.* Hayward, CA: Activity Resources Co., 1974. A set of small pamphlets that provide practice in basic algebra skills.

School Science and Mathematics. Bowling Green, OH: School Science and Mathematics Association. This monthly journal is published nine times a year and includes pedagogy and research in mathematics education that is useful for the secondary/postsecondary teacher.

The Skills Group, *Equations, Module Five.* New York: Center for Humanities, 1983. Slides, filmstrip, tape cassette dealing with solving equations in algebra.

Two Linear Equations. Chicago: LaPine Scientific Company, 1983. Includes two filmstrips for solving two linear equations algebraically.

5

Working with Polynomials

CONTENT OVERVIEW

Much of the remaining algebra to be discussed centers around the very important mathematical concept of a *function*. While the concept of function will be discussed in detail in Chapter 7, a discussion of polynomials will help to bridge the gap between the introductory topics already considered and this central idea to follow. In particular, students will encounter a considerable amount of new symbols and terminology.

The skills developed in this chapter are the foundation for continued success in the course (and in advanced courses). It is therefore necessary to provide drillwork using the algorithms provided. Students should be encouraged to check their answers throughout this chapter by substituting a given number(s) for the variable(s).

OBJECTIVES

As a result of the learning experiences in this chapter, the student should be able to:

1. Express a given expression in exponential form

2. Apply the *Laws of Exponents* to simplify a given expression

3. Add, subtract, multiply, and divide polynomials

4. Multiply binomials mentally

5. Determine common monomial factors

6. Factor a given polynomial

LEARNING EXPERIENCES

Topic 1: Factors and Exponents

1. *Activity:* Supply each student with a copy of Reproduction Page 60 and use a transparency of it on the overhead projector.

   While working through the problem, the students will quickly see a need for a shorthand notation for $3 \cdot 3 \cdot 3 \cdot 3 \cdot 3 \cdot 3 \cdot 3$. Introduce "$3^7$" to represent this multiplication of seven 3's together. (This will *not* be a new concept to most students.)

   Discussion Question: What does the exponent tell us?

   Discussion: Many students mistakenly think that the exponent indicates how many multiplications are performed (e.g., 3^4 means $3 \cdot 3 \cdot 3 \cdot 3 \cdot 3$).

   Emphasize the fact that the exponent tells us how many times the base is used as a factor.

2. *Activity:* Have the students complete Reproduction Page 61 which will provide them with practice on expressions containing exponents.

3. *Teaching Presentation:* Lead the student to discover the following Laws of Exponents:

   a. $a^x \cdot a^y = a^{x+y}$

   b. $\dfrac{a^x}{a^y} = a^{x-y}$ ⟵———————— You may wish to introduce the meaning of a° and a negative power at this point.

   c. $(a^x)^y = a^{x \cdot y}$

   What is important here is for the student to realize that these "laws" represent "shortcuts" for operations with powers. It must be pointed out to the students that:

   A. to combine powers using these laws, they *must have* the *same base*

   B. we never operate on the base, just the exponents (Keep your hands off the bases!)

   C. there is no law governing the *addition* or *subtraction* of powers having the same base

4. *Activity:* (Using a calculator.) To reinforce the students' understanding of powers and the laws of exponents, the teacher may assign Reproduction Pages 62 and 63.

Topic 2: Arithmetic Operations on Polynomials

1. *Activity:* Pass out a copy of Reproduction Page 64 to each student and use a transparency of it on the overhead. Call on individual students to complete problems 1 and 2.

   Emphasize at the end of problem 2 that we are adding the coefficients of "like" terms.

   Ask for volunteers to complete each addition in problem 3.

   The students may check each answer (part 4) for extra credit points.

2. *Teacher Presentation* (Prerequisite skills for polynomials addition):

   a. Review the rules for adding integers

b. Define what we mean by "like terms" (terms that have the identical letter-part!)

PUT	Ⓐ	Ⓑ	Ⓒ	Ⓓ	Ⓔ	Ⓕ
ON	$2x^2$	$-3x$	$-4xy$	$2x$	x^2	$-xy$
BOARD						

Have the students identify pairs of like terms.

c. Using the examples on the board, have students identify the *coefficient* of each term
d. Have the students "add" the like terms together
e. Discuss what is meant by the simple form of a polynomial:
   I. If the expression contains the same variable, e.g.,

$$2x - x^2 + 5$$

   $\boxed{\text{RULE}}$ Arrange in descending powers of the variable.

$$\therefore 2x - x^2 + 5 = \boxed{-x^2 + 2x + 5}$$

   II. If the expression contains different variables, e.g.,

$$2b - c + 3a$$

   $\boxed{\text{RULE}}$ Arrange the terms alphabetically.

$$\therefore 2b - c + 3a = \boxed{3a + 2b - c}$$

3. *Activity:* Have the students complete Reproduction Page 65 for homework. The following day, allow them to grade their own work, emphasizing that this is a survey of skills and it will help them identify their weaknesses (if any) and get help from the teacher where needed.

   Ask the students to "add" each pair of polynomials in part E.

4. *Teacher Presentation* (Subtraction): Students should be familiar with the additive inverse of a number, but review this concept nonetheless $a + (-a) = 0$ . . . the *identity element for addition.*

   Then introduce the *opposite* of a polynomial. Put the following on the board:

$$(2x - 3) + (\quad ? \quad) = 0$$

Students will quickly figure out that the missing polynomial is $-2x + 3$. Identify this as the opposite of the given.

Provide practice by having students find several opposites:

Polynomial	$x^2 + 2$	$-x + 3$	$x^2 - 4x + 3$	$2ab + 3ac - 4$
Opposite				

Introduce the way to write the opposite as "$-$(given polynomial)." Then the opposite can be found by removing parentheses [multiply each term by (-1)].

$$\text{Given} \qquad \text{Opposite}$$
$$\text{e.g., } 2x - 4y + 3; \quad -(2x - 4y + 3) = \boxed{-2x + 4y - 3}$$

Multiply by (-1)

With this background, the students can be introduced to the subtraction of polynomials.

$\boxed{\text{RULE}}$ Subtracting a polynomial is the same as adding its opposite.

Put several examples on the board, e.g.:

$(2x^2 - 3x + 4) - (4x^2 + x - 1)$
$= \underbrace{(2x^2 - 3x + 4)}_{\text{I}} \underbrace{+}_{\text{II}} \underbrace{(-4x^2 - x + 1)}_{\text{III}}$

$= \underbrace{-2x^2 - 4x + 5}_{\text{IV}}$

STEP I: Recopy first term
STEP II: Change the minus to a plus
STEP III: Replace the 2nd ( ) with its opposite
STEP IV: Combine like terms

5. *Activity.* Have the students complete Reproduction Page 66 which provides drills on subtraction, both horizontal and vertical. Students should be able to do both kinds. Vertical subtraction will be needed to do division of polynomials later in this chapter.

6. *Teacher Presentation* (Multiplication of polynomials):
   a. Review the laws for multiplying integers and for adding integers
   b. Review how to multiply monomials

   $2x \cdot 3 = \boxed{6x}$ $\qquad$ $3x \cdot x = \boxed{3x^2}$

   $4b \cdot 5a = \boxed{20ab}$ $\qquad$ $2ab \cdot 3a = \boxed{6a^2b}$

   and how to add monomials
   c. Review the Distributive Law

   $2(3x - 4) = \boxed{}$

   $x(x + 5) = \boxed{}$

   It is strongly suggested that the teacher introduce multiplication of polynomials by using the Distributive Law:

   $(2x - 4)(3y + 8) = 2x(3y + 8) - 4(3y + 8)$
   $\qquad\qquad\qquad = 6xy + 16x - 12y - 8$

   Provide students with several examples in class until they have mastered this technique.

7. *Activity.* Have students complete Reproduction Page 67 for a homework assignment.

8. *Teacher Presentation* [Multiplying $(Ax + B)(Ax + C)$]:
   Once students have mastered how to multiply polynomials using the Distributive Law, the teacher can tie what they did to the "long-multiplication" process they had in grade school in the following way:

$$
\begin{array}{r}
23 \\
\times\, 46 \\
\hline
138 \\
920 \\
\hline
1058
\end{array}
\qquad
\begin{array}{r}
2x + 3 \\
4x + 6 \\
\hline
12x + 18 \\
8x^2 + 12x \\
\hline
8x^2 + 24x + 18
\end{array}
$$

a. Start with the 6 and multiply the number above by it to get the first partial product. In algebra, we don't have to carry over.

b. On the left, we are now multiplying by 40 to get the second partial product. On the right, we line up like terms when we multiply by $4x$.

c. On the left and on the right, we now *add* our partial products. Check the result on the right by letting $x = 10$ in the answer:

$$8(10)^2 + 24(10) + 18$$
$$= 800 \quad + 240 \quad + 18$$
$$= 1058 \text{ (the answer on the left)}$$

9. *Activity.* Do a multiplication problem on the board three different ways:

Distributive	Left-handed	Right-handed
$(2x + 3)(4x - 5)$ $= 2x(4x - 5) + 3(4x - 5)$ $= 8x^2 - 10x + 12x - 15$ $= \boxed{8x^2 + 2x - 15}$	$\begin{array}{r} 2x + 3 \\ 4x - 5 \\ \hline -10x - 15 \\ 8x^2 + 12x \quad\quad \\ \hline \end{array}$ $\boxed{8x^2 + 2x - 15}$ Multiply by "–5" first	$\begin{array}{r} 2x + 3 \\ 4x - 5 \\ \hline 8x^2 + 12x \\ -10x - 15 \\ \hline \end{array}$ $\boxed{8x^2 + 2x - 15}$ Multiply by "$4x$" first

Have volunteers come up to the board and find the product of similar problems using one of the methods.

Have students vote on the method they like the best and they may use their preferred method for homework.

10. *Teacher Presentation* (Mental multiplication):

Students should now be encouraged to develop some skills in mental multiplication of two binomials by using the following procedure:

$$(3a + 4)(2a - 5) =$$

a. Write the two binomials side-by-side inside parentheses.

b. We will do four multiplications in a definite order.

$$F = (3a)(2a) \quad (+4)(-5) = L$$

$$(3a + 4)(2a - 5) = 6a^2 - 15a + 8a - 20$$

$$I = (+4)(2a) \quad\quad F \quad O \quad I \quad L$$

$$O = (3a)(-5) \quad\quad\quad \text{"add"}$$

F = the product of the first terms in each parentheses
O = the product of the *outer* terms
I = the product of the *inner* terms
L = the product of the *last* terms in each ( )

c. Then we will combine the O and I into a single term.

$$\therefore (3a + 4)(2a - 5) = 6a^2 - 7a - 20$$

    d. It should be emphasized that this technique only works when you have **two** binomials of the form $(Ax + By)(Cx + Dy)$

11. *Activity.* Have the students complete Reproduction Page 68 to practice their skills on mental multiplication. For homework, they may do each problem using one of the three prior methods.

12. *Activity.* The teacher can put the FOIL problem in fig. 5.1 on the board and draw "Mr. FOIL."

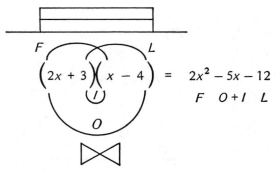

$$(2x + 3)(x - 4) = 2x^2 - 5x - 12$$
$$F \quad O+I \quad L$$

"Mr Foil"

Figure 5.1

    The students may be encouraged to draw other members of the FOIL Family that can be used to decorate the room, e.g.,

    Mrs. FOIL,   Baby FOIL,   Fido FOIL, etc.

13. *Activity.* Using the results of Reproduction Page 68 the teacher should introduce:
    a. The difference of two squares:

$$(a - b)(a + b) = a^2 - b^2$$

    b. A perfect-square trinomial:

$$(a + b)(a + b) = a^2 + 2ab + b^2$$
$$(a - b)(a - b) = a^2 - 2ab + b^2$$

    Have students identify which problems on Reproduction Page 68 illustrate each of the above.

14. *Activity.* Show the students how FOIL can be used as an aid to multiplying numbers:
    a. $(103)(97) = (100 + 3)(100 - 3) = 100^2 - 3^2$
$$= 10000 - 9$$
$$= 9991$$
    b. $(26)^2 = (20 + 6)^2$
$$= 20^2 + 2(120) + 36$$
$$= 400 + 240 + 36$$
$$= 676$$

Topic 3: Factoring

1. *Teacher Presentation.* Students are quite familiar with the prime factorization of a given number.

   Have them find the prime factors of

   $$\begin{array}{ccc} 12 & \text{and} & 20 \\ 2 \cdot 2 \cdot 3 & & 2 \cdot 2 \cdot 5 \end{array}$$

   a. Ask them to find the *Greatest Common Factor* of 12 and 20.
   b. Extend this idea to include finding the "GCF" of the following pairs:

   $$\begin{array}{lcl} 2x & \text{and} & 6y \\ 3x^2 & \text{and} & 3x \\ 8ab & \text{and} & 2a^2 \end{array}$$

   c. Introduce how to remove the GCF from a given polynomial by using the Distributive Law in Reverse:

   $$\begin{array}{l} 2x + 6y = 2(x + 3y) \\ 3x^2 - 3x = 3x(x - 1) \\ 8ab + 2a^2 = 2a(4b + a) \end{array}$$

2. *Activity.* Ask the students to find rules for divisibility by doing research in the library. When can you divide by 2? by 3? by 4?, etc.

3. *Activity.* Have students complete Reproduction Page 69 to reinforce their abilities to multiply and factor using the Distributive Law.

4. *Activity.* To get the students ready to factor trinomials of the form $Ax^2 + Bx + C$ have them complete Reproduction Page 70. Check their answers. Then have the students tear the page vertically, separating the given problems from their answers. Collect the part of the page containing the given problems.

5. *Teacher Presentation.* Using the remaining part of Reproduction Page 70, tell the students that they are now going to "unfoil," better known as "factoring."

   Their answers to numbers 1–15 are all in the form

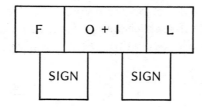

Factoring is a backwards operation:
1. We start with the *L* and find pairs of factors
2. We then look at the sign of *L* and do that operation to each pair of factors
3. We pick the pair whose answer is the number in the *O + I* position
4. Then we insert the signs into the parentheses so that when we add the two numbers in the parentheses we will get the number after x^2 in the given problem:

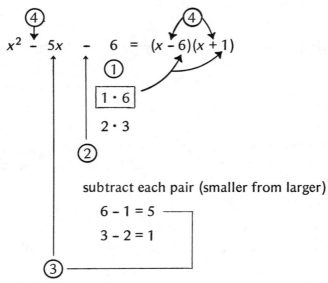

$$x^2 - 5x - 6 = (x - 6)(x + 1)$$

1 · 6

2 · 3

subtract each pair (smaller from larger)

6 − 1 = 5

3 − 2 = 1

5. These rules apply only when $A = 1$, given $Ax^2 + Bx + C$

6. *Activity*. Have students complete Reproduction Page 70, this time factoring their answers. Pass back the column they detached so that each student can check his or her answers.

7. *Teacher Presentation*. The teacher can introduce special factoring techniques at this point.
   A. The Difference of Two Squares:

   $$x^2 - 9$$
   $$4x^2 - 16$$

   B. The Perfect Square Trinomial:

   $$x^2 + 6x + 9$$
   $$4x^2 + 12x + 9$$

   Follow these with ways of factoring $Ax^2 + Bx + C$ when $A \neq 1$

8. *Activity*. Once the students have been exposed to the different types of factoring problems, they should be presented with plenty of drill work—with different types of problems plus double-factoring problems.

   Provide each student with copies of Reproduction Pages 71 and 72. Show the students how to use the flow chart for factoring any given polynomial.
   a. $2x^3 - 2x = 2x(x^2 - 1)$
   $\qquad\quad = 2x(x + 1)(x - 1)$
   b. $x^3 - 4x^2 + 4x = x(x^2 - 4x + 4)$
   $\qquad\qquad\quad = x(x - 2)(x - 2)$

   Encourage students to refine the flow chart provided as they see fit.

Topic 4: Division and Factoring by Grouping

1. *Teacher Presentation* (Division of polynomials):

Relate the division of polynomials to the "long-division" method used for whole numbers in the following way:

$$
\begin{array}{r}
41 \\
12\overline{)495} \\
4 \cdot 12 \to \quad 48 \\
12\overline{)\ 15} \\
12 \\
\overline{\text{R. }3}
\end{array}
\qquad
\begin{array}{r}
4x + 1 \\
x + 2\overline{)4x^2 + 9x + 5} \\
4x^2 + 8x \\
x + 2\overline{)\qquad 1x + 5} \\
x + 2 \\
\overline{\text{R. }3}
\end{array}
$$

I. *Trial divide* by first digit

    $1\overline{)4}$

II. Record answer above 9

III. *Multiply* newest entry in quotient times the entire division

IV. *Subtract*

V. *Bring down* next number in dividend
Go back to step I

I. Divide first term by x

    $x\overline{)4x^2}$

II. Record answer above $9x$

III. *Multiply* $4x(x + 2)$
    Divisor
    new quotient-term

IV. *Subtract* means to change the signs on the bottom row and "add"

V. *Bring down* next term

Go back to step I, then record the signs of **2nd**, 3rd, etc., terms in quotient

2. *Activity.* Have the students complete Reproduction Page 73 for developing their division skills.

3. *Activity.* Reproduction Page 68 can also be used to generate a need to group terms in order to find a common *binomial factor*. Recall that the students obtained expressions such as $5x^2 - 6x + 15x - 18$. To factor completely, they need to group terms $(5x^2 - 6x) + (15x - 18)$ and factor each group:

    $x(5x - 6) + 3(5x - 6)$

Now, it is much easier to see the common binomial factor of $5x - 6$.

The following exercises could be used as preparatory for Reproduction Page 67 or as a follow up. Notice that these can be done using two different methods.

Factor each of the following:

Example
$2bx + x + 2by + y$
$(2bx + x) + (2by + y)$ Group terms
$x(2b + 1) + y(2b + 1)$ Find common monomial factors
$(x + y)(2b + 1)$ Find common binomial factors
       or
$(2bx + 2by) + (x + y)$ Group terms
$2b(x + y) + (x + y)$ Find common monomial factors
$(2b + 1)(x + y)$ Find common binomial factors

a. $d(a + b) + f(a + b)$

b. $6w - 15 - 14wh - 35h$

c. $x^2(a + b) + y^2(b + a)$

d. $\frac{2}{3}bc - \frac{14}{3}b + c - 7$

e. $2ax^2 + bx^2 - 2ay^2 - by^2$

f. $x^2 - 8x + 16 - 49y^2$

4. *Activity.* As enrichment, students can use special products to solve equations. Students should review forms such as $(a + b)^2$ and $(a + b)(a - b)$. Present an equation such as

$$(x - 2)^2 = x^2 + 3x - 5$$

to solve for x. Students should be encouraged to focus on $(x - 2)^2$. Have students solve the following for x:

a. $4 + (x - 9)^2 = (4x + 1)^2 + 9x^2$

b. $(2x + 3)(2x - 3) + 3x^2 = 7x^2 + 2$

c. $(x + 3)^2 - (x + 5)^2 = 10$

d. $3(2x - 7) - (2x - 3)(2x - 1) = 5 - (2x - 5)^2$

CHALLENGE PROBLEMS

1. $(A + B + C)(B + A + C) = $ _____ .

2. $(x^n + y^m)^2 = $ _____ .

3. $\left(\frac{1}{4}x^n + 0.2y^{b+1}\right)^2 = $ _____ .

4. If $x^2 + y^2 = 36$ and $xy = -10$, find the value(s) of $(x + y)$.

5. Find the value of k, such that $x^2 - kx + \frac{25}{4}$ is a perfect square.

6. Let r be the result of doubling both the base and the exponent of a^b, $b \neq 0$. If r equals the product of a^b by x^b, what is the value of x?

7. Given $2^x = 8^{y+1}$ and $9^y = 3^{x-9}$; the value of $x + y = $ _____ .

8. $(y + 1)(y - 3) = $ _____ .
   a. $y^2 - 3$
   b. $y(y - 3) + 1(y - 3)$
   c. $y^2 - y - 1$
   d. $y^2 - 2y$

9. Factor completely:

   $$x^3(x - 6)^2 + x^4(x - 6)$$

10. $\sqrt{x^2y^2 + x^3y^4} = 3xy$

    $x^2y = $ _____ .

EVALUATION

1. Fill in the following table:

Factor Form	Exponent Form
$5 \cdot 5 \cdot 5$	
———	a^5
$a \cdot a \cdot b \cdot b \cdot b \cdot b$	———
$x \cdot y \cdot x \cdot y$	———
———	$s^4 t^3$

2. Evaluate each of these:

   a. $2^5 \cdot 2^2 =$

   b. $(4^3)^2 =$

   c. $a^5 \div a^3 =$

   d. $3^4 \div 3^6 =$

   e. $\dfrac{5^3 \cdot 5^{10}}{5^9} =$

   f. $6^0 \div 2 =$

3. Do each of the following:

   a. $(4x^2 + 3x - 7) + (6x^2 - 2x + 1) =$

   b. $(2y^3 - 4y + 7) - (y^3 + 3y - 2) =$

   c. $(7x^2 + 4x - 1) + (3x^2 + 2x) =$

   d. $(a + 4)(a - 6) =$

   e. $(b + 7)^2 =$

   f. $(s - 4)(s + 4)$

   g. $(a + 2)[(a^2 + 1)(a^2 - 1)] =$

4. Factor each of the following completely:

   a. $6a + 7b =$

   b. $ax^2 + ab + 2a =$

   c. $-5x^2 - 10t^2 =$

   d. $x^2 + 6x + 9 =$

   e. $16a^2 - 36 =$

   f. $x^2 + 7x + 12 =$

   g. $2a^2 + 13a - 7 =$

   h. $5x^2 + 9x - 2 =$

5. Do each of these.

   a. $(x^2 - 16x + 60) \div (x - 6) =$

   b. *Factor:* $a(b + 4) - c(b + 4)$

   c. Solve for x: $(x - 3)^2 = x^2 - 5x - 8$

6. Calculate each of the following. Show how each can be done without actually multiplying these numbers.

   a. $(9999)^2 =$

   b. $56 \cdot 44 =$

7. Evaluate each:

   a. $(x^{\frac{1}{2}} - 3)(x^{\frac{1}{2}} + 3) =$

   b. $(x^2 + 2x + 1)(x + 1) =$

8. Find the missing length.

   a. | Area $= x^2 + 5x + 6$ | ?

      $x + 2$

   b. | Area $= x^2 + 13x + 12$ | ?

      ?

9. When is a number divisible by 4?

10. Factor each:

a. $8x^2 - 10xy + 3y^2 =$ c. $y^2 - 7 =$

b. $4 - 20b + 25b^2 =$

11. Within a large square whose side is a units is a small square whose side is b units. What is the area of the large square? Area of the small square? What is the area of the region between the two squares?

12. Find the area for each figure:

a.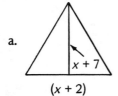

$x + 7$

$(x + 2)$

b.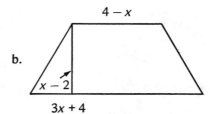

$4 - x$

$x - 2$

$3x + 4$

13. Find the number such that the square of 4 more than the number is the same as the square of the number.

Notes to Teacher

1. The problems found in this section could be used for both ongoing and final evaluation. Some or all of these problems could be used.

2. Other applications can be found in Chapter 9.

RESOURCES

Below is a selected list of resources for teaching the topics considered in this chapter. Addresses of publishers can be found in Appendix A.

Bitter, Gary G., and Mikesell, Jerald L., *Activities Handbook for Teaching with the Hand-Held Calculator*. Newton, MA: Allyn and Bacon, 1980. Familiarizes teachers with basic methods for using the calculator as a teaching tool.

Boyle, Patrick, and Juanez, William, *Accent on Algebra*. Palo Alto, CA: Creative Publications, 1971. Emphasis on the vocabulary, concepts, and skills of elementary algebra in interesting ways.

Clark, Alice, and Leitch, Carol, *Amusements Developing Algebra Skills, Volume 1*. Pacific Grove, CA: Midwest Publications, 1983. Provides an ideal combination of extensive algebra practice exercises embedded in cross number puzzles, line designs, decodes, picture graphs, optical illusions, and others.

National Council of Teachers of Mathematics, *The Mathematics Teacher*. Reston, VA: NCTM. This monthly journal is published nine times each year and includes useful suggestions for teaching various topics in the secondary mathematics curriculum.

National Council of Teachers of Mathematics, *The Teaching of Secondary School Mathematics (33rd Yearbook)*. Reston, VA: NCTM, 1970. This yearbook contains sections about preparing plans for teaching algebra.

Plan, Algebra 1. Oak Lawn, IL: Plan Products, 1983. Provides the complete introductory algebra curriculum advocated by the School Mathematics Study Group. The teacher's kit includes placement tests, achievement tests, and duplicating masters.

Rasmussen, Peter, *Key to Algebra*. Hayward, CA: Activity Resources, 1975. A set of small pamphlets that provide practice in basic algebraic skills.

School Science and Mathematics Association, *School Science and Mathematics.* Bowling Green, OH: SSMA. This monthly journal is published nine times each year and includes pedagogy and research in mathematics education useful for the secondary teacher.

Special Products and Factoring. San Francisco: Modern Learning Aids, 1983. One of a film series dealing with algebra.

6

Working with Rational Expressions

CONTENT OVERVIEW

Facility in operating with rational expressions is an essential skill needed for applying algebra in all sciences. Elementary algebra concentrates on building this skill on a foundation of underlying principles. Although students have studied how to perform arithmetic operations involving fractions, many have merely learned techniques based on memorized facts. In this chapter rational expressions are explored in relation to the real number system. The multiplicative identity element plays a major role, e.g., cancellation is avoided; instead, "forms of one" are found when reducing rational expressions. By emphasizing the *why* of the methods used to work with fractional expressions, previously learned erroneous techniques of some students will not be reinforced.

Students' success in this chapter will be directly proportional to their previously mastered skills of multiplying and factoring monomials and/or polynomials. Therefore, we strongly suggest that a "Daily Dozen Quiz" be administered each day as an opening exercise in the class. A dozen such quizzes are provided on Reproduction pages 74–76.

Algorithms are provided for each arithmetic operation with rational expressions in this chapter. Shortcuts should not be allowed at the elementary algebra level; instead, students should follow each step of the algorithm. Encourage students to keep equal signs underneath equal signs and to identify "forms of one" when appropriate. The last step in each algorithm is to check the answer. We feel that it is very important for students continuously to relate their work with rational expressions to concrete numerical computations. If calculators are available, they may be used in the checking process.

OBJECTIVES

As a result of the learning experiences in this chapter, the student should be able to:

1. Simplify rational expressions

---

2. Multiply and divide rational expressions and simplify the results

3. Simplify a complex fraction

4. Add and subtract rational expressions and simplify the results

5. Solve equations containing rational expressions

6. Solve proportions

LEARNING EXPERIENCES

Topic 1: Simplifying

1. *Activity.* Success in this unit depends on the students' ability to multiply mentally with proficiency and to recognize prime factors. On Reproduction Pages 74, 75, and 76 are twelve Daily Dozen Quizzes that should be administered at the beginning of each class throughout this chapter (see insert). The students whose scores improve the most during the week, as well as the high scorers, can be honored with something like a "Daily Dozen Honor Roll" on the bulletin board. No more than five minutes should be allowed for each quiz. Papers can be exchanged and graded by the students as the teacher goes over each answer using a transparency reproduction on the overhead projector.

2. *Teacher Presentation.* Rational expressions having the value of 1 shall be referred to as "forms of one" throughout this chapter.

    Have the students evaluate the following expressions written on the chalkboard (assign a different value of x to each row of students).

$$
\begin{array}{ccccccc}
A & B & C & D & E & F & G \\
\dfrac{x}{x} & \dfrac{-x}{-x} & \dfrac{x+2}{x+2} & \dfrac{x+2}{2+x} & \dfrac{x-2}{x-2} & \dfrac{x-2}{2-x} & \dfrac{x+8}{x-8}
\end{array}
$$

Point out the following:

a. A, B, C, D, E are all "forms of one"

b. F reduces to (-1) for all values of x, $x \neq 2$

    i. Ask the students: Why are C and D equivalent while E and F are not?

    ii. Establish the rule: $\dfrac{a-b}{b-a} = -1$ if $b \neq a$.

c. G is not a form of one

d. There are some restrictions ($x \neq 0$ in A and B)

3. *Teacher Presentation.* Students usually know that division by zero is undefined. Therefore, a rational expression such as $\dfrac{4x}{x-2}$ is undefined when $x = 2$.

    Write the following expressions on the board and ask students to identify the values that make them "disappear" (undefined)!

$$\begin{array}{ccccc} A & B & C & D & E \\[4pt] \dfrac{2}{x} & \dfrac{x}{x-3} & \dfrac{x-2}{x+5} & \dfrac{x-4}{x^2-9} & \dfrac{x^2+3x+4}{x^2+5x+6} \end{array}$$

Afterwards, discuss the algorithm used to identify values of the variable that must be excluded from the domain of the expression.

4. *Activity.* Have the students complete the exercises on Reproduction Page 77 in class. After sufficient time, have them compare their answers to those on the over-head projector (make a transparency of this page and insert the answers in red).
   Ask pertinent questions such as:

a. Why is it that we get the same answers for problems 3 and 4?
   Write on board:

$$\begin{array}{cc} 3 & 4 \\[6pt] \dfrac{x+2}{x-3} & = \dfrac{x^2+5x+6}{x^2-9} \end{array}$$

b. How can a "form of one" be used to change 3 into 4?

$$\dfrac{x+2}{x-3}\;\boxed{}\; = \dfrac{x^2+5+6}{x^2-9}$$

c. Why is it that we get a (–1) in all three columns of 8 and 9?
d. Can you find a reduced form of 10?

5. *Activity.* Write the following problems on the board and have students find the correct "form of one" needed for each.

$$\dfrac{2}{6} = \boxed{}\;\dfrac{1}{3} \qquad \dfrac{2x}{x^2} = \boxed{}\;\dfrac{2}{x} \qquad \dfrac{2x}{2x-6} = \boxed{}\;\dfrac{x}{x-3}$$

$$\dfrac{x^2-9}{x+3} = \boxed{}\;\dfrac{x-3}{1} \qquad \dfrac{3x-6}{x^2-4} = \boxed{}\;\dfrac{3}{x+2} \qquad \dfrac{3ab-3a}{3a} = \boxed{}\;\dfrac{b-1}{1}$$

6. *Teacher Presentation.* Put the following problems on the chalkboard and have students substitute 2 for a and 5 for b to determine if the statement is true or false:

a. $\dfrac{ab+5a}{2a^2} \stackrel{?}{=} \dfrac{b+5}{2a}$

b. $\dfrac{a^2+b^2}{a+b} \stackrel{?}{=} a+b$

c. $\dfrac{a^2-b^2}{a-b} \stackrel{?}{=} a+b$

d. $\dfrac{a-b}{b-a} \stackrel{?}{=} -1$

e. $\dfrac{2}{6a+2} \stackrel{?}{=} \dfrac{1}{3a+1}$

Demonstrate how to simplify rational expressions. Using a transparency of Reproduction Page 78, simplify a, c, and e above (as each step of the algorithm is displayed) in the example column.

Step

1. $\dfrac{(ab + 5a)}{2a^2}$

2. $\dfrac{a(b + 5)}{2 \cdot a \cdot a}$

3. $\dfrac{a(b + 5) \cdot 1}{2 \cdot a \rfloor a}$

4. $\dfrac{1 \cdot a \cdot (b + 5)}{2 \cdot a \cdot a}$

5. $\dfrac{1}{2} \cdot \dfrac{a}{a} \cdot \dfrac{b + 5}{a}$

6. $\dfrac{1}{2} \cdot \dfrac{b + 5}{a} = \dfrac{b + 5}{2a}$

7. *Activity.* Have the students copy the algorithm on Reproduction Page 78 into their notebooks. Then assign Reproduction Page 79.

8. *Activity.* Have the students check their answer to each problem on Reproduction Page 79 by replacing the variable(s) with an assigned value.
   Example:

$$\frac{3x}{6} \overset{?}{=} \frac{x}{2}$$

$$\boxed{\text{Let } x = 7}$$

$$\frac{3 \cdot 7}{6} \qquad \frac{7}{2}$$

$$\frac{21}{6}$$

$$3\frac{1}{2}$$

$$\frac{7}{2}$$

Encourage students to draw a vertical line underneath the equal sign. Both sides must result in the same value.

Students may be encouraged to use a second value for *x* as an additional check.

9. *Activity.* Write the following on the chalkboard: $\dfrac{x}{x + 3}$

   Have each student multiply it by their own private "form of one." Call on each student and have the class determine what "form of one" the classmate used.

10. *Teacher Presentation.* If slopes have been covered, the teacher may plot two given points on the graphboard and have the students determine the slope, the *x*-intercept, and the *y*-intercept by inspection. See fig. 6.1.
    Demonstrate that the students can use the following formulas to find the *x* and *y* intercepts of a line which passes through (x_1, y_1) and (x_2, y_2):

$$y\text{-intercept} = \frac{x_1 y_2 - x_2 y_1}{x_1 - x_2} \qquad x_1 \neq x_2$$

$$x\text{-intercept} = \frac{x_1 y_2 - x_2 y_1}{y_2 - y_1} \qquad y_1 \neq y_2$$

$A(4,3)$

$B(-2,-6)$

$m = \dfrac{3}{2}$

$(2,0) - x\text{-intercept} = 2$

$(0,-3) - y\text{-intercept} = -3$

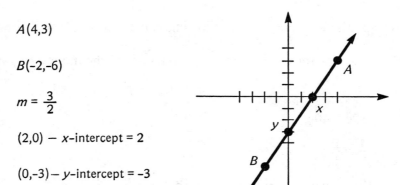

Figure 6.1

List several pairs of points on the board and have the students use the formulae to find the x and y-intercepts. The better students can be challenged to verify the formulas.

11. *Activity.* Ask students what is wrong with the following method of reducing fractions:

$$\frac{26}{65} = \frac{2\!\!\!/6}{6\!\!\!/5} = \frac{2}{5}$$
$$\frac{16}{64} = \frac{1\!\!\!/6}{6\!\!\!/4} = \frac{1}{4}$$

Challenge students to find other examples where this "crazy" form of "cancellation" works. But caution them that the only legitimate way of reducing rational expressions is to find "forms of one."

12. *Activity (Enrichment).* Divide the class into four groups and assign to each group the task of graphing one of the following sets of equations.

a. $y = 4x$ and $y = \dfrac{1}{4}x$

b. $y = 2x - 3$ and $y = \dfrac{1}{(2x - 3)}$

c. $y = \dfrac{(x + 5)}{3}$ and $y = \dfrac{3}{(x + 5)}$

d. $y = (6 - 3x)$ and $y = \dfrac{2}{(6 - 3x)}$

Students are to graph both functions on the same coordinate system. A discussion of their results should follow. Compare the graphs of the equations in each pair. What relationship exists between each pair?

Topic 2: Multiplying and Dividing

1. *Teacher Presentation.* Place eight dimes on a student's desk and ask the class: What fractional part of a dollar did I give _____ ?

Accept the answer $\frac{4}{5}$. The following could also be done if the student replied with $\frac{8}{10}$. Instruct the student to return one-half of the money to you. Write on the board:

$$\frac{1}{2} \text{ of } 80\cancel{c} = 40\cancel{c}$$

$$\frac{1}{2} \text{ of } \frac{4}{5} = \frac{2}{5}$$

Ask the students to convince you that $\frac{1}{2} \cdot \frac{4}{5} = \frac{2}{5}$.

a. Most students will remember the rule $\frac{a}{b} \cdot \frac{c}{d} = \frac{ac}{bd}$ $b \neq 0, \; d \neq 0$ and apply it immediately

b. Others will "cancel" before they multiply: $\frac{1}{\underset{①}{\cancel{2}}} \cdot \frac{\overset{②}{\cancel{4}}}{5} = \frac{2}{5}$

Challenge students to do the problem without cancelling: instead, look for a "form of one."

$$\frac{1}{2} \cdot \frac{4}{5} = \frac{1 \cdot 4}{2 \cdot 5}$$

$$= \frac{\boxed{1 \cdot 2} \cdot 2}{\boxed{1 \cdot 2} \cdot 5}$$

$$= 1 \cdot \frac{2}{5}$$

$$= \frac{2}{5}$$

The above method will be used in this chapter exclusively (cancelling should not be allowed).

Make a transparency of Reproduction Page 80 and demonstrate the solution to example problems at each step of the algorithm.

Example

$$\boxed{\frac{5x-5}{3} \cdot \frac{9}{x^2-1}}$$

Step 1. $\dfrac{(5x-5)}{3} \cdot \dfrac{9}{(x^2-1)}$

Step 2. $\dfrac{(5x-5) \cdot 9}{3(x^2-1)}$ ⟵———— This is the answer

Step 3. $\dfrac{5(x-1) \cdot 3 \cdot 3}{3(x+1)(x-1)}$

Step 4. $\dfrac{3(x-1) \cdot 3 \cdot 5}{3(x-1)(x+1)}$

We reduce the answer.

Step 5. $\boxed{\dfrac{3(x-1)}{3(x-1)}} \dfrac{3 \cdot 5}{(x+1)}$ We reduce the answer.

Step 6. $1 \cdot \dfrac{15}{(x+1)} = \dfrac{15}{(x+1)}$

Write on transparency

2. *Activity.* Write the following on the chalkboard: $\dfrac{x^2-9}{6x} \cdot \dfrac{6x-18}{x^2-6x+9}$

Have the students follow the algorithm at their seats and find the answer.

Reveal the correct solution on the overhead and have them check their work. Students will then *check* their answers by replacing the variable with a number (have each row use a different value of *x*).

3. *Activity.* Have the students complete Reproduction Page 81. Provide them with a copy of the algorithm.

Discuss the correct procedure for simplifying the expressions correctly at the bottom of the page.

4. *Teacher Presentation.* Write the following problems on the chalkboard and ask the students how to do the problem.

$$\boxed{\dfrac{4}{5} \div \dfrac{1}{7}} \qquad \boxed{\dfrac{3}{5} \div 4}$$

Almost immediately they will chant "change the division sign to a multiplication sign and invert the divisor." So do just that . . .

$$\boxed{\dfrac{4}{5} \cdot \dfrac{7}{1}} \;!! \qquad \boxed{\dfrac{3}{5} \cdot 4} \;!!$$

The algebraic way of saying invert the divisor is "multiply by the *reciprocal* (the multiplicative inverse) of the divisor." Have students complete the following chart.

Number	2	$-\dfrac{2}{3}$	x	$x+2$	$\dfrac{x+3}{4}$	$-\dfrac{5}{x+1}$
Reciprocal	$\dfrac{1}{2}$	$-\dfrac{3}{2}$	$\dfrac{1}{x}$	$\dfrac{1}{x+2}$	$\dfrac{4}{x+3}$	$-\dfrac{x+1}{5}$

Verify each answer by applying the rule Number $\cdot$ Reciprocal = 1

5. *Teacher Presentation.* Have the students compare the following:

$4\overline{)12}$ $\qquad \dfrac{1}{4}$ of 12

$12 \div 4$ $\qquad \dfrac{1}{4} \cdot 12$

All represent the same number.

Therefore dividing 12 by 4 is the same as multiplying 12 by $\dfrac{1}{4}$. $12 \div 4 = 12 \cdot \dfrac{1}{4}$.

This specific example should make the following rule more understandable for the student. $\dfrac{a}{b} \div \dfrac{c}{d} = \dfrac{a}{b} \cdot \dfrac{d}{c} = \dfrac{ad}{bc}$ $b \neq 0, c \neq 0, d \neq 0$

6. *Activity.* Have the students complete Reproduction Page 82.

7. *Teacher Presentation.* Ask the students to find the reciprocal of $\frac{1}{2} + \frac{1}{3}$. It obviously isn't $\frac{2}{1} + \frac{3}{1}$!!

   Reciprocal is only defined for any rational expression of the form $\frac{p}{q}$ where $p \neq 0$, $q \neq 0$. Thus any divisor made up of a polynomial expression such as $\left(\frac{x}{2} + \frac{3}{x}\right)$ must be expressed as a single fraction before its reciprocal can be found.

   Since this requires the skill of addition or subtraction of rational expressions which has not been covered to date, the following procedure can be used at this time (demonstrate to the class):

   Divide: $\dfrac{x - y}{3} \div \left(\dfrac{1}{x} - \dfrac{1}{y}\right)$

   Step 1. Write the division problem as a fraction

   Dividend = Numerator
   Divisor   = Denominator

   $$\dfrac{\dfrac{x - y}{3}}{\dfrac{1}{x} - \dfrac{1}{y}}$$

   Step 2. Find the *LCD* for the fractions within the fraction.

   $LCD = 3xy$

   Step 3. Multiply the fraction in step 1 by 1 in the form *LCD/LCD*.

   $$\boxed{\dfrac{3xy}{3xy}} \cdot \dfrac{\dfrac{x - y}{3}}{\dfrac{1}{x} - \dfrac{1}{y}} \qquad\qquad \text{Use the Distributive Law.}$$

   Step 4. The resulting fraction should have no fractions within it.

   $$\dfrac{xy(x - y)}{3y - 3x}$$

   Step 5. Simplify the resulting fraction, if possible.

   $$\dfrac{xy\,\boxed{(x - y)}}{3\,\boxed{(x - y)}} = \dfrac{xy}{3}$$

   Have students do at least two similar problems.

8. *Teacher Presentation.* The presentation above contains an algorithm which can be used to simplify complex fractions. Demonstrate the simplifying process for each of the following on the chalkboard:

   a. $\dfrac{\dfrac{3}{2}}{5}$

b. $\dfrac{1 + \dfrac{1}{a}}{a - \dfrac{1}{a}}$

c. $\dfrac{\dfrac{1}{4} - a^2}{a - \dfrac{1}{2}}$

9. *Activity.* Do the example problem alongside the algorithm on Reproduction Page 83 with the students. Then have the students complete the page independently.

Topic 3: Adding and Subtracting

1. *Teacher Presentation.* When presenting the rule $\dfrac{a}{c} + \dfrac{b}{c} = \dfrac{a+b}{c}$, point out that just as the common factor x is retained when the sum of $2x + 7x$ is expressed as $9x$, the common denominator c (the common factor $\dfrac{1}{c}$) should also be retained.

Illustrate this fact to the students in the following manner:

$2x + 7x$	*vs.*	$\dfrac{2}{x} + \dfrac{7}{x}$
$= 2 \cdot x + 7 \cdot x$		$= 2 \cdot \dfrac{1}{x} + 7 \cdot \dfrac{1}{x}$
$= (2 + 7) \cdot x$		$= (2 + 7) \cdot \dfrac{1}{x}$
$= 9 \cdot x$		$= 9 \cdot \dfrac{1}{x}$
$= 9x$		$= \dfrac{9}{x}$

2. *Activity.* Have the students follow the algorithm on Reproduction Page 84 and complete the exercises.

   As a followup, assign six students to record a given problem and their answers on the chalkboard and then *check* by using the number of the problem as the replacement for the variable.

3. *Teacher Presentation.* The teacher should point out that there is one basic rule for adding fractions, namely

$$\frac{a}{c} + \frac{b}{c} = \frac{a+b}{c} \qquad c \neq 0$$

Therefore, to add $\dfrac{3}{5} + \dfrac{2}{15}$ one could convert the first fraction to an equivalent form having 15 for its denominator. How do we do this?

We could simply insert a "1" in front of the 5, but mathematically, that would be a grievous error. Why?

There is only one correct way to change the denominator 5 to 15: *use the identity element for multiplication* (a "form of one"), such as $\frac{2}{2}, \frac{3}{3}, \frac{4}{4}$. Thus,

$$\frac{3}{5} + \frac{2}{15} = \boxed{\frac{3}{3}} \cdot \frac{3}{5} + \frac{2}{15} = \frac{9}{15} + \frac{2}{15} = \frac{11}{15}$$

Which form (or forms) to use in each problem is the mystery that students must solve. Here is where "prime factorization" and "least common multiples" enter the scene. Review these ideas with the students and have them complete Reproduction Page 85.

4. *Activity.* After the students have completed Reproduction Page 85, have them convert each problem in part C to an addition problem and find the sum.
Example:

$$\boxed{\frac{5}{5}} \cdot \frac{2}{3} + \frac{4}{15} = \frac{10}{15} + \frac{4}{15} = \frac{14}{15}$$

5. *Activity.* Have two volunteers add the following on the board:

a. $\dfrac{49}{35} + \dfrac{-9}{15}$ 　　　　　　 b. $\dfrac{9}{6} + \dfrac{-1}{2}$

When the correct solution is on the board, point out that they could have gotten their answers by simply adding the numerators *and* the denominators!!

a. $\dfrac{49}{35} + \dfrac{-9}{15} = \dfrac{49 + (-9)}{35 + 15}$ 　　　　 b. $\dfrac{9}{6} + \dfrac{-1}{2} = \dfrac{9 + (-1)}{6 + 2}$

$$= \frac{40}{50} \qquad\qquad\qquad = \frac{8}{8}$$

$$= \frac{4}{5} \qquad\qquad\qquad\quad = 1$$

Challenge the students to find other examples that adhere to the rule

$$\frac{a}{b} + \frac{c}{d} = \frac{a+c}{b+d} \qquad b \neq 0, d \neq 0$$

The better student may be asked to find under what circumstances this "crazy" way of adding fractions will work.

6. *Teacher Presentation.* All fractions can be combined according to the rule:

$$\frac{a}{b} \pm \frac{c}{d} = \frac{ad \pm bc}{bd} \qquad b \neq 0, d \neq 0$$

Put the following examples on the chalkboard:

A	B	C
$\dfrac{3}{x} \diagdown\!\!\!\!\diagup \dfrac{2}{5}$	$\dfrac{3}{5} \diagdown\!\!\!\!\diagup \dfrac{2}{15}$	$\dfrac{3}{x-2} \diagdown\!\!\!\!\diagup \dfrac{-2x}{x+3}$
$= \dfrac{2x + 15}{5x}$	$= \dfrac{45 - 10}{75}$	$= \dfrac{2x^2 - 4x + 3x + 9}{x^2 - x - 6}$
	$= \dfrac{35}{75} = \dfrac{7}{15}$	$= \dfrac{2x^2 - x + 9}{x^2 - x - 6}$

Ask students the following questions:
a. Why did we have to reduce the result in *B* but not in *A* or *C*?

b. Would we have to reduce the result if we were given $\frac{3}{2} - \frac{x-2}{4x}$? Why?

Have the students complete Reproduction Page 86.

7. *Teacher Presentation.* Write the following problems on the chalkboard and have student volunteers find the sums:

a. $\frac{9}{8} + \frac{5}{-8}$ b. $\frac{5}{-x} + \frac{8}{x}$ c. $\frac{b^2}{b-2} + \frac{4}{2-b}$

d. $\frac{2x+7}{x-6} + \frac{3x}{6-x}$ e. $\frac{a-3}{a^2-9} + \frac{a-3}{9-a^2}$

Lead students to discover how to add fractions when the given denominators are additive inverses: *multiply one fraction by the "form of one"* $\frac{-1}{-1}$.

8. *Teacher Presentation.* Present the following problems to the class; solicit and write their answers on the chalkboard.

a. $2\frac{1}{3} = ?$

b. $2 + \frac{1}{3} = ?$

c. $x + \frac{1}{3} = ?$

Discuss the fact that $2\frac{1}{3}$ is a shorthand way of writing $2 + \frac{1}{3}$. Therefore $x + \frac{1}{3}$ can be treated as a mixed number and the answer is analogous to an improper fraction. Write the following on the chalkboard.

$$2\frac{1}{3} = \frac{3 \cdot 2 + 1}{3}$$

Add
$$x + \frac{1}{3} = \frac{3 \cdot x + 1}{3} = \frac{3x + 1}{3}$$
multiply

This method can also be used when a minus sign occurs

d. $(x + 2) - \frac{3}{x} = \frac{x(x+2) - 3}{x} = \frac{x^2 + 2x - 3}{x}$

9. *Activity.* Reproduction Page 87 contains a variety of addition of fractions problems. Have students do each problem the standard way (using forms of one). Afterwards, pass out another copy of this page and discuss with the class which problems could have been done more easily using the methods presented in Teacher Presentations 6, 7, and 8.

10. *Teacher Presentation.*
a. Review the meaning of the additive inverse (the "opposite") of real numbers; emphasize the rule that $a + (-a) = (-a) + a = 0$.

Number	Its Opposite	
5	-5	because $5 + (-5) = 0$
$x - 3$	$-x + 3$	because $(x - 3) + (-x + 3) = 0$
$\dfrac{4x + 5}{2}$	$\dfrac{-4x - 5}{2}$	because $\dfrac{4x - 5}{2} + \dfrac{-4x - 5}{2} = 0$

Point out that the opposite of a polynomial is found by multiplying it by -1: $(-2x + 3)$; $-(-2x + 3) = +2x - 3$

Point out that the opposite of a fraction is equivalent to replacing the numerator with its opposite.

b. Review the rule for subtraction of real numbers:

$$a - b = a + (-b)$$
$$\text{e.g.,} \quad 2x - (3x - 4) = 2x + (-3x + 4)$$

opposites

c. Therefore, to subtract rational expressions, change the problem to an equivalent addition problem by doing the following:
   A. change the minus sign to a plus sign
   B. replace the following numerator with its opposite

$$\text{e.g.,} \quad \frac{a + 3}{2} - \frac{a - 5}{2} = \frac{a + 3}{2} + \frac{-a + 5}{2} = \frac{8}{2} = 4$$

11. *Activity.* Make a transparency of Reproduction Page 88 for the overhead projector and pass out dittoed copies to the students. Discuss each section with the class after soliciting individual student answers.

    For homework, the students can actually find the differences for each problem in section B and check their results.

12. *Teacher Presentation.* Once students have been exposed to addition and subtraction of rational expressions using the rule $\dfrac{a}{b} + \dfrac{b}{c} = \dfrac{a + b}{c}$, demonstrate how this rule can be used in reverse for simplifying expressions:

$$\frac{2x + 6}{2} \text{ is the result of adding } \frac{2x}{2} \text{ and } \frac{6}{2}$$

$$\text{Therefore,} \quad \frac{2x + 6}{2} = \frac{2x}{2} + \frac{6}{2} = \frac{2x}{2} + \frac{2 \cdot 3}{2} = x + 3$$

Do several problems on the board with the class:

a. $\dfrac{3a + 12}{3a} = \boxed{} + \boxed{}$

b. $\dfrac{8 - 4b}{4} = \boxed{} - \boxed{}$

c. $\dfrac{x + 1}{x + 2} = \boxed{} + \boxed{}$

13. *Activity (Enrichment).* Briefly discuss *shapes of numbers* with the entire class. (See fig. 6.2.)

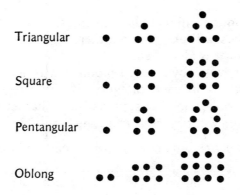

Figure 6.2

Divide the class into four groups. Assign a different shape number to each group. Each group must find the first dozen numbers having its assigned shape; then, figure out a formula for the nth such number.

Afterwards, have the groups interact with one another to see if there is any relationship that is true about their shapes, and, if so, generalize it.

Example:
Square numbers = sum of two triangular numbers

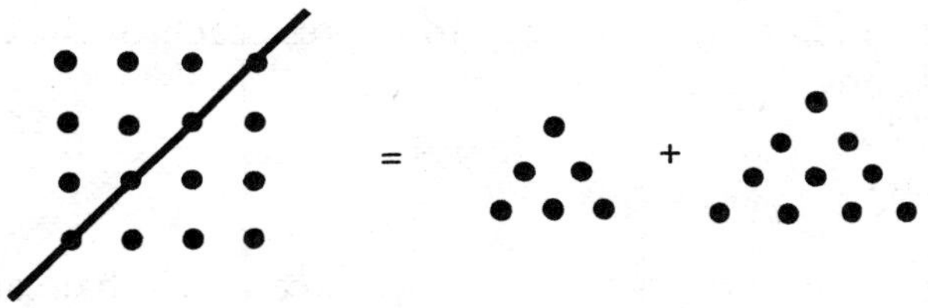

$$4^2 \quad = \quad \frac{3(3+1)}{2} + \frac{4(4+1)}{2}$$

$$n^2 \quad = \quad \frac{(n-1)(n)}{2} + \frac{n(n+1)}{2}$$

Activity. The class can be divided into groups of three students. Each group will play a game of Tic-Tac-Know. The categories will be as shown in fig. 6.3.

Reducing Fractions	Multiplying Fractions	Dividing Fractions
Adding Like Fractions	Adding Unlike Fractions	POTLUCK
Subtracting Like Fractions	Subtracting Unlike Fractions	Complex Fractions

Figure 6.3

One student will act as the monitor, the other two will be the opponents. Once a category is chosen and answered correctly, an *X* or *O* card will cover that category; the monitor will pick up the others, shuffle, and redistribute the available categories. Winners will play one another, monitors will become players, etc. until a grand prize winner is identified.

The teacher will provide each monitor with a copy of Reproduction Page 89 containing questions in each category. If the category chosen is in the middle space, the last problem in that set is assigned (harder problem). Once a problem is asked, the monitor will scratch it from the list.

15. *Activity (Enrichment).* Ancient Egyptians had an interesting way of working with fractions. With very few exceptions (e.g., $-\frac{2}{3}$), they used only distinct unit fractions (fractions having a numerator of 1). For example, they wrote $\frac{2}{5}$ as $\frac{1}{3} + \frac{1}{15}$.

The following identity containing the exception $\frac{2}{3}$ was very useful to them.

$$\boxed{\frac{2}{3} \cdot \frac{1}{x} = \frac{1}{2x} + \frac{1}{6x}}$$ Have the students verify that this *is* an identity.

Show the students how they used this identity to express $\frac{2}{9}$ as the sum of unit fractions:

$$\frac{2}{9} = \frac{2}{3} \cdot \frac{1}{3} = \frac{1}{2(3)} + \frac{1}{6(3)}$$

Have the students use this identity to express each of the following as the sum of two unit fractions.

$$\frac{2}{15} \quad \text{and} \quad \frac{2}{21}$$

Challenge the students to find other exceptions that cannot be written as two unit fractions.

Topic 4: Solving Fractional Equations

1. *Teacher Presentation.* Before solving fractional equations (where the variable appears in the denominator) it is beneficial to present a lesson which reviews skills necessary for success. Proceed as follows:
   A. Review "*LCD*" and have the students find the *LCD* of
      a. 2 and 6
      b. 4 and 5 and 10
      c. $5x$ and $2x$
   B. Review the product of a whole number and a fraction
      a. $2\left(\frac{2}{3}\right)$ d. $x\left(\frac{6}{x}\right)$
      b. $x\left(\frac{x}{3}\right)$ e. $x^2\left(\frac{2}{x}\right)$
      c. $6\left(\frac{x}{2}\right)$ f. $[2(x+3)] \cdot \frac{x}{2}$

C. Review the distributive property

    a. $12(2a + 3b)$

    b. $12\left(\dfrac{x}{2} + 3\right)$

    c. $x\left(\dfrac{x}{3} + \dfrac{1}{x}\right)$

D. Review the meaning of expressions such as $\dfrac{1}{2}x$

$$\frac{1}{2}x = \frac{1}{2} \cdot x = \frac{x}{2}$$
$$\frac{2}{3}a = \frac{2a}{3}$$

E. Have students complete Reproduction Page 90.

2. *Activity.* To increase the students' ability to find *LCD*'s quickly the following game can be played.

    Pass out a copy of Reproduction Page 91 to each student and have each make an "I-Know" card by placing each selection from the available list in a random space. Collect the cards, shuffle, and redistribute to the students. The teacher will write each of the following on a 3 x 5 index card:

a. $3, x$	g. $3, x + 2$	m. $x + 2, 2 + x$	s. $x - 2, 2x - 4$
b. $3, 6x$	h. $2, x - 2$	n. $x + 2, x^2 + 2x$	t. $x + 2, 2x + 4$
c. $3, 3x$	i. $2, 2x - 4$	o. $x + 2, x - 2$	u. $x + 2, x + 3$
d. $x, 6x$	j. $x, x + 2$	p. $x - 2, x^2 - 4$	v. $x - 2, x + 3$
e. $2x, 3x^2$	k. $x, x^2 + 2x$	q. $2 + x, x^2 - 4$	w. $2 - x, 2 - x$
f. $6x, x^2$	l. $-2, 4 - 2x$	r. $x - 2, x - 2$	x. $x + 3, x - 2$

    The game is played like "Bingo": the teacher will draw a card and the students will cover only one square containing the *LCD* of the two expressions on that card.

3. *Teacher Presentation.* Make a transparency of Reproduction Page 92 and demonstrate how to solve an equation containing rational coefficients following the algorithm. One of the examples used should be a linear system such as:

$$\frac{x}{2} + y = -1$$
$$\frac{5x}{14} - \frac{y}{7} = 1$$

4. *Activity.* Have the students complete Reproduction Page 93 following the algorithm used in the above presentation.

5. *Teacher Presentation.* The algorithm on Reproduction Page 92 can also be followed to solve equations where the variable appears in the denominator of the fraction—with one exception: a step is needed before Step 1.

Step 0: The student must determine what values of the variable must be excluded from the domain of the variable.

    If the student is cautioned to do this first, then he or she will automatically reject those values if they appear in Step 6. Demonstrate the use of the algorithm in the following manner.

Example:

$$\frac{3}{x} + \frac{2x}{x-2} = 3 - \frac{x^2}{x^2 - 2x}$$

Step 0: $x \neq 0$ or $+2$

Step 1: Not needed

Step 2: $\dfrac{3}{x} + \dfrac{2x}{(x-2)} = 3 - \dfrac{x^2}{(x^2 - 2x)}$

Step 3: Not needed

Step 4: $LCD = x(x-2)$

Step 5: $[x(x-2)] \cdot \dfrac{3}{x} + [x(x-2)] \cdot \dfrac{2x}{(x-2)} = 3[x(x-2)] - \dfrac{x^2}{x^2 - 2x}[x(x-2)]$

Step 6: $\boxed{\dfrac{x}{x}} \dfrac{(x-2)\cdot 3}{} + \dfrac{x \boxed{(x-2)}}{\boxed{(x-2)}} \cdot 2x = 3(x^2 - 2x) - x^2 \dfrac{\boxed{[x(x-2)]}}{\boxed{x(x-2)}}$

$$\begin{aligned}
(x-2)\cdot 3 + x \cdot 2x & & = 3x^2 - 6x \;\; - x^2 \\
3x - 6 \quad\;\; + 2x^2 & & = 2x^2 - 6x \\
3x - 6 & & = -6x \\
9x &= 6 \\
x &= \frac{2}{3} \text{ (not one of the rejected values)}
\end{aligned}$$

Step 7: Check the answer

Review operations with students that produce equivalent equations. Note that if $a = b$, then $a \cdot c = b \cdot c$ provided $c \neq 0$. Likewise if $a = b$, then $a/c = b/c$ provided $c \neq 0$. *Multiplying or dividing an equation by zero is prohibited.*

A caution sign ⬡ containing this message can be displayed in a strategic location in the classroom.

6. *Activity.* Challenge the students to find the error in the following mathematical fallacy.

Prove: $1 = 2$

Proof

a. Let $a = b = 1$

b. $a = b$

c. $a^2 = ab$

d. $a^2 - b^2 = ab - b^2$

e. $\dfrac{a^2 - b^2}{a - b} = \dfrac{ab - b^2}{a - b}$

f. $\dfrac{(a+b)\boxed{(a-b)}}{1 \cdot \boxed{(a-b)}} = \dfrac{b\boxed{(a-b)}}{1 \cdot (a-b)}$

g. $a + b = b$

h. $1 + 1 = 1$

i. $2 = 1$

7. *Activity.* Distribute dittoed copies of Reproduction Page 94 to students and have them solve each problem following the algorithm on Reproduction Page 92. *Note to teacher:* Quadratic equations do *not* appear when solving any of the problems on this page.

8. *Teacher Presentation.* While completing Reproduction Page 94, the students may discover a "shortcut" for solving certain equations [numbers 3, 5, 8].
   Example 3:

$$\frac{5}{a+3} = \frac{3}{a-1} \qquad LDC = (a+3)(a-1)$$

$$(a+3)(a-1) \cdot \frac{5}{a+3} = \frac{3}{a-1} \cdot (a+3)(a-1)$$

$$(a-1) \cdot 5 \qquad\quad = 3 \cdot (a+3) \quad *$$

This step can be omitted since we can get the same result by simply "cross-multiplying":

$3(a+3) = 5(a-1)$ is equivalent to * because of the property of symmetry: If $a = b$, then $b = a$.

9. *Activity.* Reproduction Page 95 has the students transform equations into the form of a proportion and then solve by "cross-multiplying." This activity provides drill and practice in working with mixed numbers in algebra.

10. *Teacher Presentation.* Another method for solving a system of linear equations (different from the methods discussed in Chapter 4) can be demonstrated to the students as follows:

$$\text{Solve} \begin{cases} 7x - 3y = 7 \\ 5x + 2y = 34 \end{cases}$$

Step 1: Solve both equations for "y"

$$7x - 3y = 7 \qquad\qquad 5x + 2y = 34$$
$$-3y = 7 - 7x \qquad\qquad 2y = 34 - 5x$$
$$\boxed{y = \frac{7 - 7x}{-3}} \qquad\qquad \boxed{y = \frac{34 - 5x}{2}}$$

Step 2: Set the two expressions for y equal to each other and insert ( ) around any polynomial involved.

$$\frac{(7 - 7x)}{-3} = \frac{(34 - 5x)}{2}$$

Step 3: Solve the proportion by "cross-multiplying."

$$-3(34 - 5x) = 2(7 - 7x)$$
$$\vdots$$
$$x = 4$$

Step 4: Find y by substituting the value for x in one of the rectangles in Step 1.

$$7 = \frac{7 - 7(4)}{-3} = \frac{-21}{-3} = 7$$

Step 5: Check the answer in the given system.

This method provides drill and practice with (a) isolating a variable and (b) solving proportions. Assign several systems of linear equations to be solved in the manner presented above.

11. *Teacher Presentation.* Systems of equations can be solved in another way that provides drill and practice with solving an equation containing fractions.

   Directions: Isolate one variable in one equation and substitute the resulting expression for that variable in the other equation.

$$\begin{cases} A: 7x - 3y = 7 \\ B: 5x + 2y = 34 \end{cases}$$

Isolate x in A: $x = \dfrac{7 + 3y}{7}$

Substitute into B: $5\left(\dfrac{7 + 3y}{7}\right) + 2y = 34$

Solve the resulting fractional equation.

12. *Activity* (Enrichment). The following is a list of more challenging problems for this chapter. They may be assigned one at a time throughout the chapter, they may be presented at the beginning of the chapter as a unit project due after the chapter test, or they may simply be presented as a challenge for better students.

   a. Solve for x: $\dfrac{2x - 3}{3x - 2} + \dfrac{2x + 3}{2x + 5} = \dfrac{2(5x^2 - 3)}{6x^2 + 11x + 10}$

   b. Replace a in $\dfrac{a + 1}{a - 1}$ with $\dfrac{a + 1}{a - 1}$. Write the resulting fraction in simplest form

   c. Find: $\left(1 - \dfrac{1}{3}\right)\left(1 - \dfrac{1}{4}\right)\left(1 - \dfrac{1}{5}\right) \cdots \left(1 - \dfrac{1}{8}\right)$

   d. Solve for x: $\dfrac{a + x}{a} - \dfrac{2x}{a + x} - \dfrac{1}{3} = \dfrac{x^2(a - x)}{a(a^2 - x^2)}$

   e. Solve for x: $\dfrac{x + 3}{x + 6} - \dfrac{x + 6}{x + 9} + \dfrac{x + 5}{x + 8} - \dfrac{x - 2}{x + 5} = 0$

   f. Simplify:

$$\left\{ \left(\dfrac{1}{\frac{1 - x}{1 + x}}\right) \cdot \left[\dfrac{(1 + x) - (1 - x)}{(1 + x)^2}\right] \right\} \cdot \left[\dfrac{x(1 + x^2) - (2x)(2x)}{(1 + x^2)^2}\right]$$

$$\div \left[\dfrac{-2x(1 + x^2) - (1 - x^2)(2x)}{(1 + x^2)^2}\right]$$

13. *Calculator Activity.* The following exercises can be assigned to the students who have access to a hand-held calculator.

   a. Multiply: $\dfrac{625}{a + 345.1} \quad \dfrac{34.2}{a - 345.1} \qquad \dfrac{0.0058}{p + 68.421} \quad \dfrac{64000}{p - 68.421}$

   b. Evaluate the following when $x = 1, 2, 4, 100, 1000$

$$\dfrac{1}{x - 3}, \quad \dfrac{2x}{x - 1}, \quad \dfrac{x + 1}{x^2}, \quad \dfrac{2x}{x^2 - x}, \quad \dfrac{x + 1}{x^2 - 1}$$

What happens to the value of each expression as x becomes very large?

c. Add: $\dfrac{244a + 8.913}{a - 41.882} + \dfrac{322a - 70.561}{41.882 - a}$

$\dfrac{30r - 7.664}{r - 109.84} + \dfrac{469r + 80.504}{109.84 - r}$

d. Subtract: $\dfrac{365b - 67.453}{b - 78.98} - \dfrac{89.223 - 402.1b}{78.98 - b}$

$\dfrac{448x - 8.7750}{x - 208.36} - \dfrac{556x - 9.3440}{208.36 - x}$

e. Solve for x:

$$\dfrac{64442 + x}{52345 - x} = \dfrac{.00238}{.01201} \qquad \dfrac{650000}{x - 0.00911} = \dfrac{250000}{x + 0.2011}$$

14. *Activity.* The life of the famous Greek mathematician Diophantus is described in the puzzle below:

He was a boy for $\dfrac{1}{6}$ of his life.

After $\dfrac{1}{12}$ more, he grew a beard.

After another $\dfrac{1}{7}$, he married.

In the 5th year after his marriage his son was born.

His son lived $\dfrac{1}{2}$ as many years as his father.

He died 4 years after his son.

Display this puzzle on the overhead projector as you lead the students in finding out how old Diophantus was when he died.

Assign a library research project to some students: "Contributions of Diophantus to Mathematics," or "The Life of Diophantus."

CHALLENGE PROBLEMS

1. Simplify $\dfrac{t - \dfrac{t^2 - 1}{t}}{1 - \dfrac{t - 1}{t}}$

2. The expression $\dfrac{P + Q}{P - Q} - \dfrac{P - Q}{P + Q}$ where $P = x + y$ and $Q = x - y$ can be simplified to
_____.

3. If $2x - 3y - z = 0$ and $x + 3y - 14z = 0$, $z \neq 0$, the numerical value of $\dfrac{x^2 + 3xy}{y^2 + z^2} =$
_____.

4. Reduced to lowest terms, $\dfrac{a^2 - b^2}{ab} - \dfrac{ab - b^2}{ab - a^2} =$ _____.

5. In the expression xy^2, the values of x and y are each decreased 25%; the value of the expression is:
   a. decreased 50%

   b. decreased 75%

   c. decreased $\dfrac{37}{64}$ of its value

   d. decreased $\dfrac{27}{64}$ of its value

   e. none of these

6. The fraction $\dfrac{5x - 11}{2x^2 + x - 6}$ was obtained by adding the two fractions $\dfrac{A}{x + 2}$ and $\dfrac{B}{2x - 3}$. The values of A and B are _____ .

7. Find the least positive integral value of n for which $\dfrac{n - 12}{5n + 23}$ is a nonzero reducible fraction.

   Hint: A nonzero fraction is reducible if and only if its reciprocal is reducible.

8. If $\dfrac{x}{x - 1} = \dfrac{y^2 + 2y - 1}{y^2 + 2y - 2}$, then $x =$ _____ .

9. $ab - 2cd = p$ $\dfrac{p}{r} =$ _____ .
   $6cd - 3ab = r$

10. What is the value of $\dfrac{4(x - y) - 8y}{6y - 2x}$? _____

EVALUATION

A. Simplify each of the following; record your answer in the box provided.

1. $\dfrac{12x^3y^2}{16xy}$ 2. $\dfrac{a^2 - 16}{a^2 - 8a + 16}$ 3. $\dfrac{2r - 2s}{s - r}$ 4. $\dfrac{x^2 - 2x + 1}{x^2 + 2x - 3}$

B. Perform the indicated operations and simplify the results if necessary. Record your answer in the box provided.

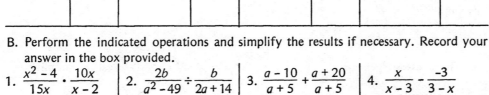

1. $\dfrac{x^2 - 4}{15x} \cdot \dfrac{10x}{x - 2}$ 2. $\dfrac{2b}{a^2 - 49} \div \dfrac{b}{2a + 14}$ 3. $\dfrac{a - 10}{a + 5} + \dfrac{a + 20}{a + 5}$ 4. $\dfrac{x}{x - 3} - \dfrac{-3}{3 - x}$

5. $\dfrac{7}{x+2} + \dfrac{x-4}{3x+6}$

6. $\dfrac{3c}{c^2-1} - \dfrac{5}{2c-2}$

7. $\dfrac{ab - \dfrac{b}{x}}{a^2 - \dfrac{1}{x^2}}$

8. $(x-2) - \dfrac{3x^2-4}{x+5}$

C. Find the solution set of each of the following equations. Record your answer in the box provided.

1. $\dfrac{5}{c+3} = \dfrac{3}{c-1}$

2. $\dfrac{x}{x-3} + 2 = \dfrac{3}{x-3}$

3. $\dfrac{n+4}{n-2} - \dfrac{n+5}{n-3} = 0$

4. $\dfrac{1}{2}x - \dfrac{x-4}{3} = 8x$

D. Find the solution set of the following system:

$$\dfrac{2x}{3} - \dfrac{1}{5}y = 2$$

$$\dfrac{4}{3}x + 4y = -4$$

RESOURCES

Below is a selected list of resources for teaching rational expressions. Addresses of publishers can be found in the alphabetical list in Appendix A.

Boyle, Pat, *Accent on Algebra*. Palo Alto, CA: Creative Publications, 1971. Includes a set of enrichment activities for use with any level algebra student. Cross number puzzles, algebra adages, and alphametics provide motivating practice.

Clark, Alice, and Leitch, Carol, *Amusements in Developing Algebra Skills, Volume II*. Pacific Grove, CA: Midwest Publications, 1983. Provides an ideal combination of extensive algebra practice exercises embedded in cross number puzzles, line designs, decodes, picture graphs, optical illusions, and others.

The Math Group, *Journey into Algebra*. Clinton, IA: EDUCAT, 1983. A set of clever puzzles and other activities for learning and practicing the skills of algebra.

National Council of Teachers of Mathematics, *The Mathematics Teacher*. Reston, VA: NCTM. This monthly journal is published nine times a year and includes useful suggestions for teaching various topics in the secondary school mathematics curriculum.

Rasmussen, Peter, *Key to Algebra*. Hayward CA: Activity Resources, 1975. A set of small pamphlets that provide practice in basic algebraic skills.

Rational Expressions. Chicago: LaPine Scientific Company, 1983. A set of three filmstrips and three cassettes on addition, subtraction, multiplication, and division of rational expressions —also solving equations with fractional coefficients.

Stallings, Pat, *Puzzling Your Way to Algebra*. Hayward, CA: Activity Resources, 1978. A collection of twenty-four cross number puzzles on various algebraic topics, including rational expressions.

7

Functions

CONTENT OVERVIEW

As discussed in the introductory chapter, one of the unifying concepts in algebra is that of *function*. The concept of function is powerful in that it provides a framework for much of what is to follow in algebra; notice that later students will move on to linear functions as well as quadratic, absolute value, step, circular, exponential, and logarithmic functions. Certainly each type of function differs from the others in some respects, but it will be important to have a general common approach to all of them so that students may more easily compare and contrast them. It will be the purpose of this chapter to establish a general approach to functions with particular emphasis on linear functions.

Thus the major emphasis at this point should be to help students develop an understanding of function in a general sense. One aspect of this emphasis will be to consider the input-output action of function. Second, the students must consider the domain, range, and various properties of functions. Finally, certain graphing techniques and properties can be used to further develop understanding of the concept of functions and their properties, as well as to aid in investigating particular functions.

Overall, the goal is for students to develop a deep structural understanding of function that will help them organize their knowledge of particular functions. They should then be in a better position to ask questions when essential ingredients appear to be missing or when the facts seem to be incongruous. They will be better able to maintain their own learning and make the best use of instructional resources such as teachers, texts, and peers.

OBJECTIVES

As a result of the learning experiences in this chapter, the student should be able to:

1. Find the set of ordered pairs determined by a relation defined on a given set

2. Identify the domain and range of a given relation

3. Determine if a given relation is a function

4. Given a function, $f(x)$, evaluate $f(a)$ for a in the domain of f

5. Given a function, identify the domain and range of the function

6. Given several input-output pairs, determine the rule defining a particular function

7. Given a function, use point-plotting to graph this function

8. Given two points on a line or the slope and y-intercept of the line, determine the equation for the line

9. Given the equations for two lines, determine if the lines are parallel (perpendicular)

10. Given an equation for a line, determine the slope and y-intercept of the line

11. Solve proportions

12. Determine when a function is a direct variation

LEARNING EXPERIENCES

Topic 1: Relations

1. *Teacher Presentation.* Introduce the idea of a set of ordered pairs representing a relation. Use some examples such as those found on Reproduction Page 96. Emphasize the importance of the order in the pairs.

2. *Activity.* Have the students complete Reproduction Page 96. Emphasize the various ways of describing a relation—listing the ordered pairs, a table, a rule (equation, etc.)

3. *Activity.* Give the students several equations and have them list some ordered pairs determined by each equation.
   Examples:

$y = 2x$	$(0,0), (1,2), (2,4), (-1,-2), (-3,-6) \ldots$
$d = 32t$	$(1,32), (2,64), (3,96) \ldots$
$y = \dfrac{x}{2}$	$(0,0), (2,1), (4,2), (-2,-1), (-6,-3) \ldots$

   Note the importance of order!

$y = x + 3$	$(0,3), (-1,2), (1,4), (-2,1), (2,5) \ldots$
$y = \sqrt{x}$	$(0,0), (4,2), (9,3) \ldots$

4. *Activity.* Have the students complete Reproduction Page 97.

5. *Teacher Presentation.* State a rule, say "add 2," and have the students complete the following set of ordered pairs. Point out how the rule "add 2" states a relation between the coordinates of the pairs.

   $(0,\underline{\hspace{1em}}), (3,\underline{\hspace{1em}}), (-2,\underline{\hspace{1em}}), (5,\underline{\hspace{1em}}), (\underline{\hspace{1em}},6)$

   This rule expresses a *relationship*, not just how to get the second coordinate if we know the first. State other rules and have them complete the ordered pairs.

6. *Activity.* Have students construct rules and challenge each other.

Topic 2: Domain and Range of Relations

1. *Activity.* Have the students work through Reproduction Page 98 identifying sets of first elements and second elements in a set of ordered pairs. This activity is designed to help prepare the students for domain and range. Students should work with these examples before they encounter the definitions.

2. *Teacher Presentation.* Define domain and range of a relation by referring back to the examples the students have completed on Reproduction Page 98. Also, ask the following:

Discussion Question: Given Domain = {1,2,3} and Range = {2,4} of a relation, find the relation.

Discussion: The students will discover that there are many possible answers. This point should be emphasized. The domain and range of a relation tell us only something about the relation, not all. Very different relations may have the same domain and range.

$$R_1 = \{(1,2),(1,4),(2,2),(3,4)\}$$
$$R_2 = \{(1,4),(2,3),(3,2)\}$$

Both R_1 and R_2 have the domain and range specified above.

3. *Activity.* Give the students some examples that involve finding a relation given the domain and the rule governing the relation.

Example:

If we drop an object the relation between the distance d it falls (in feet) and the time t it falls (in seconds) is given by the equation $d = 16t^2$. Find the relation $R_1 = \{(t,d)\, d = 16t^2)\}$ if Domain = {1,2,3,4,5}

Answer:

$$R_1 = \{(1,16), (2,64), (3,144), (4,256), (5,400)\}$$

Other examples could be used such as:

$$V = 32t \qquad \text{(Velocity related to time)}$$
$$F = \frac{9}{5}C + 32$$

4. *Activity.* Have the students complete Reproduction Page 99, identifying the domain and range of a relation stated as an equation. Point out that certain equations will have restrictions (division by zero, square root of negative number, etc.). Also, for a relation represented by an equation, the range will be determined by the domain.

Equation:

Let $y = 3x + 4$

a. If Domain = {whole numbers} find the range.

b. If Domain = {2,4,6, . . .} find the range.

Topic 3: Types of Functions

1. *Activity.* Have students complete Reproduction Page 100 comparing two relations.

This activity is to give them a more concrete experience with a relation that also satisfies the definition of a function.

2. *Teacher Presentation.* Lead into the definition of function by reviewing the example from Reproduction Page 100. Emphasize each domain element being matched (paired) with *exactly one* range element. Refer to the examples often! For $y = 3.50x$, what would it mean for one x value to have two different y values? Of course, this is impossible since it would mean that there could be two different rental fees for the same hours used. Make sure that students encounter relations that are not functions (in a variety of settings).
Example:
Consider the ordered pairs $(1,A)$, $(1,B)$, $(2,C)$, $(2,A)$, etc., that are used in locating cities on road maps. Is this relation a function?
Domain = $\{1,2,3,\ldots,12\}$ vertical location
Range   = $\{A,B,C,\ldots,N\}$ horizontal location

3. *Activity.* Have students find (or make up) examples of relations that are functions and some that are not. Encourage them to use various means of representing the relations.
Examples (not functions):
a. $x = 3$
b. $|y| = x$
c. $\{(1,3),(1,4),(2,3),(4,7)\}$
d. Matchings such as automobile color schemes, map locations, etc.

4. *Activity.* Have students complete Reproduction Page 101 introducing the $f(x)$ notation. This page is designed to help students *understand* the relation between the concepts and the notation. You may also want to use this notation

$$(x, f(x))$$

to emphasize that x represents domain values while $f(x)$ represents range values. Also, the $f(x)$ notation tells us the "rule" defining the function.
Example:
Let $f(x) = 3x + 2$
$f(1) = 5$ or we can say $(1, f(1)) = (1,5)$ is in the relation (function).

5. *Activity.* Have students put some of the relations considered so far into $f(x)$ notation.
Examples:
a. Map Scale $f(x) = 50x$ Have them identify what "x" means here (where it comes from). Same for $f(x)$.
b. Hours-Rent $f(x) = (3.50)x$

6. *Activity.* Using the previous examples have students complete the following.
a. For $f(x) = 50x$, find $f(1)$, $f(2)$, $f(5)$, $f(10)$, $f(3.5)$, $f(7.5)$.
Have the students tell what each of these $f(x)$ values mean.
b. For $f(x) = (3.50)x$, find $f(1)$, $f(2.5)$, $f(3)$, $f(10.5)$.

7. *Teacher Presentation.* Vary the notation and examples in the following ways.
a. Use $g(x)$, $h(x)$, $s(x)$, etc.
b. Have the students consider the following:

$f(x) = x + 7$

x	$f(x)$
1	8
2	
4	
3	
6	
12	
9	
$2a$	
☐	☐ + 7

It should be emphasized that there is nothing "magic" about x. $f(x) = x + 7$ tells us that whatever domain value we choose is paired with 7 greater than that number.

8. *Activity.* Introduce "function machines." These machines follow specified rules (functions).
   Examples:
   a. $f(x) = x - 4$
      $x = 1, 2, 3$

   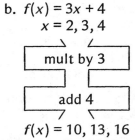

   b. $f(x) = 3x + 4$
      $x = 2, 3, 4$

   a. $f(x) = -3, -2, -1$

   b. $f(x) = 10, 13, 16$

   Have the students complete Reproduction Page 102.

9. *Activity.* Again, using the rent and map examples give students $f(x)$ values and have them find the corresponding x.
   Example:
   If Mr. Jones had to pay a rental fee of $14.00, for how long did he rent the mower?

   $f(x) = (3.50)x$ ⟶ $(3.50)x = 14.00$
   $f(x) = \$14.00$ ⟶ $x = 4$

   Can be found by solving equivalent equations or with a table.

   Example:
   Fill in the following table for $f(x) = 50x$ when x represents the number of inches on the map.

Inches on Map	Actual Miles Represented
2	——
7	——
——	450
10.5	——
——	600

10. *Teacher Presentation.* Remind the students that a function is a relation and as such will have a domain and range. Consider again $f(x) = (3.50)x$. What is its

domain? Computationally, x could be any real number. Of course, for this example, negative numbers make no sense. Also, what about fractions (representing fractions of hours)? Present the following cases.

a. Domain = {counting numbers} whole hours
   Range = {3.50, 7, 10.50, ...} multiples of $3.50

b. Domain = $\{x | x = \frac{a}{2}, a \in C\}$ nearest half-hour
   Range = {1.75, 3.50, 5.25, 7.00, ...} multiples of $1.75

11. *Activity.* Have students work Reproduction Page 103 identifying the domain and range of various functions. You may want to return to some of the same activities that were used for domain and range of relations. (Especially activity 3 under Topic 2.)

12. *Activity.* Have the students find examples of phenomena that can be modeled by a function.
    Examples:

    hours — rental fee
    hours — distance traveled
    hours worked — salary
    products per hour — total output

    Their examples should be linear functions. Have them use $f(x)$ or $(x, f(x))$ notation and describe the domain and range of each.

13. *Teacher Presentation.* "Guess My Rule": Let the teacher (later one might let a student operate the function) select a process such as "add five" which is to be applied to all input values. Since students are to guess the rule, they should not be told or shown the rule ahead of time, but the teacher might want to write it down for verification later. For example, the function is:

    $f(x) = x + 5$

    Let students take turns naming input values for which the teacher reports the corresponding output value.

Student	Teacher
7	12
0	5
6	11

    The students are to try to guess the common process connecting outputs to inputs. One might keep score on who is the first to get each function and/or the number of ordered pairs it took before the rule was correctly determined. (One might consider penalties for guessing incorrectly.) The rules chosen can range from easy to difficult. Some examples follow:

    a. $y = 5$
    b. $y = x$
    c. $y = x + 5$
    d. $y = x - 1$
    e. $y = 2x$

  f. $y = 2x + 1 = (x) + (x + 1)$
  g. $y = x^2$
  h. $y = x^2 + 1$
  i. $y = 2x^2$

14. *Teacher Presentation.* The teacher might begin by naming some functions in a certain area and have students volunteer others. Some examples follow:

Area	Function
Conversions	Fahrenheit $\longrightarrow$ Celsius : $C = \frac{5}{9}(F - 32)$
Conversions	Yards $\longrightarrow$ Meters : $M = \frac{3600}{3937}Y$
Postage	Letter weight $\longrightarrow$ postage
Wages	Work time $\longrightarrow$ pay
Wages	Units produced $\longrightarrow$ pay

15. *Activity* (Enrichment). Simply mention an area or situation and students are to identify related functions.

	Input	"Rule"	Output
Mailing letters	mailing	address	deliver
Telephone calling	dialing	routing	ring
Telephone conversation	speaking	transmission	reproduction
Radio	—	—	—
TV	—	—	—
Movies	film	transmission of light	screen

16. *Activity* (Enrichment). Games and functions: The teacher might illustrate how many games are compositions of functions.
   a. Chess: In chess, on a single move, the knight must choose one of eight functions; his movement constitutes a composition of such functions.
   b. Number search games: Beginning with two functions say, $f(x) = x - 7$ and $g(x) = x + 11$ and using them as the only legal moves, start with some number, e.g. 99, and try to generate some goal, say 100.
   Sample solution:

$$\overset{f}{99 \quad} \overset{g}{92 \quad} \overset{f}{103 \quad} \overset{g}{96 \quad} \overset{f}{107 \quad} 100$$

Legal Moves	Start	Goal
$f(x) = x + 7, g(x) = x - 11$	99	100
$h(x) = \frac{x}{3}, k(x) = x + 5$	13	11
" "	13	10

17. *Activity.* The purpose of this activity is to show how a complicated function can sometimes be broken up in terms of several elementary functions.
   Begin with a function rule such as

$$f(x) = 2x - 1$$

This function can be thought of as the combination of first doubling the number, and then subtracting one from the intermediate result.

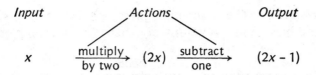

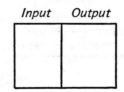

To build an activity around this idea, the teacher should prepare a chart for recording the outputs generated for selected inputs such as the following:

Input	Output

Now choose four students; say *A, B, C,* and *D*; and give them, respectively, the following assigments.

A: Any time *A* receives an input number, *A* records it in the input column and also writes it on a sheet of paper which is then given to *B*.

B: Taking the paper from *A*, *B* multiplies the written number by two. *B* records the result, either on the same or a different sheet of paper. That paper is passed along to *C*.

C: Taking the paper from *B*, *C* subtracts one from *B*'s result. *C* then sends the difference along to *D*.

D: *D* records the final result in the output column of the chart, next to the input.

The teacher can vary this in several ways. The jobs for *A* and *D* could be taken over by *B* and *C* respectively if fewer students are to be involved. Instead of paper, a calculator could be passed along (caution—it could get dropped), or some type of display (an abacus or score cards, etc.) could be set up at each station and arranged so that only the next person in line can see the needed result. With such secrecy, the team *A-B-C-D* could act as the function and the "Guess-My-Rule" activity could be played. Too, like workers on an assembly line, *B* and *C*, only having direct contact with a small part, might wonder what the finished product is like. Finally, several teams could be formed and relay races be conducted—speed would be judged second to accuracy. More challenging examples can now be presented to the class.

18. *Activity* (Enrichment). Geometric functions or transformations may be introduced as special projects for your better students. These include line reflections, point reflections, translations, and rotations.

Topic 4: Graphing Relations and Functions

1. *Activity.* Suppose the reports of population size for a certain year were

Year	Population
1920	5,000
1930	8,000
1940	11,000
1950	12,000
1960	11,000
1970	10,000

Graph the population as a function of time and draw a polygonal line connecting the points.

2. *Activity.* Plot the verticies of a polygon and draw the polygon. E.g., *A*: (1,3); *B*: (2,4); *C*: (4,7); *D*: (0,4); draw quadrilateral *ABCD*. Present the class with other relations which will yield special quadrilaterals.

3. *Activity.* Use a calculator, computer, or progammable calculator to systematically input values such as –5, –4, –3, –2, –1, 0, 1, 2, 3, . . . and output the values of certain functions. The points can be hand plotted one at a time as they occur, or, if a computer is being used, automatically. Some examples to try are:

   a. $y = \frac{5}{9}(x - 32)$, changes Fahrenheit to Celsius

   b. $y = |x|$, or
   c. $y = x^2 - 5x + 6$

4. *Activity* (Enrichment). Use a programmable calculator; program it to loop using the output from one calculation as input for the next. Use a function such as

   $$y = \frac{5}{9}(x - 32)$$

   and starting at $x = 0$, let it run and plot the points as the output coverges on the fixed point (–40,–40).

5. *Activity.* Have your students consider the graphs in fig. 7.1. Which are functions and which are not?

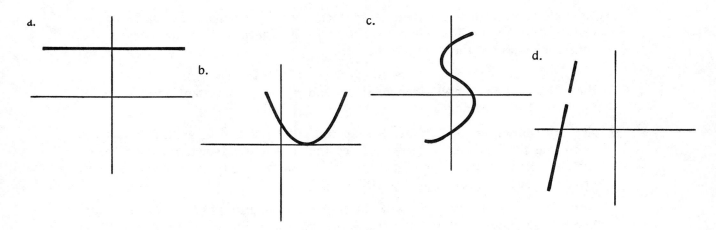

Figure 7.1

Introduce the vertical line test. Have the students complete Reproduction Page 104.

Topic 5: Slope of a Line

1. *Teacher Presentation.* Present students with linear functions of the form $f(x) = mx + b$. Point out to the students that the graphs of these functions being straight lines amounts to the same thing as constant growth rates. We need to verify this mathematically.

2. *Activity.* For a given linear function, have each student find two points (x_1, x_2) and their respective images $(f(x_1), f(x_2))$. Find the difference quotient:

$$\frac{f(x_1) - f(x_2)}{x_1 - x_2}$$

The fact that the line grows at a constant rate (slope) is thus verified by showing that the difference quotient is indeed constant. Repeat this exercise with the examples found on Reproduction Page 105.

3. *Teacher Presentation.* Present the students with the graphs of several linear functions. Let them guess the slopes (steepness) of each line. Point out that the slope and additional values of the function can be found more accurately from the equation than by reading the graph.

4. *Teacher Presentation.* Point out that equations of the form $ax + by = c$ may easily be changed to the slope-intercept form, and hence, the slope and y-intercept may be read directly.

5. *Activity.* Consider the equation $3A - 2B = 6$. Construct a table of values:

A	3	4	6	10
B	$\frac{3}{2}$	3	6	12

Now plot points on a graph and let $A = mB + b$ or $B = mA + b$. Set up two equations $4 = m \cdot 3 + b$ and $6 = m \cdot 6 + b$ and solve for m and b. Put them back in general equation of the form $y = mx + b$.

6. *Activity.* Present the students with equations of the form $y = mx + b$. Investigate the effects on the graph when m varies and b remains constant and vice versa. Consider Reproduction Page 106.

7. *Activity* (Enrichment). Consider the equation of a line and its graph. Reflect the given line through the line $y = x$. Have the students comment on the slope of the given line and the slope of its image. What about reflections through the x-axis or y-axis? See Reproduction Page 107.

8. *Activity.* Present the students with the graphs and equations of a family of parallel lines. They should see that the slopes are the same. Furthermore, it should be emphasized that the graph of $y = mx + b$ is the graph of $y = mx$ shifted b units vertically on the y-axis.

9. *Teacher Presentation.* Point out the fact that parallel (or coincidental) lines having the same slope leads to the result that certain systems of linear equations have no (or infinitely many) solutions. Hence the lines $ax + by = c$ and $ax + by = d$ are parallel ($c \neq d$).

10. *Activity.* Repeat the previous exercise with pairs of perpendicular lines. Students should see that slopes of perpendicular lines are negative reciprocals of one another. Better students should be able to show that the lines $ax + by = c$ and $bx - ay = d$ are perpendicular. See Reproduction Page 108.

11. *Teacher Presentation.* Attention should be called to the fact that the m and b, or the slope and y-intercept, are two conditions that determine the position (equation) of a straight line, just as two points determine its position. This discussion should lead to the following summarizing generalization: *To determine the position of a straight line in a plane, it is necessary to have two independent conditions.*

12. *Activity.* Give students the slope and y-intercept of several lines and have them determine the equation of the lines by using the slope-intercept form $y = mx + b$. Point out to students that given the slope and y-intercept (or any point), a second point could be determined by simply applying the vertical move divided by horizontal move definition of slope to the given point. This should assist students in seeing the similarities in the "different" forms.

13. *Activity.* Present students with two points on a Celsius scale and their corresponding points on the Fahrenheit scale. Have students determine the formula equation. What is the slope?

14. *Teacher Presentation.* At this time it should be apparent that if two points determine the position of a straight line, then two points will also determine the equation of a line. Students should now be introduced to the point-slope form of the equation of a line $y - y_1 = m(x - x_1)$. Have students choose a different $(x_1 y_1)$.

15. *Activity.* Repeat the previous activity using physical problems. Students should write the equations of these physical problems using the point-slope form. Examples include:
    a. A five-minute long-distance phone call costs $2.50. A 10-minute phone call costs $6.25. However, the first 3 minutes only cost $1.00. Write an equation for the cost C, of a call lasting n minutes longer than 3 minutes.
    b. The death rate per thousand was 10.5 in 1930 and 7.5 in 1970. Write an equation to predict the death rate, given the last two digits of the year. Hint: Use (30,10.5) and (70,7.5).

16. *Activity* (Enrichment). Emphasize to students that linear equations can be thought of as prediction equations. For example, the length of a spring is a linear function of the weight attached to it. Hence have students estimate or predict the length of a spring given certain weights. Students should be asked to make up their own problems (e.g., the cost of cutting a yard is a linear function of the hours spent).

Topic 6: Proportion and Variation

1. *Teacher Presentation.* The concepts of ratio and proportion are used, at least intuitively and by implication, even in the arithmetic of the elementary school, and to a

greater extent in the subsequent work of the junior high school. It would be well to review the concept of proportion for the subsequent study of variation.

2. *Activity.* Present students with many practical examples (e.g., recipes, fuel mixtures, dietetic compositions) where proportions may be useful as mathematical models. Point out that the first component of each ratio refers to the same kind of object and the second component refers to the same kind of object.

3. *Teacher Presentation.* Show students how to solve systems of linear equations by ratio and proportion. For example, if

$$x - y = 3$$
$$x + y = 5$$

let us determine the ratio $x:y$. We can rewrite as

$$\frac{x - y}{x + y} = \frac{3}{5}$$

Hence $5x - 5y = 3x + 3y$ or $2x = 8y$ which implies $x = 4y$. Therefore,

$$\frac{x}{y} = \frac{4}{1}.$$

There are infinitely many rational numbers equivalent to $\frac{4}{1}$, but we want those which satisfy our original system. Hence $x = 4$ and $y = 1$.

4. *Activity.* Have the students solve other systems of linear equations found on Reproduction Page 109.

5. *Teacher Presentation.* The concept of variation is inseparable from the concept of function, and the two should be stressed together, both concepts being abstracted and clarified through the interweaving of graphic illustrations and numerical evaluations of formulae. It should be emphasized that direct and inverse variations are functions. Let students compare tabular values for $y = 3x$ and $y = \frac{3}{x}$.

6. *Activity.* The discovery that direct variation produces straight lines and inverse variation produces curved lines (hyperboles) is significant and instructive. Hence, have students graph the equations found on Reproduction Page 110.

7. *Teacher Presentation.* Variation may be regarded as an aspect of ratio and proportion. $y = Kx$ implies:

$$\frac{y_1}{x_1} = \frac{y_2}{x_2} = K.$$

Present this table to the students.

$y = 4x$

x	y	$\frac{y}{x}$
1	4	4
2	8	4
.	.	.
.	.	.
.	.	.

8. *Activity.* Present students with a judicious number of physical examples illustrating direct and inverse variation. They may be drawn from arithmetic, geometry, physics, etc. For example:
   a. The perimeter of a square varies directly to the side
   b. The area of a square varies directly to the square of a side
   c. The base of a rectangle of constant area varies inversely to the altitude
   d. The gravitational force between two objects varies inversely to the square of the distance between them
   In each case the students should be asked to translate the statement into an equation involving a constant K and to indicate the numerical value of K where they can. Now have students construct their own example problems. Present these to the other members of the class and ask them to solve the problems using proportions.

9. *Teacher Presentation.* The nature of functional relationships should be continually stressed throughout the study of variation. Your better students may even wish to consider some problems illustrating joint or inversely as the square variation.

CHALLENGE PROBLEMS

1. R varies directly as S and inversely as T. When $R = \frac{3}{4}$ and $T = \frac{9}{14}$, $S = \frac{3}{7}$. Find S when $R = \sqrt{48}$ and $T = \sqrt{75}$.

2. If $f(x) = \dfrac{5 + 3\sqrt{5}}{10}\left(\dfrac{1 + \sqrt{5}}{2}\right)^x + \dfrac{5 - 3\sqrt{5}}{10}\left(\dfrac{1 - \sqrt{5}}{2}\right)^x$ then $f(x + 1) - f(x - 1)$, expressed in terms of $f(x) =$ _____.

3. If $f(x) = \dfrac{x(x - 1)}{2}$, then $f(x + 2)$ equals
   a. $f(x) + f(2)$
   b. $(x + 2) f(x)$
   c. $x(x + 2) f(x)$
   d. $x \cdot f(x)/x + 2$
   e. $\dfrac{(x + 2) f(x + 1)}{x}$

4. $f(a) = a - 2$ and $F(a,b) = b^2 + a$, then $F[3, f(4)] =$ _____.

5. $f(x)$ is a linear function. If $f(3x) = 4x - 2$ and $f(n) = 8$, find n.

6. The function f is not defined for $x = 0$, but, for all nonzero real numbers x,

   $$f(x) + 2f\left(\frac{1}{x}\right) = 3x.$$ The equation

   $f(x) = f(-x)$ is satisfied by how many real numbers.

7. If the function f defined by

   $$f(x) = \frac{cx}{2x + 3}, \quad x \neq -\frac{3}{2},$$

   satisfies $f(f(x)) = x$ for all real numbers x except $-\frac{3}{2}$, then $c =$ _____.

8. What is the domain of h if $h(x) = \dfrac{\sqrt{x}}{x-1}$?

9. Find the equation of a line which passes through the point (p,q) and is parallel to $ax - by = c$.

10. The coordinates of A and B are $(2a, 2b)$ and $(4a, 3b)$, respectively, the slope of the line perpendicular to $\overleftrightarrow{AB}$ is _____.

EVALUATION

1. Circle the ordered pairs that satisfy the relation $2x - 3y = 6$:

   $(0, 2)$ $(3, 2)$ $(3, 0)$ $(-6, -6)$ $(3, -2)$

2. Given: $B = \{(2, 1)\ (3, 1)\ (2, 3)\ (4, 5)\}$
   Identify the domain _____
   Identify the range _____
   Is this relation a function? _____

3. Given: $f(x) = 3x + 5$
   Find: $f(0)$ = _____
          $f(2)$ = _____
          $f(a + 4)$ = _____

4. Complete the following table for the function $y = x^2 + 3$:

x	-2	-1	0	1	2
y					

   Using the ordered pairs determined by this table,

5. Determine the range and the rule of the function pictured below:

   $x = 0, 1, 2, 3, 4$

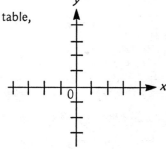

   Range = _____
   Rule: _____

6. Determine the equation of the lines, given
   a. points (2, –3) and (–1, 4) are on the line _____
   b. its slope is 3 and its y-intercept is (0, –5) _____

7. Solve the following systems of linear equations.

   a. $x + y = 2$ b. $2x + y = 6$ c. $x - 4y = 4$
      $x - y = 4$ $x - 3y = 3$ $y = \frac{1}{4}x + 6$
   By ratio and proportion   By graphing

   By any method

8. Given: $2x - 3y = 12$
   Find: a. Slope _____
         b. y-intercept _____
   Graph on the grid provided.

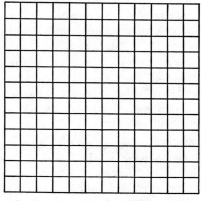

9. Identify the following pairs of lines as being parallel, perpendicular, the same line, or none of these.
   a. $2x + y = 6$
      $x - 2y = 6$ _____
   b. $2x + y = 6$
      $x + 2y = 6$ _____
   c. $2x + y = 6$
      $x + \frac{1}{2}y = 3$ _____
   d. $2x + y = 6$
      $2x + 6 = 0$ _____
   e. $2x + y = 6$
      $4x + 2y = 12$ _____

10. Graph the following: $x = 2y$. Identify as a direct or indirect variation.

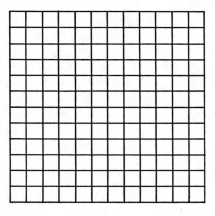

RESOURCES

Below is a selected list of resources for teaching functions. Addresses of publishers can be found in Appendix A.

Clark, Alice, and Leitch, Carol, *Amusement Developing Algebra Skills, Volume II.* Pacific Grove, CA: Midwest Publications, 1983. Provides an ideal combination of extensive algebra practice exercises embedded in cross number puzzles, line designs, decodes, picture graphs, optical illusions, and others.

Crouse, Richard I., and Sloyer, Clifford W., *Mathematical Questions from the Classroom.* Newton, MA: Allyn and Bacon, 1983. A collection of questions and suggested answers for secondary school mathematics students.

Gelfand, I. M., *The Method of Coordinates and Functions and Graphs.* Cambridge, MA: M.I.T. Press, 1968. This pamphlet, illustrating the relationship between functions and their graphs, is part of the "Library of School Mathematics" series.

National Council of Teachers of Mathematics, *The Mathematics Teacher.* Reston, VA: NCTM. This monthly journal is published nine times a year and includes useful suggestions for teaching various topics in the secondary school mathematics curriculum.

National Council of Teachers of Mathematics, *Growth of Mathematical Ideas.* (24th Yearbook). Reston, VA: NCTM, 1959.

National Council of Teachers of Mathematics, *Enrichment Mathematics for High School.* (28th Yearbook). Reston, VA: NCTM, 1963.

Plan, Algebra 2. Oak Lawn, IL: Plan Products, 1983. Algebraic concepts are developed through carefully sequenced and clearly stated objectives and activities. The teacher's kit includes placement tests, achievement tests, and duplicating masters.

School Science and Mathematics Association, *School Science and Mathematics.* Bowling Green, OH: SSMA. This monthly journal is published nine times a year and includes pedagogy and research in mathematics education useful for the secondary/post-secondary teacher.

8

Problem Solving and Applications of Algebra

CONTENT OVERVIEW

Although it is very doubtful, one might (???) justify presenting algebra as an abstract formal system without real-world relevance to those few destined to be professional research mathematicians. However, this is far from the characterization of algebra that is needed for the secondary school population in general. In fact, all students of algebra need meaningful parallels as they learn algebra. Then, to see via algebra the power and ubiquity of mathematics, they need numerous domains of application to explore and conquer, to exercise and reinforce their knowledge, to extend their range of understanding, and to see algebra as a valuable conceptual tool. It is in this broad context, consistent with recommendations for utility and relevance from professional organizations, that we developed the following presentation of the algebraic method organized rather uniquely around general notions of cognitive processes and problem-solving behavior.

The essence of the method as presented here, given a problem situation, is to construct an algebraic representation or model such as a system of equations, thus producing a corresponding algebraically expressed problem. It is in the latter mode that previously learned algebraic skills and techniques have a direct bearing, leading, hopefully, to at least an algebraic solution. Then, depending on the links between the model and the real situation, it might be possible to carry the algebraic solution back and to construct a solution to the original problem in the original domain. Hence, algebra acts as a mediator for solving problems in other arenas!

The development here, however, is intended to be supplementary, complementing textbook presentations rather than being a replacement for such. Whereas traditional textbooks do not provide adequately for teaching how to translate from the given situation to an algebraic model, the bulk of the learning experiences here are aimed at this specific phase of the process. Items 1 and 2 of Topic 1, for example, are geared to the perceptual feat of detecting which operations to use and in which order. Item 3 of Topic 1 extends this as a vocabulary-building exercise to include relationships and to help students learn both similarities and differences in meaning between various words and phrases. Topics 6 and 7

113

explicitly acknowledge the necessity of having at least a minimal knowledge about the mechanisms and relationships active in the domain of application.

To help students realize the nature and potential of the algebraic method, we emphasize its general aspects rather than specialized techniques. Thus, translating to a system of equations and using substitution are presented before the specialization of constructing a single equation for the limited range of problems to which the technique applies. The latter approach is included, however, because of its general use. But it is presented here without the pedantic insistence on producing a single equation when a system with two or more equations might seem quite natural to the student.

Furthermore, left to their own devices, students rarely develop the concept of algebraic equivalence, instead relating problems on the basis of context, the quantities involved, or other superficialities. Topic 5 addresses this issue, aiming at the development of an explicit notion of algebraic equivalence. Students should come closer to appreciating the power of algebra once they are cognizant of the fact that, in its abstractness, a given algebraic model may be representative of a multitude of situations.

Since it is possible to give only a limited supply of problems in this publication, we encourage teachers to search for interesting, motivating problems that embody suitable mathematical learning objectives and which are appropriate for the capabilities of their students. To assist with the "treasure hunt," several sources of excellent problems are listed among the references to this chapter.

OBJECTIVES

As a result of the learning experiences in this chapter, the student should be able to:

1. Analyze verbally stated problems for algebraic operations and relationships across a range of contexts, developing a vocabulary of words and phrases that have algebraic interpretations

2. Choose, from among various alternatives, those equations which can be used to model a given problem situation, explaining the links between the variables of the model and the unknowns of the problem

3. Use the algebraic method of constructing a suitable algebraic model (an equation, system of equations . . .), solving the algebraic version of the problem, and translating to a solution of the original, for the standard types of word problems (coin, rate-distance, lever . . .)

4. Use certain basic formulae in solving selected problems to which such apply

5. Identify, from among alternatives, those problems which are algebraically identical or equivalent

6. Detect the sometimes needed "extra" information for certain problems and to seek out such implicit or hidden information

7. Detect and possibly resolve inconsistencies in information for certain given problems

8. Develop an appreciation for algebra as a conceptual and problem-solving tool with a wide range of applications

LEARNING EXPERIENCES

Topic 1: The Algebraic Method for Solving Problems

1. *Teacher Presentation.* Very soon we will be trying to solve story problems like:

   Jim has $2.55 in dimes and nickels. If the number of nickels is one less than twice the number of dimes, how many dimes does he have?

   In algebra we learn how to use equations like

   $$5(2x - 1) + 10x = 255 \quad \text{or}$$
   $$\frac{255 - x}{5} = 2x - 1$$

   to solve such problems. Notice how these equations are constructed using the arithmetic operations of addition, subtraction, multiplication, or division. As a review and to get ready to solve algebra story problems, we shall do some arithmetic story problems. However, instead of just finding the answers, we need to concentrate on the operations, being sure to note which operations we use and why we should use them.

   Example 1.
   If we share $2.55 equally among 5 children, how much will each one get?
   Operation: Division, because we are "sharing equally."
   Solution: $5\overline{)2.55}$ with $.51$ above; each gets $0.51 or 51¢.

   Example 2.
   Mary, Bobby, and Annie are respectively 12, 10, and 5 years old. What is the average of their ages?
   Operations: Addition, then division. To compute an average, one first gets the total of all of the items and then divides by the number of items.
   Solution: $12 + 10 + 5 = 27$, $3\overline{)27}$ with 9 above. Therefore, 9 is the average of their ages.

   Example 3.
   Jim has 13 dimes and 25 nickels. How much money is that all together?
   Operations: Multiply, multiply, and add.
   Solution: $13 \cdot 10 = 130$, is the number of cents in dimes
   $\quad\quad\quad\; 25 \cdot 5 = \underline{125}$, is the number of cents in nickels
   $\quad\quad\quad\quad\quad\quad\quad 255$, is the total in cents.
   This is $2.55 all together.

2. *Activity.* Have the students do the exercises on Reproduction Page 111. They should use an approach similar to the above, first planning which operations need to be used and in what order, and then carrying out the plan. As a follow-up, we suggest a discussion of their results and comments leading to the next activity.

3. *Activity.* Suggest to students that they construct their own thesaurus (or dictionary) to help with the "translation" phase of the algebraic method. The four fundamental arithmetic operations should definitely be included. Entries could be placed

on separate cards to provide for expansion and still be able to maintain alphabetical order. We illustrate a possible entry for *addition.*

    Addition—the binary operation symbolized by "+"

        related—Add, combine, increase, more than, plus, sum, total

        idioms—_____ added to _____, exceeds _____ by _____, _____ greater than _____, _____ increased by _____, sum of _____ plus _____

        contrasted—decrease, difference, less than, minus, subtract, subtraction

Note: One should not be too naive in interpreting the inclusion of such terms as *total* being related to *addition.* Depending on the problem conditions, *total* may imply other processes than just *addition.* It would be helpful, then, if terms like *total* and *average* were provided with separate entries in the thesaurus.

Topic 2: Using Equations as Models

1. *Teacher Presentation.* Let's turn our attention directly to the most important part of the algebraic method for solving problems: using variables and number operations in equations or formulae to model problem situations. Here are some examples.

    Example 1.

    Using an equation to model a simple arithmetic problem.

    Problem: After getting 20 meters of new track for his miniature railroad, Kim has 24 meters all together. How many meters of track did he begin with?

    Discussion: Many of you already know to take 24 minus 20 to get the answer, but wait, right now we are more concerned about an equation for the problem. Do you see that

$$T + 20 = 24,$$

where T represents the initial number of meters of track, is a model equation for the problem? The new amount would be added to the amount he already had to get the total.

    Another interesting thing will happen if we look at some steps for solving the equation.

a. $T + 20 = 24$ Given
b. $(T + 20) - 20) = 24 - 20$ Subtraction Property of Equality
c. $T = 24 - 20$ Simplifying the left member
d. $T = 4$ Subtraction fact

Thus, Kim began his set with 4 meters of track.

    Notice that the third step includes the subtraction of 24 - 20 that we mentioned at the beginning for the arithmetic solution to this problem. So using equations does not eliminate the necessity of doing the computation, it only delays it. The advantage, however, is that the equation captures all the operations and relationships in the problem situation. Thus, for more complicated problems one can focus one's attention on the processes needed to solve the equation without being concerned with or distracted by the meaning in terms of the problem situation. One need only to look for such meaning when the equation is first established and then again once it has been solved.

Example 2.

Using an appropriate model formula.

Problem: What was Mr. Traveler's average speed if it took him 3 hours to travel 246 km?

Discussion: The rate of speed, the time spent, and the distance traveled (quantities in the problem situation) are interrelated as in the formula

$$r \cdot t = d$$

where we know to *multiply* the rate in km/hr times the time in hours to get the distance measured in kilometers. The time and distance are known to be 3 hours and 246 km, respectively, while the rate is unknown. Thus, substituting into the formula,

$$r \cdot 3 = 246$$

is an algebraic model expressing the operations and relations in the problem situation. Then, solving for *r* will help us solve the problem.

a. $r \cdot 3 = 246$

b. $r = \dfrac{246}{3}$

c. $r = 82$

Answer: He (Mr. Traveler) averaged 82 km/hr.

Again, we have used a simple example so that you can follow the important strategy of establishing an algebraic model for the problem, leaving the computational steps to be done while solving the equation.

2. *Activity.* Have students do the matching exercises on Reproduction Page 112, connecting problems and model equations. As a follow-up discuss the fact that two or more problems might use the same model equation. This should help support the abstract nature of algebra. While constructing an algebraic model, the students should analyze the problem in terms of its algebraic qualities and relationships, emphasizing these over other qualities.

Answers:

1	5
2	12 and 2 and 3 (possibly 14)
3	11 and 14 (possibly 2 and 3)
4	1 and 10
5	8
6	15 or 13
7	16
8	7

Topic 3: Systems of Equations as Models

1. *Teacher Presentation.* The algebraic model for some problems will contain not just one, but two or more equations and perhaps several different variables corresponding to different unknowns. Such a model is called a *system of equations.* (Loosely speaking, for completeness, one equation involving only one variable can also be

called a system.) To prepare for such an occasion we will show how the *substitution principle* can be used to solve a system of equations.

Example 1.

Formulae and assigned values.

System: $A = \frac{1}{2}h(B + b)$, $A = 120$, $B = 11$, $b = 5$, find h.

Discussion: This system of four equations in four unknowns represents a very common type of situation working with formulae. Given values for all the variables except one, the last one is determined by the relationship. This example will help to illustrate the substitution principle.

Focusing our attention on the formula

$$A = \frac{1}{2}h(B + b)$$

and knowing $A = 120$, $B = 11$, and $b = 5$, we can replace each unknown by its corresponding value; i.e., substitute these values into the formula. We get:

$$120 = \frac{1}{2}h(11 + 5)$$

This result is worth noting. It is a single equation in one unknown, the type we have learned to solve.

Finishing,

$$\frac{1}{2}h(16) = 120$$
$$8h = 120$$
$$h = 15$$

Example 2.

Two equations in two unknowns; one explicitly solved.

System: $5x + 10y = 185$
$\qquad\quad y = (20 - x)$

Discussion: Notice the second equation in this system. This equation gives y in terms of x (there are no other occurrences of y in this equation). This expression $(20 - x)$ can be used relative to the substitution principle just like the numbers 120, 11, and 5 were used in the preceding example. Thus, focusing on the first equation

$$5x + 10y = 185$$

we substitute $(20 - x)$ for y giving us

$$5x + 10(20 - x) = 185,$$

a single equation in one unknown. (The solution is left for later.)

Example 3.

Two equations in two unknowns, the most common case.

System: $5x + 10y = 185$
$\qquad\quad x + y = 20$

Discussion: This example differs from the preceding one in that neither equation gives one of the variables in terms of the other. As a subproblem, then, we need to solve one equation. If we choose the second equation

$$x + y = 20$$

and solve for y, we get

$$y = (20 - x)$$

(*Note:* The parentheses were introduced to help avoid errors in the upcoming substitution.)

This brings us to the point where we started in the earlier example. Substituting $(20 - x)$ for y in the first equation gives us (once again)

$$5x + 10(20 - x) = 185$$

Finishing,

$$5x + 200 - 10x = 185$$
$$-5x + 200 = 185$$
$$-5x = -15$$
$$x = 3$$

Here we have x, but what about y? "Back substituting" 3 for x in the equation $y = (20 - x)$,

$$y = 20 - 3$$
$$y = 17$$

2. *Activity.* Have students solve the systems of equations on Reproduction Page 113, using substitution techniques.

Topic 4: The Single-Equation Alternative to Simple Systems

1. *Teacher Presentation.* Problems that may use systems of equations. Problem: Barbara has 35 coins, some are dimes and the rest are quarters. If their total value is $5.30, how many of each kind does she have?

Discussion: We will show, first, how this problem can be solved using a system of two equations and then suggest how one could formulate a single equation initially.

Letting d stand for the number of dimes and q the number of quarters, we can write

$$d + q = 35$$

based on information in the first sentence. Working toward the total value, the dimes are worth $10d$ cents and the quarters are worth $25q$ cents. Therefore

$$10d + 25q = 530$$

where $5.30 has been changed to the corresponding number of cents. Thus, our algebraic model for the problem situation is the system

$$d + q = 35$$
$$10d + 25q = 530$$

Solving for d and q will help us answer the question in the problem. Let us solve the first equation for q in terms of d.

$$d + q = 35$$
$$q = (35 - d)$$

Now substituting $(35 - d)$ for q in the second equation

$$10d + 25(35 - d) = 530$$

Finishing

$$10d + 875 - 25d = 530$$
$$-15d + 875 = 530$$
$$-15d = -345$$
$$d = 23$$

So
$$q = 35 - 23$$
$$q = 12$$

Answer: Barbara has 23 dimes and 12 quarters.

Since the expression $(35 - d)$ can be understood through mental processes, instead of introducing the second variable, we offer an alternative approach going directly to the single equation:

$$10d + 25(35 - d) = 530$$

Again letting d correspond to the number of dimes, the rest of them, namely $(35 - d)$ must be quarters. These quarters have a value of $25(35 - d)$ cents. This together with $10d$ cents in dimes gives us the total. Hence,

$$10d + 25(35 - d) = 530$$

With the exception of explicitly writing q, the rest is the same as before.

2. *Activity.* Have students solve the story problems on Reproduction Page 114. Encourage them to use either a system of several equations or a single equation if they wish. Alert them to the necessity of having the same number of equations as unknowns in their algebraic models.

Topic 5: Algebraically Identical or Equivalent Problems

1. *Activity.* Follow-up to exercises on Reproduction Page 114. Referring to Reproduction Page 114, direct students' attention to a reexamination of their solutions for problems 5 and 6, comparing the two. Indicate that we want to build another layer of knowledge using comparison and contrast. We want to develop a deeper understanding of algebra's role in problem solving. Point out to those who have not yet seen the relation that probably the exact same equation was used as the algebraic model for both, namely:

$$4(x - 2) = 3(x + 2)$$

(Aside: Allow for minor adjustments due to commutativity, symmetry, and different choice of variable.)

The links to the two problem situations are, respectively,

no. 5 · the number of years in Jenny's age.

no. 6 · the average number of kilometers per hour at which "Wheeler" traveled for the trip.

With these assignments, the algebraic models are identical. In such a case we say that the two problems are *algebraically identical.*

Exercise:

At this point, assign students the task of writing a third problem which is *algebraically identical* to these two.

2. *Activity.* Once one sees the idea of being *algebraically identical,* one can relax the restriction concerning the use of identical constants (but not the variable nor the operations) between the two problems. We only want to preserve the algebraic structure of the equations. Thus, instead of the specific constants 4, 2, 3, and 2 in

a. $4(x - 2) = 3(x + 2)$

Let us switch to generalized constants *a, b, c,* and *d* giving us

b. $a(x - b) = c(x + d)$

Given any two equations which have the structure (pattern) shown in (b), regardless of whether the specific values for *a, b, c,* and *d* in one of them are the same as in the other, we say the two equations are *algebraically equivalent.* As an example, the equation

c. $25(x - 7) = 10(x + 20)$

is *algebraically equivalent* to

a. $4(x - 2) = 3(x + 2)$

With this in view, have students examine their solution to problem 7, Reproduction Page 115.

Letting x be the number of items Rhoda wants to buy, equation (c) is an algebraic model for problem 7. (Aside: Again allow for minor adjustments.) So, problems 5, 6, and 7 all use algebraically equivalent models. We say, then, that these problems are *algebraically equivalent* too. (Sometimes, "they have the same *algebraic structure.*")

Exercise:

At this point have students produce examples of problems which are algebraically equivalent but not algebraically identical to problems 5 and 7.

3. *Activity.* The ideas of *algebraically identical* and *algebraically equivalent* can be extended to problems modeled by systems of (two or more) equations. For examples of algebraically identical problems of this type see problems 3 and 4. These both (with proper assignments for x and y) can be modeled by the system.

$$x + y = 17$$
$$4x + 18y = 236$$

The general structure can be characterized by either

$$x + y = a$$
$$bx + cy = d$$
$$\text{or}$$
$$ax + by = c$$
$$dx + ey = f$$

depending on one's interpretation. In either sense, problem 8 is algebraically equivalent to problems 3 and 4 by virtue of the system

$$x + y = 17$$
$$10x + 25y = 350$$

which can be used to model it.

Exercise:

Have students produce examples of problems that are *algebraically identical* to number 8 and problems *algebraically equivalent* but not *identical* to problems 3 and 8.

Topic 6: Using Formulae and/or Situation-Specific Knowledge

1. *Teacher Presentation.* Consider the problem:

How old is Jimmy, if twice his age is nine more than half of it? This problem represents a type whose model equation can be constructed by direct analysis of the problem statement in terms of numerical quantities (either known or unknown) and mathematical operations and relations. Fig. 8.1 illustrates the process and a resulting model equation.

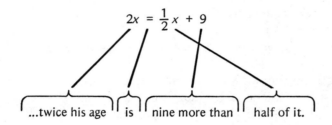

Figure 8.1. Problem Situation ⟶ Model. The arrows indicate the analysis and model construction processes of the algebraic method for solving problems.

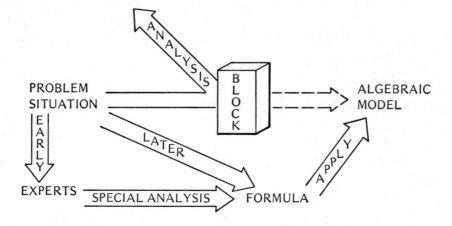

Figure 8.2. The formula alternative within the algebraic method for solving problems.

For simple problems the *basic analysis* route might be possible. However, for more complicated problems we might be blocked from this pursuit of a model (see fig. 8.2) by our unfamiliarity or lack of special knowledge for the problem situation. What people sometimes do when their own individual efforts are blocked is to consult with experts. The right experts might know a formula or be able to develop one using special analysis techniques. So, in one's earliest encounters with a certain type of problem, one might spend considerable time seeking an appropriate formula. Later, however, one's memory can help one think of the formula which, properly applied, will get around the obstacle. Fig. 8.3 shows a sample of formulae gleaned from experts in business, finance, industry, science, mathematics, and so on. Notice how algebra is relevant across a wide range of influences for our lives.

$$S = C + M \qquad\qquad A = p + prt$$

$$p = \frac{d^2 n}{2 \cdot 5} \qquad\qquad F = \frac{9}{5}C + 32$$

$$rt = d \qquad\qquad\qquad E = mc^2$$

$$I = \frac{E}{R} \qquad\qquad\qquad A = \pi r^2$$

$$P = 2(1 + w) \qquad\qquad x = \frac{-b \pm \sqrt{b^2 - 4ac}}{2a}$$

Figure 8.3.   Sample formulae in our heritage.

Let's look now at a sample problem and solution to highlight the kinds of knowledge and concerns to have for using formulae. Consider the problem:

At 75 meters per second, how long will it take to travel 1 kilometer?

Discussion: We can solve this problem with an application of the relatively simple (and common) formula

$rt = d$

In devising this formula, the experts selected letters to help them distinguish between the different quantities in the problem situation (a mnemonic device). You are doing the reverse process and you need to know the quantities which correspond to each letter. Our example illustrates the fairly common and easy-to-break coding system of initials. Thus, r = rate, t = time, and d = distance. Were this not the case you might, again, consult the experts to find out their conventions. We are not finished by just knowing the type of quantity represented by the letter, we must also know about the units of measure which can be used, e.g., rates can be measured in miles per hour, meters per second, kilometers per hour, or various other possibilities.

Still this is not sufficient. There must also be agreement concerning which units may be used throughout the formula. The following table shows some of the permissible combinations for our example. Continuing with our application, these units can help us identify the quantities from the problem statement. Hence 75 meters per second is a rate, 1 kilometer is a distance, and, of course, "how long" indicates a measure of time, in this case (it could be a distance elsewhere).

Quantity	Rate	Time	Distance
units	miles per hour	hours	miles
"	meters per second	seconds	meters
"	kilometers per hour	hours	kilometers

Comparing these with the table we see another potential difficulty: the units in the problem *do not* form a permissible combination. Additional knowledge is needed—namely conversion facts. We could, for example, convert the distance of 1 kilometer into the corresponding number of meters (here 1000) by knowing

$1\ km = 1000\ m$

Then with a free choice of units for time (none were specified) we can choose seconds, giving us the permissible combination.

Quantity Units Number	Rate meters per second 75	Time seconds ?	Distance meters 1000

Substituting into the formula, staying with *t* for the unknown, we have, finally, the model

$75t = 1000$

Finishing:

$t = 13\dfrac{1}{3}$

Answer: At the given rate it will take $13\dfrac{1}{3}$ seconds to go the given distance.

2. *Discussion Continued.* This has been an extensive look at a familiar and rather simple example. But, let's see what we've obtained from our investment. We now know a number of questions which need to be answered if a formula is to be used in the algebraic method.
   A. What formula should we use?
   B. Referring to the letter code, to which quantities do the symbols refer?
   C. Referring to a specific quantity, what is it and in what possible units can it be measured?
   D. For agreement in the formula, what constitutes a permissible combination of units across the quantities?
   E. In case they are needed, what are the conversion facts for changing between different units measuring the same quantity?

3. *Teacher Presentation.* Choose another example of a problem whose solution may use a formula.
   Problem: What is the width of a rectangle 1 foot long whose area is 100 square inches?

Lead students in a discussion through the solution, asking each of the five questions above in turn.

4. *Activity.* Have students practice these formulae using techniques with the problems on Reproduction Page 115. Students should be helped to realize that a certain formula may be only one of several conditions in the algebraic model; note problem 2, for example.

Topic 7: Hidden or Implicit Relationships

1. *Teacher Presentation.* From your experience with Reproduction Page 115, try to imagine how many different formulae there are, and the wide variety of situations where algebra can be applied. You realize there are far too many such situations for us to practice examples of each. Indeed, many of you will soon be preparing to work professionally in specific areas of business, science, and technology. In the course of your study you will learn how to measure the quantities of interest and of the relationships (formulae) between them.

Even as you specialize and learn about one area, in your everyday lives there will still remain encounters with areas for which you have no special preparation. What can you do then? One choice is whether you want to do your own scientific analysis or to consult resources for ready-made knowledge. In the second case you could consult an encyclopedia for general information or a book written about the topic of interest.

2. *Activity.* Pick a topic, say the "Law of Gases," and have students make a brief report of what they find in an encyclopedia and then what they find in a book containing this as a special topic. It is better if they can find a chemistry or physics book on their own rather than being directed to one. If you choose to do your own analysis of the situation, in lieu of more sophisticated techniques, try collecting data systematically and putting it into tables and/or graphs. Fig. 8.4 is a simulation on how we might discover the "Balance Principle of Levers."

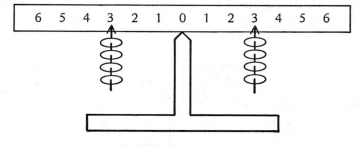

Figure 8.4

The figure shows a balanced beam (lever) with the same number of weights (one unit each) at the same locations (distance from the fulcrum or zero point) on each side. This is not a very informative situation concerning the principle, but at least it can help us identify the categories for our table. See headings below.

| Left Side | | Right Side | |
Weight	Distance	Weight	Distance
4	3	4	3

Now for the systematic experimentation. Leaving one side (say the right side) as is, see if weights at some other location on the left can be used to maintain the balance. (Remove those from the distance 3 location.) Try first peg (distance) 1, then 2, then 3 again, then 4, and so on. The results are in the following extension of our table.

| Left Side | | Right Side | |
Weight	Distance	Weight	Distance
4	3	4	3
12	1	4	3
6	2	4	3
4	3	4	3
3	4	4	3
*	5	4	3
2	6	4	3

*2 is not enough, 3 are too many, so one would need 2 and some fractional part of a weight to make it balance.

Now look for a pattern in the table, using operations like addition, subtraction, multiplication, and division to see if you can discover the principle. Here you might notice that

(weight left side) · (distance left side) =
(weight right side) · (distance right side)

Although this is *not* the principle in its most general form at least you see it is important to multiply each weight times its distance. Scientists have a name for each such product, calling it the *torque*. Those tending (no other weights on the lever) to twist the lever clockwise are called clockwise torques (right side from our point of view); the others are counterclockwise torques. Look at the next table to see if you can discover the fully generalized principle. (Hint: look for patterns using addition, subtraction, multiplication, and division.)

| | Left Side Counterclockwise Torques | | Right Side Clockwise Torques | |
At:	First Position	Second Position	First Position	Second Position
Pictured	4 · 5 = 20	6 · 2 = 12	4 · 3 = 12	5 · 4 = 20
Others	20	12	4 · 2 = 8	4 · 6 = 24
	20	12	2 · 4 = 8	4 · 6 = 24

The "Balance Principle for Levers," then, in its most general form is:

The sum of the counterclockwise torques must be equal to the sum of the clockwise torques for the lever to balance.

3. *Activity.* Have students practice using their newly discovered Balance Principle while doing the exercises on Reproduction Page 116. The follow-up discussion

should reflect on the algebraic method, the use of formulae (principles), and how one might go about discovering such a formula or principle.

4. *Activity.* Refer to an algebra textbook which has special categories of problems—work problems, investment problems, mixture problems, geometry problems, and so on. Help students learn the specific principles or formulae that operate in these situations, and have them practice using the same. Like the thesaurus activity, have students keep a notebook of types of problem situations and the principles or formulae which apply. Later give students an assorted set of problems containing a variety of the types of problems for which they have a record of the principles and formulae.

5. *Teacher Presentation:* Implicit, Extra, Inconsistent, or Hidden Information. Most problems that appear in textbooks are carefully designed to help you exercise a certain technique or principle. Thus, the authors usually supply just enough of the right kind of information to present a problem which is uniquely solvable. The most difficult case then is when problems are implicit rather than explicit about needed information. This usually happens when a formula or principle like the previous ones are needed but not given in the problem. This is quite realistic in nature, but there are other realistic possibilities too. Let's look at illustrations of the possibilities suggested above. Compare the following three problems.

a. Mr. Jones is now 28 years older than Jenny. In 20 years he will be exactly twice as old as she. How old is Jenny now?

b. Mr. and Mrs. Jones have a daughter Jenny born to them when they were respectively 28 and 27 years old. The Joneses live in a red brick house at 2827 North Division Street in Yourtown, U.S.A. Twenty years from now there is no telling where they might live, but at that time Mr. Jones will be just twice as old as his daughter. How old is Jenny now?

c. Their daughter Jenny was born to Mr. and Mrs. Jones when they were respectively 28 and 27 years old. Presently Mr. Jones is 4 times as old as Jenny and Mrs. Jones is 3 times as old as Jenny. How old is Jenny at the present?

Discussion: Problem a. is a concisely stated problem needing implicit information as well as that explicitly stated. Let x be Jenny's age now and let $(x + 28)$ be Mr. Jones' age now based on the *explicitly* stated "Mr. Jones is now 28 years older than Jenny." Twenty years from now each of these will increase giving the values $(x + 20)$ and $(x + 28) + 20$ respectively. This is based on the implicit principle of "getting one year older each year." Finally,

$$2(x + 20) = (x + 28) + 20$$

is justified by the explicit information ". . . he will be exactly twice as old as she." Solving gives us $x = 8$ and $(x + 28) = 36$ so that Jenny is now 8 years old and Mr. Jones is 36.

This example illustrates how both *implicit* and *explicit* relationships might be needed to solve a given problem. Problem b. is almost the same as a. with a few minor exceptions. The idea that Mr. Jones is now 28 years older than Jenny is given more subtly (implicitly) instead of being stated explicitly as in a. Otherwise this version contains irrelevant but not inconsistent information either to add interest or to cause distraction. Learning to filter out such distraction is important since in everyday applications to real problems there will often be a great deal of nonmathematical information clouding up our view of the mathematical structure of the problem. Problem c. sounds all right but there is an inconsistency, i.e., it is not possible for all of the relationships to exist which have been claimed or implied. It is possible, however, that this impossibility could go undetected if the solver does not check each of the conditions. Let's see how this might happen.

Letting x be Jenny's age now, we note that Mr. Jones is now $(x + 28)$ years old. Since this is four times as old as Jenny,

$$4x = (x + 28)$$

As

$$3x = 28$$
$$x = 9\frac{1}{3}$$

We seem to have answered the question—Jenny is $9\frac{1}{3}$ years old—without any need of the other information. Suppose, however, that since we got a fractional part we were just skeptical enough to try doing the problem another way as a check. Say, $(x + 27)$ is Mrs. Jones' present age and

$$3x = (x + 27)$$
$$2x = 27$$
$$x = 13\frac{1}{2}$$

Now we don't know which answer is correct. Would you be confident enough in your own methods and skill to identify the problem statement itself as the source of difficulty? Let's take one more stab at it. Mrs. Jones is $3x$ years old and Mr. Jones is $4x$ years old. Since they were 1 year apart when she was born, they will always be 1 year apart. Thus,

$$3x + 1 = 4x$$
$$x = 1$$

So it looks like Jenny is 1 year old, Mr. Jones is 29, and Mrs. Jones is 28. But wait! $3(1) = 3$ says that Mrs. Jones is 3 years old and $4(1) = 4$ says that Mr. Jones is 4 years old. Will biological wonders never cease?

6. *Activity.* Have each student choose a problem, from the textbook, of interest to him or her. Have them rewrite the problem with embellishment, making several copies of the new version to give the problem to other students. These students should either solve the problem or identify possible inconsistencies. These could be discussed in small group settings along with how to distinguish relevant from irrelevant information and the different algebraic models that might be used.

7. *Activity.* The following problem involves redundant information, i.e., extra, but not inconsistent, information. Have students solve the problem and discuss their solutions, bringing out the identification and disposition of the redundant information.
   Problem: Find two consecutive integers such that 4 times the smaller is 2 less than 3 times the larger but such that twice the larger is also 3 more than the smaller.

8. *Teacher Presentation.* Now let's look at a problem which just does not seem to

have enough information to identify a unique solution. Hidden deeply in the problem situation, however, are conditions which help produce *the* answer.

Problem: Mr. Prince formed a group of students and adults to go to a special concert with him as his guests. Tickets cost $3 for students and $5 for adults. If it cost Mr. Prince $27 for tickets, how many students and how many adults (including him) were in the group?

Discussion: Letting S = the number of students and A = the number of adults in the group, we have

$$3S + 5A = 27$$

This is one equation in two unknowns so, typically, we should look for another equation. Lo and behold, there is none. The algebraic model for this problem consists of just this one equation in two unknowns. In general, such an equation has an infinite number of solutions, each being a pair of numbers, one for S, and the other for A. If, then, there is to be a unique solution, it must depend on other types of information interacting with this relationship. Let us continue the investigation. Think about the possibility that no adults were in the group, then

$$3S + 5 \cdot 0 = 27$$
$$3S = 27$$
$$S = 9$$

From this we can realize that there were at most 9 students. If we acknowledge Mr. Prince, we can refine this a bit, claiming there were at most 8 students. Let us use the latter. Now supposing only adults

$$3 \cdot 0 + 5A = 27$$
$$5A = 27$$
$$A = 5\frac{2}{5}$$

This tells us there were at most 5 adults, but since we rounded off we know furthermore that there was at least one student. In summary, we have

$$1 \leqslant A \leqslant 5$$
$$1 \leqslant S \leqslant 8$$

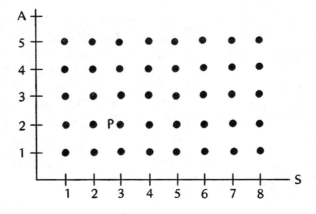

Figure 8.5

By now you have also identified a subtle but very important condition, namely that A and S both be natural numbers; it's not polite to dismember your guests.

Giving the last 3 conditions a graphic representation (see fig. 8.5), all of the possible (40) combinations are shown by the dots in the array. Point P. for example, represents the combination $S = 3$ and $A = 2$. Checking this in the equation (just the left side), we have $3 \cdot 3 + 5 \cdot 2 = 9 + 10 = 19$ which is not enough since the cost was $27.

Rather than proceeding with trial and error, let's superimpose the conditions $3S + 5A = 27$ on our graph. That is, let's also graph the line given by this equation. We see point Q in fig. 8.6 if $A = 0$, $S = 9$. Also, if $S = 0$, $A = 5\frac{2}{5}$, we see point R.

Drawing the line RQ, the only points close to this are shown in the figure. The third entry in each case represents the cost for that combination.

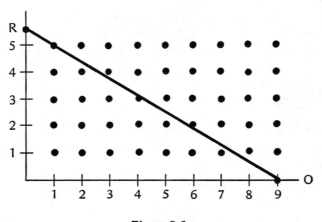

Figure 8.6

S	1	2	4	6	7
A	5	4	3	2	1
Cost	28	26	27	28	26

Hence 4 students and 3 adults were in the group. None of the other points are on line RQ, and therefore the solution is unique! Looking back over this problem what was the hidden information that lead to the uniqueness of the answer? (The restriction to nonnegative, nonzero integers and the two inequalities are expected answers. More subtle is the realization that a line such as RQ might pass through an array (lattice) of points touching only one or two, or missing them all. This is much like the scientific discovery that neutrons can be shot through a thin sheet of gold without hitting any particles.)

9. *Activity.* Have students find another line of the form $3S + 5A =$ (constant) which passes through this same 40-point array touching exactly two points, or no points—by specifying a proper constant.

10. *Activity.* Have students do the exercises on Reproduction Page 117, looking for

implicit, extra, inconsistent, or hidden information. Be sure to bring these out in follow-up discussions of any of the problems.

CHALLENGE PROBLEMS

1. A library needed to bind some English, French, and German books whose number was in the ratio 3:2:1. Three shops offered to do the job, each working independently, the first one in 20 days, the second in 30 days, the third in 60 days. So that the job could be done as soon as possible, it was decided to give the job to all three shops at once. In how many days will the shops do the job, working simultaneously?

2. Two tourists are at points A and B, respectively. The first travels the distance between A and B in x hours, the second in y hours. In how many hours will the tourists meet if they leave points A and B at the same time in order to meet each other?

3. A plant is supposed to turn out a tools over a definite period, and therefore planned to make b tools a day. The workers exceeded the quota and each day made m tools more than was planned. How many days before the projected deadline did the plant fill its order?

4. The sum of two numbers is 20. If one number is increased by 5 times and the other by 4 times, the sum of the numbers will be 92. Find the numbers.

5. I am now 3 times as old as I was when my brother was my age. When I am as old as my brother is now, together we will have lived 96 years. How many years old is each of us right now?

6. A two-digit numeral represents a number which is 3 times the product of its digits. What is the number? Hint: There may be more than one answer.

7. How many pounds of water must be added to p pounds of alcohol to make a solution which is x% alcohol?

8. When 6 gallons of gasoline are put into a car, the indicator goes from $\frac{1}{4}$ to $\frac{5}{8}$. The total capacity of the gasoline tank is _____.

9. Faye has h hours of homework. After spending 3 hours, what *part* of her homework is still left undone? _____.

10. Mr. A invests x dollars, while Mr. B and Mr. C each invest y dollars to form a corporation. What part of $100 profit should Mr. A receive if each shares in the profits in proportion to the amount invested?

    a. $\frac{1}{2}y$

    b. $\frac{1}{2}$

    c. $\frac{x}{x} + 2y$

    d. $\frac{100x}{x + 2y}$

    e. $\frac{100}{2y}$

EVALUATION

Following are some sample questions to assess some of the nonstandard as well as standard objectives associated with solving verbal problems using the algebraic method.

1. Jim traveled for 2 hours at 45 miles per hour and then $\frac{1}{2}$ an hour at 30 miles per hour. Explain how to compute the total distance that he traveled.

2. The average of 3 consecutive odd integers is 28. Explain how to find their sum.

For numbers 3 to 7, refer to the problem:

> *Jennifer is 5 centimeters taller than Bobby.* The sum of their heights is 185 cm. How tall is each?

Consider the italicized portion of the above problem. Indicate which of the following are (use "Yes") and which are not (use "No") equivalent replacements for the underlined condition.

_____ 3. Bobby is 5 cm. shorter than Jennifer.

_____ 4. Jennifer's height exceeds Bobby's by 5 cm.

_____ 5. Jennifer's height is greater than Bobby's.

_____ 6. Jennifer is taller than Bobby, by 5 cm.

_____ 7. Bobby is 5 cm. less than Jennifer.

For numbers 8 to 11, refer to:

> When Anita was introduced to Sally's 2-year-old little brother, she told Sally several age relationships. She said, "My Dad is 4 years older than my Mom. My Mom is 3 times as old as I am, and I am 5 times as old as your little brother."

Find the words or phrases in the above situation which translate into the given algebraic symbol or operation.

8. = : _____

9. > : _____

10. + : _____

11. Multiplication: _____

For numbers 12 to 16, consider the following:

> Andrea is 7 years younger than Cheryl. Six years from now, Andrea's age will be 1 more than $\frac{1}{2}$ of Cheryl's. How old is each now?

Determine if the given algebraic sentence can be used in modeling the above situation. Use "Yes" if it can, "No" if it cannot; explain the connections between quantities in the problem and the variables in the algebraic sentences, or why the sentence won't work.

12. $x + 1 > \frac{1}{2}y$ _____

13. $x + 7 = y$ _____

14. $x = \frac{1}{2}y + 1$ _____

15. $x - 7 = y$ _____

16. $x = \frac{1}{2}(x - 7) + 1$ _____

For numbers 17 to 21, solve the indicated problem using the algebraic method of translating to an algebraic representation, solving the algebraically expressed problem, and translating back to construct an answer to the original problem in the original context. Show your work in good form.

17. Jackie broke a meter stick (cleanly) into 2 pieces. The longer piece was 8 cm short of being 3 times the other. Find the length of each piece.

18. Billy has 3 dollars in nickels, dimes, and quarters. There are 2 more dimes than nickels, but the number of quarters is the same as the number of nickels. How many coins does he have?

19. Mr. Seller mixed 5 pounds of peanuts worth 89¢ per pound with 3 pounds of cashews worth $1.37 per pound. How much should he charge per pound for the 8 pounds of mix in order to make the same amount of money compared to selling each type of nut separately?

20. Lesley bought 3 pounds of peanut clusters and 2 pounds of chocolate covered raisins at the "Ye Olde Sweet Shoppe" for $4.65 (not including tax) to share with her friends. Rochelle liked the peanut clusters the best and wanted to know how much per pound they cost. Lesley could not remember directly, but knew that the chocolate covered raisins cost $1.05 per pound. Help Lesley answer Rochelle's question.

21. Seventy-five pound Jason could not balance 105 pound Jamie, each sitting 5 feet from the center on opposite sides of the teeter-totter. When little Lynn, sitting 3 feet from center, joined Jason, everything balanced. How much did Lynn weigh?

For numbers 22 to 27, consider:

The sum of 2 numbers is 22. If 3 times the smaller is 1 more than twice the larger, what are the numbers?

Without actually solving the problem, decide which of the following pieces of information are consistent (use "C") and which are inconsistent (use "I") with the conditions of the problem.

_____ 22. Twice the larger is 1 less than 3 times the smaller.

_____ 23. The smaller number is less than 11.

_____ 24. The smaller is 22 less than the larger.

_____ 25. Twenty-two exceeds the smaller by the amount of the larger.

_____ 26. If they are integers, both numbers are odd.

_____ 27. Two-thirds of the larger is 4 less than half the smaller.

For numbers 28 to 33, consider:

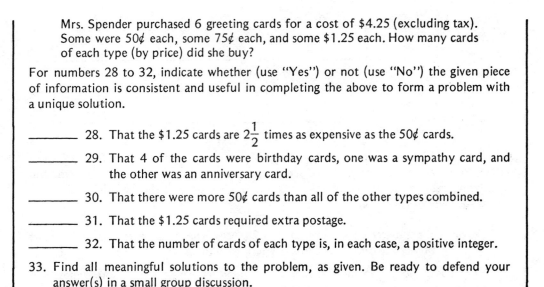

Mrs. Spender purchased 6 greeting cards for a cost of $4.25 (excluding tax). Some were 50¢ each, some 75¢ each, and some $1.25 each. How many cards of each type (by price) did she buy?

For numbers 28 to 32, indicate whether (use "Yes") or not (use "No") the given piece of information is consistent and useful in completing the above to form a problem with a unique solution.

_____ 28. That the $1.25 cards are $2\frac{1}{2}$ times as expensive as the 50¢ cards.

_____ 29. That 4 of the cards were birthday cards, one was a sympathy card, and the other was an anniversary card.

_____ 30. That there were more 50¢ cards than all of the other types combined.

_____ 31. That the $1.25 cards required extra postage.

_____ 32. That the number of cards of each type is, in each case, a positive integer.

33. Find all meaningful solutions to the problem, as given. Be ready to defend your answer(s) in a small group discussion.

RESOURCES

Below is a selected list of resources for teaching problem solving with special emphasis on word problems. Addresses of publishers can be found in Appendix A.

Applied Mathematical Problem Solving. Columbus, OH: ERIC Clearinghouse for Science, Mathematics, and Environmental Education, 1983. A collection of papers presenting varied perspectives on applied problem solving.

Conquering Word Problems in Mathematics. Glen Ellyn, IL: Math House, 1983. Includes ten audiocassettes with spirit duplicating masters and Teacher's Guide for teaching word problem strategies.

Dodson, Joseph W., "Characteristics of Successful Insightful Problem Solvers," Doctoral Dissertation, University of Georgia, 1970. Dissertation Abstracts International 37A, 1977.

Fisher, Lyle, and Medigovich, William, *Problem of the Week*. Palo Alto, CA: Dale Seymour, 1983. A set of thirty posters depicting problems to help students focus on problem-solving skills. A 192-page Problem Book which includes reproducible masters of the poster problems, detailed solutions, and teaching suggestions is also available.

Haber, Philip, ed., *Mathematical Puzzles and Past-*

times. Mount Vernon, NY: The Peter Pauper Press, 1957.

Krulik, Stephen, and Rudnick, Jesse, *Problem Solving: A Handbook for Teachers*. Newton, MA: Allyn and Bacon, 1982. Activities, problems, games, and blackline masters for teaching and learning the skills needed for successful problem solving.

Krutitskii, V. A., *The Psychology of Mathematical Abilities in School Children*. Chicago: The University of Chicago Press, 1976.

National Council of Teachers of Mathematics, *The Arithmetic Teacher*. Reston, VA: NCTM, November 1977. A special issue of problem solving.

National Council of Teachers of Mathematics, *Hints for Problem Solving, Booklet 17*. Reston, VA; NCTM, 1983. A pamphlet entirely devoted to strategies for teaching problem solving.

National Council of Teachers of Mathematics, *Journal for Research in Mathematics Education*. Reston, VA: NCTM.

National Council of Teachers of Mathematics, *The Mathematics Teacher*. Reston, VA: NCTM. This monthly journal is published nine times a year and includes useful suggestions for teaching various topics in the secondary school mathematics curriculum.

National Council of Teachers of Mathematics, *Problem Solving in School Mathematics*. Reston, VA: NCTM, 1980. A series of articles with wide appeal to all teachers of mathematical problem solving.

Newell, Allen, and Simon, Herbert, *Human Problem Solving*. Englewood Cliffs, NJ: Prentice-Hall, 1972. A psychological approach to human problem solving based on detailed analyses of human behavior.

Polya, George, *How To Solve It*. New York: Doubleday, 1957. A classic book on the methods of solving problems. A list of strategies and problems is presented in a very readable style.

"Problem Solving," *The Forty-First Yearbook of the National Society for the Study of Education, Part II, The Psychology of Learning*, 1942.

School Mathematics Study Group NLSMA Reports. Leland Stanford Junior University, 1968.

School Science and Mathematics Association, *School Science and Mathematics*. Bowling Green, OH: SSMA. This monthly journal is published nine times a year. A special issue on problem solving was dated March, 1978.

Soracco, Lionel J., Jr., *Solving Word Problems in Algebra*. Glen Ellyn, IL: Math House, 1983. Includes sixteen audio-cassettes with sixty-five spirit duplicating masters. The lessons correlate with most standard textbooks for first-year algebra.

Tops Problem Card Decks. Palo Alto, CA: Dale Seymour, 1980. Contains 200 illustrated problem decks, color coded for level of difficulty.

Wickelgren, Wayne, *How To Solve Problems*. San Francisco: W. H. Freeman, 1974. General problem-solving methods and solutions to example problems are presented gradually.

9

Quadratic Equations and Functions

CONTENT OVERVIEW

There are various methods for solving quadratic equations. Purely algebraic treatments include factoring, completing the square, and applying the quadratic formula. A geometric approach involves solving by graphing. Although this is tedious and yields only an approximate result, it assists students' intuitive understanding for the meaning of the roots of an equation and the zeros of a function. Our efforts in this chapter will concentrate on the methods of factoring, applying the quadratic formula, and graphing. Students should already possess some familiarity with factoring polynomials, graphing points on a coordinate plane, and working with squares and square roots. Principles of these concepts will be applied by the student to the solution and analysis of quadratic equations.

Although the major focus of this chapter will be on the solution of quadratic equations, the relationship between the graphs of quadratic functions and their respective properties will also be examined. The properties include vertex, symmetry, and shape. Finally, applications of quadratic functions will be discussed.

OBJECTIVES

As a result of the learning experiences in this chapter, the student should be able to:

1. Distinguish quadratic equations from other kinds of equations (e.g., linear)

2. Determine a, b, and c in a quadratic equation $ax^2 + bx + c = 0$

3. Solve quadratic equations of the form $x^2 = a$

4. Solve quadratic equations by factoring

5. Solve quadratic equations by completing the square

6. Solve quadratic equations by using the quadratic formula

137

7. Use the discriminant of a quadratic equation to determine the nature of the roots

8. Graph quadratic functions on a coordinate plane

9. Describe the relationship between the graph, the roots, and the discriminant of a quadratic equation

10. Use the geometric definition of a parabola to write its equation and to determine its properties

11. Appreciate the applications of parabolas in real-world situations

LEARNING EXPERIENCES

Topic 1: Solving by Factoring

1. *Teacher Presentation.* Briefly review the concept of linear/first degree equations. Ask the students to discuss the contrasting features of the equations $2x + 3 = 7$ and $x^2 + 7x + 6 = 0$. These may include the degree of the polynomial, the solution or number of solutions, or the number of terms.

   Define a quadratic equation as an equation of the form $ax^2 + bx + c = 0$, where a, b, and c are real numbers and $a \neq 0$. Why the restriction on a? It will be helpful to identify: a = leading coefficient; b = linear coefficient; c = constant.

2. *Activity.* Give the students the following examples and ask them to determine which equation(s) are quadratic.

   a. $x^2 + 2x + 1 = 0$ f. $6x = 2x^2$
   b. $2x + 1 = 0$ g. $x(x + 3) = 0$
   c. $x^2 = 4$ h. $(x - 1)(x + 2) = 5$
   d. $-6 = x^2 - 3x$ i. $2x - 1 = x^2 + 3x + 5$
   e. $x^3 + 2x^2 + 5x - 1 = 0$ j. $x^2 - 2 = x^2 + x$

3. *Activity.* After deciding which of the above equations are quadratic, rewrite them in the "equivalent" form $ax^2 + bx + c = 0$. Have students determine a, b, and c for each quadratic equation. Refer to leading coefficient, linear coefficient, and constant.

4. *Teacher Presentation.* The solution of a linear equation (e.g., $2x + 3 = 7$) was that value of the variable which made the equation true. In a similar manner, the solution(s) of a quadratic equation are those value(s) of the variable which make the quadratic equation true.

   Consider $x^2 = 4$. From our knowledge of squaring, we know that 2 and –2 are the needed values. Hence $\{2, -2\}$ is the solution set for the equation $x^2 = 4$. If the x term is missing, only specific information is needed to solve the quadratic equation.

5. *Activity.* Use the following examples to discuss quadratic equations of the form $x^2 = a$. The replacement set is the set of real numbers.

   Equation: $x^2 = \frac{4}{9}$ $x^2 = 16$ $x^2 = 5$ $x^2 = 0$ $x^2 = -4$

Solution Set: $\left\{-\frac{2}{3},\frac{2}{3}\right\}$, $\{4,-4\}$, $\{-\sqrt{5},\sqrt{5}\}$, $\{0\}$, $\emptyset$

The first three examples show that any time x^2 is equal to a positive real number, there are two roots—sometimes rational, sometimes irrational. These roots are always the opposites of each other. If x^2 is zero, only zero is a root. If x^2 is negative, there are no *real* roots. (You may now wish to discuss the number of roots of any quadratic equation.)

Have students complete the exercises on Reproduction Page 118.

6. *Teacher Presentation.* It may be useful to review certain concepts (e.g., multiplying monomials and binomials, solving linear equations, etc.) before proceeding to other methods of solving quadratic equations.

7. *Teacher Presentation.* Present to the class the following scenario: I am thinking of two numbers. Their product is zero. Can you tell me one of the numbers? Ask the class to state formally their conclusions.

    For all real numbers a and b, $ab = 0$ if and only if $a = 0$ or $b = 0$. Refer to this as the zero-product property. (Students will need to be reminded that this also implies that a and b could both be equal to zero.)

8. *Teacher Presentation.* What values of x make $x^2 - 5x + 6 = 0$ true? This equation can be solved by inspection for the values $x = 2, 3$. Have students factor $x^2 - 5x + 6$.

    Now $(x - 3)(x - 2) = 0$. Students should see how $(x - 3)(x - 2) = 0$ fits the pattern $a \cdot b = 0$.

    Hence, according to the property, $x - 3 = 0$ *or* $x - 2 = 0$. If we solve these linear equations, we will have $x = 3$ *or* $x = 2$.

    Checking, we have
    for $x = 2$, $2^2 - 5 \cdot 2 + 6 = 4 - 10 + 6 = 0$
    Therefore, $x = 2$ is in the solution set.
    For $x = 3$, $3^2 - 5 \cdot 3 + 6 = 9 - 15 + 6 = 0$
    Therefore, $x = 3$ is in the solution set.

9. *Activity.* As a review for factoring, have students complete Reproduction Page 119.

10. *Teacher Presentation.* Provide students with the following step-by-step procedure for solving quadratic equations by factoring:
    a. Write the equation in standard form: $ax^2 + bx + c = 0$
    b. Factor the lefthand side
    c. Set each factor equal to zero
    d. Solve the resulting equations
    e. Check in original equation
    Example: $x^2 - 7x = -10$
    a. Rewrite as $x^2 - 7x + 10 = 0$
    b. $(x - 5)(x - 2) = 0$
    c. $x - 5 = 0$ *or* $x - 2 = 0$
    d. $x = 5$ *or* $x = 2$
    e. $5^2 - 7 \cdot 5 = -10$ $2^2 - 7 \cdot 2 = -10$
    Reemphasize the zero-product property.

11. *Teacher Presentation.* Rewriting a given quadratic equation in standard form and then factored form is really a matter of finding equivalent equations—hence the solutions are identical.

Examples:

1. $x^2 = 3x$ is equivalent to $x^2 - 3x = 0$ and $x(x - 3) = 0$.
2. $x^2 + 4x + 4 = 0$ is equivalent to $(x + 2)^2 = 0$ and $(x + 2)(x + 2) = 0$.
3. $\frac{x}{3} = \frac{x + 6}{x}$ is equivalent to $x^2 = 3x + 18$ and $x^2 - 3x - 18 = 0$.
4. (Extension) $3a^3 + 14a^2 = -8a$ is equivalent to $3a^3 + 14a^2 + 8a = 0$ and $a(3a^2 + 14a + 8) = 0$ and $a(3a + 2)(a + 4) = 0$.

12. *Teacher Presentation.* Point out to students that the zeros of a function f are the same as the roots of the equation $f(x) = 0$.

    Example:

    $f(x) = x^2 + 3x - 4$.
    $f(x) = 0$ implies $x = -4, 1$.
    $f(-4) = 0$ and $f(1) = 0$

    At this point, you may wish to discuss multiple roots and double roots.

13. *Activity.* Have students complete Reproduction Page 120.

14. *Teacher Presentation.* Students should now recognize the relationship between the number of roots of a quadratic equation and the degree of the polynomial expression.

15. *Activity.* Ask students to provide a quadratic equation in standard form if the solutions are as follows:

    a. $x = 2$ or $x = -3$
    b. $x = \frac{1}{2}$ or $x = 4$
    c. $x = 0$ or $x = -1$
    d. $x = 5$ or $x = -5$
    e. $x = \frac{1}{3}$ or $x = -\frac{2}{3}$
    f. $x = 5$ or $x = -5$

    Example:

    $x = 2$ or $x = -3$
    $(x - 2)(x - (-3)) = 0$
    $(x - 2)(x + 3) = 0$
    $x^2 + x - 6 = 0$

16. *Activity* (Enrichment). Play "Guess My Equation." Think of an equation. A student will choose a number for x, and you will supply the value of the expression evaluated at that number. Continue this process until a student has determined the equation.

    Example:

    Think of the equation $2x^2 - 3x - 2$. Let students select values to substitute for x.

x	$2x^2 - 3x - 2 = 0$
0	-2
1	-3
2	0
-1	-3
$-\frac{1}{2}$	0
.	.
.	.
.	.

If students happen to guess the roots, it will be easy to find the equation. In the example above, $(x - 2)(x + \frac{1}{2})$ will yield the desired equation. This may not happen very often.

More generally, consider an equation in standard form, $ax^2 + bx + c = 0$. Select values of 0, 1, and 2.

Example:

Suppose you are thinking of the equation $x^2 - x - 6 = 0$.

From $2a = 2$, we know $a = 1$. We also know $a + b = 0$ or $1 + b = 0$. Consequently, $b = -1$. For $x = 0$, we find $c = -6$.

We will be able to find a, b, c from the knowledge of any three *consecutive* integers. Ask your class to think of other equations.

Topic 2: The Quadratic Formula

1. *Teacher Presentation.* The method of completing the square is of value primarily because it leads to the quadratic formula. In order to understand and appreciate this method, students should first review the concepts of (a) solving quadratic equations of the form $x^2 = a$, and (b) perfect-square trinomials—$x^2 + 2kx + k^2$. Ask students to do exercises on Reproduction Page 121.

2. *Teacher Presentation.* The method of completing the square is really one of transforming any quadratic equation into the equivalent form $(x + k)^2 = c$. $(x + k)^2$ can be represented graphically.
   For example, $(x + 3)^2 = x^2 + 3x + 3x + 9$

	x	3
x	x^2	$3x$
3	$3x$	$?$

   What term is missing?

   This is similar to the exercises on Reproduction Page 121.

3. *Teacher Presentation.* Work through an example that can be solved by either factoring or completing the square.

Factor	*Completing the Square*
$x^2 + 4x - 5 = 0$	$x^2 + 4x - 5 = 0$
$(x + 5)(x - 1) = 0$	$x^2 + 4x = 5$
$x = -5$ or $x = 1$	$x^2 + 4x + 4 = 5 + 4$
	$x^2 + 4x + 4 = 9$
	$(x + 2)^2 = 9$
	$x + 2 = \sqrt{9}$
	$x = -3 - 2$ or $x = 3 - 2$
	$x = -5$ or $x = 1$

   Emphasize the fact that each step in the solution represents an equivalent equation. Also when the coefficient of the x term is odd, one will be dealing with fractions.

4. *Activity.* Ask students which of the following quadratic equations they would solve by factoring and which they would solve by completing the square. Why?
   a. $3x^2 + 1 = 2$
   b. $3(x - 4)^2 + 5 = 9$
   c. $x^2 + 4x - 1 = 0$
   d. $x = 4x^2$

5. *Teacher Presentation.* Students should be provided with the following step-by-step procedure for solving quadratic equations using the method of completing the square.
   a. Write the equation in the form: $ax^2 + bx = -c$

b. Divide all terms by a: $x^2 + \dfrac{b}{a}x = -\dfrac{c}{a}$

c. Find one-half of the coefficient of the linear (x) term: $\dfrac{1}{2} \cdot \dfrac{b}{a} = \dfrac{b}{2a}$

d. Square it. $\left(\dfrac{b}{2a}\right)^2 = \dfrac{b^2}{4a^2}$

e. Add this result to both sides of the equation. $x^2 + \dfrac{b}{a}x + \dfrac{b^2}{4a^2} = -\dfrac{c}{a} + \dfrac{b^2}{4a^2}$

f. Rewrite the left-hand side as the square of a binomial: $\left(x + \dfrac{b}{2a}\right)^2 = \dfrac{-c}{a} + \dfrac{b^2}{4a^2}$

g. Take the square root of both sides: $x + \dfrac{b}{2a} = \pm\sqrt{\dfrac{-c}{a} + \dfrac{k^2}{4a^2}}$

h. Simplify. (Some review may be necessary.) $x + \dfrac{b}{2a} = \pm \dfrac{\sqrt{b^2 - 4ac}}{2a}$

i. Solve.

j. Check.

6. *Activity.* Have students complete the exercises on Reproduction Page 122.

7. *Teacher Presentation* (Enrichment). Completing the square operates on the ax^2 and bx terms, with a view that $ax^2 + bx$ is incomplete in a certain sense, the process depending on the special knowledge that

$$m^2x^2 + 2mnx + n^2 = (mx + n)^2$$

and matching m^2x^2 with ax^2, $2mnx$ with bx. Consider the example $16x^2 + 8x = 3$. Now matching $16x^2$ with $m^2x^2 \rightarrow 16 = m^2 \rightarrow m = 4$ (there is no loss in taking the nonnegative root).

Also $m = 4$ and $2mnx = 8x \rightarrow 2 \cdot 4 \cdot n \cdot x = 8x \rightarrow 2 \cdot 4 \cdot n = 8 \rightarrow 2 \cdot n = 2 \rightarrow n = 1 \rightarrow n^2 = 1$.

Now the n^2 term which was missing from the $16x^2 + 8x$ is known. Hence, we have $16x^2 + 8x + 1 = (4x + 1)^2$, the expression on the left being a perfect-square trinomial.

Be certain your students compensate by adding 1 to the right-hand side of the equation. Not doing so is a common error.

8. *Teacher Presentation.* The method of completing the square is quite deterministic because there is no trial-and-error stage like that involved in factoring. The procedure presented for solving quadratic equations by the method of completing the square is quite tedious. This was done purposely.

Refer students to step h.

$$x + \frac{b}{2a} = \pm\frac{\sqrt{b^2 - 4ac}}{2a}$$

Subtracting $\dfrac{b}{2a}$ from both sides yields

$$x = -\frac{b}{2a} \pm \frac{\sqrt{b^2 - 4ac}}{2a}$$

or

$$x = \frac{-b \pm \sqrt{b^2 - 4ac}}{2a}$$

This is called the *quadratic formula*. Consequently, completing the square for the general case $ax^2 + bx + c = 0, a \neq 0$ gives us mechanisms for arithmetic computation of the roots using only the coefficients a, b, and c.

9. *Teacher Presentation.* A somewhat elegant method for deriving the quadratic formula can be found in nineteenth-century textbooks.
   a. $ax^2 + bx + c = 0$
   b. $4a(ax^2 + bx + c) = 0 \cdot 4a$
   c. $4a^2x^2 + 4abx + 4ac = 0$
   d. $4a^2x^2 + 4abx = -4ac$
   e. $4a^2x^2 + 4abx + b = b^2 - 4ac$
   f. $(2ax + b)^2 = b^2 - 4ac$
   g. $2ax + b = \pm\sqrt{b^2 - 4ac}$
   h. $2ax = -b \pm\sqrt{b^2 - 4ac}$
   i. $x = \dfrac{-b \pm \sqrt{b^2 - 4ac}}{2a}$

   Once again, emphasize that all the above equations are equivalent. Whichever method of derivation is preferred, the formula itself is indispensable. Students should be required to memorize it and use it.

10. *Activity.* In the following problems, ask students to find a, b, $-b$, b^2, $4ac$, $b^2 - 4ac$ and solve using the quadratic formula.
    a. $x^2 - 3x - 10 = 0$
    b. $3x^2 + x = 2$
    c. $7x^2 - 14x + 1 = 0$
    d. $2x^2 + 3x - 2 = 0$
    e. $2x^2 + 2x + 1 = 0$
    f. $x^2 - 6x + 9 = 0$

11. *Teacher Presentation.* Students may decide that problems (a) and (b) above are more easily solved by factoring. There is often a choice among methods of solution.

    In the derivation of the quadratic formula, it was shown that $ax^2 + bx + c = 0$ is equivalent to $(2ax + b)^2 = b^2 - 4ac$. Hence, in problem (d),

$$2x^2 + 3x - 2 = 0 \Leftrightarrow (4x + 3)^2 = 25$$
$$\Rightarrow 4x + 3 = \pm 5$$
$$\Rightarrow 4x = \pm 5 - 3$$
$$\Rightarrow x = \frac{1}{2}, -2$$

The solution to (e), using the quadratic formula, is

$$\frac{-2 \pm \sqrt{-4}}{4}$$

For first-year algebra students, we recommend that problem (e) be classified as having *no* (real) solutions.

Define discriminant to be the value of $b^2 - 4ac$. Students should understand that the discriminant will determine the number of roots as well as the nature (rational or irrational) of the roots.

12. *Activity.* Have students complete the exercises on Reproduction Page 123.

13. *Teacher Presentation.* Students should now be able to verbalize the following: If the discriminant is a *positive* number, the equation has *two* real solutions. If it is equal to *zero*, the equation has *one* real solution. If it is *negative*, the equation has *no* real solutions.

14. *Activity.* Given that the roots of a quadratic equation are

$$x = \frac{-b + \sqrt{b^2 - 4ac}}{2a}$$

or

$$x = \frac{-b - \sqrt{b^2 - 4ac}}{2a}$$

have the students find the sum and product of the roots.

Sum of roots $= -\dfrac{b}{a}$

Product of roots $= \dfrac{c}{a}$

Example:

$x^2 + 6x + 5 = 0$

$x = -5, -1$

$(-5) + (-1) = -\dfrac{6}{1} = -6$

and

$(-5)(-1) = \dfrac{5}{1} = 5$

Hence, this method provides another method (besides direct substitution) for *checking* our solutions. Caution your students, however, that the quadratic equation must be in the form $x^2 + \dfrac{b}{a}x + \dfrac{c}{a} = 0$ in order to use the preceding checking solution.

Complete exercises on Reproduction Page 124.

15. *Activity* (Enrichment). Finding equations with no real roots is difficult for many students. It is true that equations of the form $nx^2 + (n + 1)x + n + 2$ have no real roots if $n \neq 0, -1,$ or -2.

Consequently, $x^2 + 2x + 3 = 0, 4x^2 + 5x + 6 = 0$, etc., have no real roots.

Furthermore, equations of the form $nx^2 + (n + 2)x + n + 4$ have no real roots if $n \neq 0, -1, -2, -3,$ or -4.

Hence, $x^2 + 3x + 5 = 0, 6x^2 + 8x + 10 = 0$, etc., have no real roots.

Can your students find other patterns?

Topic 3: Graphing Quadratic Functions

1. *Teacher Presentation.* Consider the linear equation $2x + 10 = 0$ and its corresponding linear function $y = 2x + 10$. The solution of the linear equation is -5. It should

also be noted that this number (–5) is the point where the linear function intercepts the x-axis. This is, indeed, a significant result because it is true for *all* polynomial equations written in standard form.

2. *Teacher Presentation.* Before discussing the graphical method of solution of quadratic equations, consider the following hint for graphing quadratic functions.

Given a quadratic function $y = ax^2 + bx + c$, students often have difficulty plotting to find the complete graph. For example, in $y = x^2 + 2x - 3$, if students use $x = 0, 1, 2, 3, 4, 5$, they would get less than half of the curve. Hence, find the value $x = \frac{-b}{2a}$ which is halfway between the two places where the graph cuts the x-axis, since it equals half the sum of the roots. The line $x = \frac{-b}{2a}$ is the equation of the line of symmetry; the turning point of the curve is on this line. Hence, have students find the turning point, then take points, one point to the left and right alternately, until the graph crosses the x-axis.

Example:

$$y = x^2 - 2x - 15$$
$$\frac{-b}{2a} = \frac{-(-2)}{2 \cdot 1} = 1$$

x	1	0	2	–1	3	–2	4	–3
y	–16	–15	–13	–12	–12	–7	–7	0

Now the graph can be easily plotted.

Once the coordinates of the turning point are known, $x = 1, y = -16$, we have the axis of symmetry, $x = 1$, and the minimum value of the function, –16.

3. *Activity.* Ask students to complete the exercises on Reproduction Page 125. A table of values should be constructed for each graph. Remind students that in order to use the previous hint, they should have quadratic functions in standard form, $y = ax^2 + bx + c$.

4. *Teacher Presentation.* The graphical method of solution is really the interception of $y = ax^2 + bx + c$ and $y = 0$. Yet, solving a quadratic equation by graphing its corresponding quadratic function is not very satisfactory inasmuch as the results are approximate.

Reemphasize the fact that the real solutions of the equation are the values of x where the graph crosses the x-axis. These same values are also called the real zeros of the function. Hence, the graph can be used to show why two real and distinct roots may exist, why the roots are sometimes real and equal (double root), and why, in certain cases, there are no real roots. This same information was available by knowledge of the discriminant.

5. *Activity.* Have students complete the table found on Reproduction Page 126.

6. *Teacher Presentation.* The students should now formalize what they have learned from Reproduction Page 126.

a. If the discriminant of a quadratic equation is positive, the equation has two real solutions, and its corresponding graph will cross the x-axis twice.

b. If the discriminant of a quadratic equation is zero, the equation has one real solution, and its corresponding graph crosses the x-axis once (tangent to axis).

c. If the discriminant of a quadratic equation is negative, the equation has no real roots, and its corresponding graph does not intersect the x-axis.

7. *Teacher Presentation.* Consider the quadratic function $y = x^2 - 2x - 8$. The roots (zeros) of this function are $(x - 4)(x + 2) = 0 \Rightarrow x = \{4, -2\}$.

What part of the graph lies above the x-axis?

where

$$(x - 4)(x + 2) > 0$$

This implies

$$(x - 4) > 0 \quad \text{and} \quad (x + 2) > 0$$
$$\text{or}$$
$$(x - 4) < 0 \quad \text{and} \quad (x + 2) < 0$$

What part of the graph lies below the x-axis?

where

$$(x - 4)(x + 2) < 0$$

This implies

$$(x - 4) > 0 \quad \text{and} \quad (x + 2) < 0$$
$$\text{or}$$
$$(x - 4) < 0 \quad \text{and} \quad (x + 2) > 0$$

Check this with fig. 9.1.

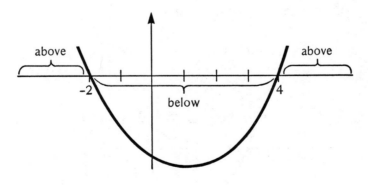

Figure 9.1

8. *Activity.* Ask students to graph $y = x^2$ and $y = -2x + 3$ on the same coordinate plane. Where are the points of intersection? $\{-3, +1\}$. These are the roots of the equation $x^2 + 2x - 3 = 0$. In general, given $ax^2 + bx + c = 0$, we can graph $y = x^2$ and $y = -\frac{b}{a}x - \frac{c}{a}$, and find their intersection.

9. *Activity* (Enrichment). Draw the graph $y = x^2$ as shown in fig. 9.2. Consider the points $(-5, 25)$ and $(8, 64)$.

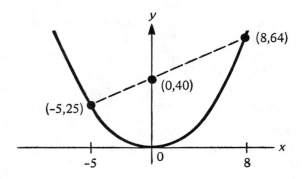

Figure 9.2

The line formed by the points (–5, 25) and (8, 64) will intersect the y-axis at the point (0, 40). Your students should be asked to show why this is true. Also note –(–5)(8) = 40. Does this hold true for other such points? (I.e., is the product of the abscissas equal to the opposite of the ordinate on the y-axis?)

Given $(a, a^2), (b, b^2)$:

$$y - a^2 = \left(\frac{b^2 - a^2}{b - a}\right)(x - a)$$
$$y - a^2 = (b + a)(x - a)$$

Letting $x = 0$, we have

$$y - a^2 = (b + a)(-a)$$
$$y - a^2 = -ab - a^2$$
$$y = -ab \ (a \text{ or } b \text{ is negative}).$$
$$-ab \text{ represents the product of } ab.$$

10. *Teacher Presentation* (Enrichment).

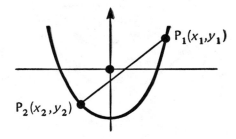

Figure 9.3

Reproduce fig. 9.3. Let $y = ax^2 + bx + c$ (c is the y-intercept).

In linear functions, $\dfrac{y_2 - y_1}{x_2 - x_1}$, $x_1 \neq x_2$ is the slope of the line with points (x_1, x_2) and (y_1, y_2).

$$\frac{y_2 - y_1}{x_2 - x_1} = \frac{ax_2^2 + bx_2 + c - (ax_1^2 + bx_1 + c)}{x_2 - x_1}$$

$$= \frac{a(x_2^2 - x_1^2) + b(x_2 - x_1)}{x_2 - x_1}$$

$$= a(x_1 + x_2) + b$$

Hence from $\frac{y_2 - y_1}{x_2 - x_1} = a(x_1 + x_2) + b$ we have a formula for finding the slope of a secant through any two points on the curve. Furthermore, if we take values of x_2 closer and closer to x_1, we can find the slope of the tangent line at $P_1(x_1, y_1)$. The "limiting" process will yield $2ax_1 + b$ as the slope of the tangent line.

Topic 4: Properties of Quadratic Functions

1. *Teacher Presentation.* Relate the following story to your students: Suppose you found a treasure map and it said that a chest of gold coins was buried at some point *equidistant* from a tree, marked with an *x*, and the edge of the river. Where would you dig? Can you mark three possible treasure locations in the drawing in fig. 9.4?

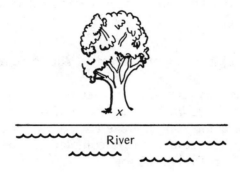

River

Figure 9.4

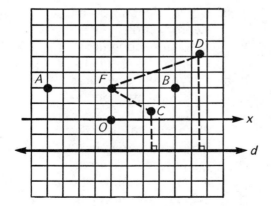

a. The origin (*o*) is one possible location for the buried treasure, since it is 2 units from *F* and 2 units from *d*.

b. Points *A* and *B* are each 4 units from *F* and 4 units from *d*.

c. Points *C* and *D* look equidistant from *F* and *d*.

Figure 9.5

Representing the tree with a point (F) and the edge of the river with a line (d), we can translate this problem onto a Cartesian Coordinate System as shown in fig. 9.5.

How many points are there equidistant from F and d?

There are infinitely many points equidistant from a given point and a given line. They are located on what we call a *parabola*.

Define *parabola* as the set of all points on a plane equidistant from a fixed point (called the *focus*) and a fixed line (called the *directrix*). Students should be informed that the shape of all parabolas are "similar." Furthermore, the graphs of quadratic functions are parabolas.

2. *Teacher Presentation.* Although the ideas of vertex and axis of symmetry can be defined in terms of focus and directrix, we tend to discourage this for first-year algebra students. An intuitive approach would be more beneficial at this stage of learning—a more extensive study of these concepts should be postponed until second-year algebra.

   Define vertex as the minimum or maximum point of the graph. In our first example the vertex (V) = (0, 0). The axis of symmetry is that line on the graph such that if the graph were folded, the two sides of the parabola would coincide. Again, in our example, the axis of symmetry was the y-axis ($x = 0$).

3. *Activity.* Ask the students to complete the exercises on Reproduction Page 127.

4. *Teacher Presentation.* The vertex of the parabola that corresponds to the quadratic equation $y = ax^2 + bx + c$ ($a \neq 0$) is $\left(-\dfrac{b}{2a}, -\dfrac{b^2}{4a} + c\right)$. It can also be shown that the line $x = -\dfrac{b}{2a}$ ($a \neq 0$) is its axis of symmetry. You could refer to activity 2 in Topic 3.

5. *Activity.* If a quadratic function is written in the form $y = a(x - h)^2 + k$, it may be shown that the vertex is (h, k) and the line of symmetry is $x = h$. Students should discover this after completing the exercises on Reproduction Page 128. It should be pointed out to the students that completing the square may be necessary in order to write the function in the form $a(x - h)^2 + k$.

6. *Activity.* Ask students to graph the function $y = x^2$ on the same cartesian plane as those on Reproduction Page 128. Then have them cut it out.

$y = x^2$

a. Which functions on Reproduction Page 128 are "congruent" to $y = x^2$? 1–8, 11–13.
b. Do you see why these functions are congruent?
c. Place cutout (see fig. 9.6) on overhead (plane) and have students determine the equation of the graph.

Figure 9.6

7. *Teacher Presentation.* Consider the "unit" parabola $y = x^2$. We have already discussed graphing of quadratic functions by constructing tables of ordered pairs (points). However, by using the concepts of vertex, axis of symmetry, and a special property of the unit parabola, we will be able to graph any quadratic function. Fig. 9.7 is the graph of $y = x^2$. What do we notice?

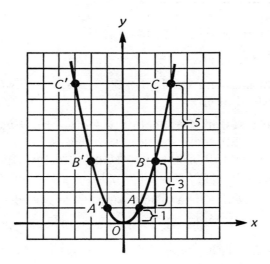

Figure 9.7

a. The graph of $y = x^2$ is a smooth, unbroken curve which is symmetric with respect to the y-axis [for any ordered pair (a, b) on the parabola, $(-a, b)$ is also on the parabola].

b. From left to right, the value of y decreases until it becomes zero at the vertex; then it steadily increases.

c. Looking at the corresponding y-values for consecutive positive integral values of x, we see that they differ by consecutive odd numbers. The movement between two points having consecutive integral abscissas constitutes what we call a "step" containing a RUN (the horizontal move) and a RISE (the vertical move). We will write $\boxed{\text{"RUN} \rightarrow \text{RISE"}}$. Therefore the steps for a unit parabola are

$$\boxed{1 \rightarrow 1, \ 1 \rightarrow 3, \ 1 \rightarrow 5, \ 1 \rightarrow 7, \dots}$$

8. *Activity.* Have the students graph $y = x^2$ using the following steps:
a. Plot the vertex $(0, 0)$
b. Identify the axis of symmetry $(x = 0)$
c. Starting at the vertex, move over one unit to the right, then up one unit . . . place a dot. $1 \rightarrow 1$
d. Starting at this new point, move over one unit to the right, then up 3 units . . . place a dot. $1 \rightarrow 3$
e. Starting at this new point, move over one unit to the right, then up 5 units . . . place a dot. $1 \rightarrow 5$
f. Find corresponding points on the other side of the axis of symmetry.

g. Draw the Unit Parabola.

9. *Teacher Presentation.* More generally, a quadratic function of the form $y = a(x - h)^2 + k$ may be graphed by using the steps:

$$1 \to 1a, \ 1 \to 3a, \ 1 \to 5a \ldots$$

Examples:
a. $y = 2x^2$ The steps are $1 \to 2, 1 \to 6, 1 \to 10, \ldots$
b. $y = \frac{1}{3}x^2$ The steps are $1 \to \frac{1}{3}, \ 1 \to \frac{3}{3}, \ 1 \to \frac{5}{3}, \ldots$
c. $y = -x^2$ The steps are $1 \to 1, \ 1 \to 3, \ 1 \to 5, \ldots$ However, the vertical steps will be *down* instead of *up*.

10. *Activity.* When $a < 0$ in the function $y = a(x - h)^2 + k$, the graph of the function opens downward. Students should discover this fact after doing the exercises on Reproduction Page 129. Since the "steps" are the same for each of these problems, students can now understand why these graphs are congruent.

11. *Teacher Presentation.* On a blackboard or overhead, graph the functions $y = x^2, y = 3x^2, y = \frac{1}{2}x^2$. When $|a| > 1$, the graph of $y = a(x - h)^2 + k$ is narrow relative to $y = x^2$. Similarly, when $|a| < 1$, the graph of $y = a(x - h)^2 + k$ is wide relative to $y = x^2$.

12. *Activity.* Students should complete the exercises on Reproduction Page 130. This should reinforce the role of a in $y = a(x - h)^2 + k$.

13. *Teacher Presentation.* Summarize by referring to the general form of the quadratic function $y = ax^2 + bx + c, a \neq 0$. An equivalent form of the function is

$$y = a\left(x + \frac{b}{2a}\right)^2 + \frac{4ac - b^2}{4a}$$

The axis of symmetry is $-\frac{b}{2a}$ and the vertex is $\left(-\frac{b}{2a}, \frac{4ac - b^2}{4a}\right)$. The vertex is the minimum point if $a > 0$ and the maximum point if $a < 0$.
a. The effect of a on the graph of the function $y = ax^2 + bx + c$: When $a > 0$, the curves are open upward and have a minimum point. When $a < 0$, the curves are open downward and have a maximum point. Furthermore as a gets larger in numerical value, the curve tends to close upward toward the y-axis, and as a gets smaller in numerical value, the curve tends to stretch away from the y-axis.
b. The effect of b on the graph of the function $y = ax^2 + bx + c$: The graph will be shifted along a horizontal axis, reflecting any change in b.
c. The effect of c on the graph of the function $y = ax^2 + bx + c$: The point $(0, c)$ is the y-intercept of the graph. The graph will be shifted along a vertical axis, reflecting any change in c.
d. We may also use the quadratic formula to find where the graph crosses the x-axis.

14. *Teacher Presentation* (Enrichment). Other properties which could be discussed include:
a. inverses of quadratic functions

b. periodicity of quadratic functions

c. odd, even functions

d. continuity

15. *Teacher Presentation.* List some real-world phenomena that look like parabolic curves.

a. path of a roller coaster

b. shooting a basketball

c. the three-point "line" in professional basketball

d. the path of a tennis ball hit with topspin

e. jumping out of a plane in a parachute

f. parabolic path of certain comets (they will never return)

g. gateway arch in St. Louis

h. the supporting cables of a suspension bridge

Ask your class to find other examples.

16. *Teacher Presentation.* Numerous natural laws can be expressed in the form of quadratic functions. Examples:

a. $s = \frac{1}{2}qt^2$; this represents the relation between time and distance pertaining to an object thrown vertically into the air, where s = distance fallen; g = gravitational constant approximately equal to 32 ft/sec^2; t = time in seconds.

b. $E = \frac{1}{2}mv^2$; this represents the kinetic energy of any moving object where m = mass of object; v = velocity; E = energy.

c. $F = \frac{mv^2}{r}$; this represents the centripetal force of a rotating object where m = mass; v = linear velocity; r = radius of path of rotation.

d. $t^2 = \left(\frac{4\pi^2}{g}\right) L$; this represents the vibrational frequency of a simple pendulum where t = time of one vibration; L = length of pendulum; g = acceleration of a freely falling body.

A knowledge of the parabola is essential to the fabrication of the mirror of the reflecting telescope, to the construction of headlights for automobiles, and to the creation of the mass spectograph.

Ask your class to research these and other topics involving parabolas.

CHALLENGE PROBLEMS

1. Factor completely: $x^2 + 8\sqrt{3}x - 60$

2. The product of two numbers is 2 and the sum of their squares is 20. Find the negative difference of the two numbers.

3. One root of the equation $x^2 + px + 11 = 0$ is $2\sqrt{3} - 1$. Find the value of p.

4. The difference between the larger root and the smaller root of $x^2 - px + \frac{(p^2 - 1)}{4} = 0$

is _____.

5. The function $f(x) = ax^2 + bx + c$ passes through the points $(-1, 12)$, $(0, 5)$, and $(2, -3)$; the value of $a + b + c$ is _____ .

6. If the reciprocal of $x + 1$ is $x - 1$, then $x =$ _____ .

7. Let n be the number of values of p for which the roots of $x^2 - px + p = 0$ are equal. Then $n =$ _____ .

8. The sum of the reciprocals of the roots of the equation $ax^2 + bx + c$ is _____ .

9. In solving a problem that reduces to a quadratic equation one student makes a mistake only in the constant term of the equation and obtains 8 and 2 for the roots. Another student makes a mistake only in the coefficient of the first degree and finds -9 and -1. The correct equation in the form $ax^2 + bx + c = 0$ is _____ .

10. Find all real values of x which satisfy

$$(x^2 - 5x + 5)^{x^2 - 9x + 20} = 1$$

EVALUATION

1. Solve each equation for its solutions(s).
   1. $x^2 + 8x = 0$ $x =$ _____
   2. $121 = k^2$ $k =$ _____
   3. $x(x + 5) = 4$ $x =$ _____
   4. $2y - 3 = -y^2$ $y =$ _____
   5. $b^2 - 8b - 12 = 0$ $b =$ _____
   6. $x^2 - \frac{2}{3}x - 1 = 0$ $x =$ _____
   7. $\frac{2}{x} = \frac{x}{8}$ $x =$ _____
   8. $(y - 3)(6y - 2) = 0$ $y =$ _____
   9. $3a^2 - 5a + 12 = 0$ $a =$ _____
   10. $\sqrt{2x - 1} - 3 = 0$ $x =$ _____
   11. $6x^2 + cx + a = 0$ $x =$ _____

2. Find the value of the discriminant (D) for each of the following quadratic equations and use it to tell how many *real* solutions the equation has.

	D	No. of real solutions
1. $x^2 - 12x = -36$	_____	_____
2. $3y^2 + 15y - 12 = 0$	_____	_____
3. $3k^2 + 12 - 5k = 0$	_____	_____
4. $10b^2 = 3 + b$	_____	_____
5. $16x^2 + 24x + 9 = 0$	_____	_____

3. Write a quadratic equation in the form $ax^2 + bx + c = 0$ whose solutions are:
   1. $\{3, -6\}$ 4. $\{1 - \sqrt{3}, 1 + \sqrt{3}\}$
   2. $\left\{-\frac{1}{2}, \frac{2}{3}\right\}$ 5. $\{0, -6\}$
   3. $\{4, 4\}$

4. If the discriminant of a quadratic equation is negative, how many times will its graph cross the x-axis? _____

5. Given the function $y = x^2 - 2x - 3$, rewrite this function in the form $y = a(x - h)^2 + k$. Hint: Use completing the square.

$y =$ _____

6. Graph each pair of parabolas on the grids provided.

   a. $y = (x - 3)^2$ a. $y = -2x^2 + 5$

   b. $y = x^2 - 2$ b. $y = \frac{1}{3}(x + 3)^2 + 2$

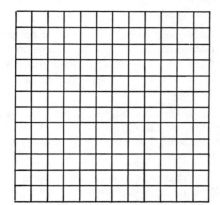 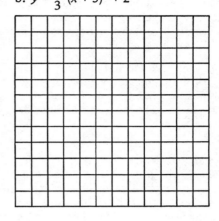

7. Complete the following chart

Parabola	Vertex	Axis of Symmetry
$y = (x - 4)^2$		
$y = 2x^2 + 6$		
$y = -3(x - 1)^2$		
$y = \frac{1}{2}(x - 1)^2 + 1$		
$y = 2x^2 + 15x + 18$		
$y = -x^2 + 6x$		

8. Write a quadratic function in the form $y = a(x - h)^2 + k$ whose vertex is (2, -1) and whose graph opens downward. _____

9. Bonus: Write a quadratic function in standard form ($y = ax^2 + bx + c$) whose vertex is (1, -4) and whose graph contains the points (2, -1) and (-1, 8). _____

RESOURCES

Below is a selected list of resources for teaching the solution of quadratic equations and the graphing of quadratic functions. Addresses of publishers can be found in Appendix A.

Clark, Alice, and Leitch, Carol, *Amusements Developing Algebra Skills, Volume II.* Pacific Grove, CA: Midwest Publications, 1983. Provides an ideal combination of extensive algebra practice exercises embedded in cross number puzzles, line designs, decodes, picture graphs, optical illusions, and others.

Journey Into Algebra, Clinton, IA: EDUCAT, 1983. Clever puzzles provide practice in skills ranging from order of operations to solving quadratic equations; reproducible for classroom use.

National Council of Teachers of Mathematics, *The Mathematics Teacher.* Reston, VA: NCTM. This monthly journal is published nine times a year and includes useful suggestions for teaching various topics in the secondary school mathematics curriculum.

National Council of Teachers of Mathematics, *The Teaching of Secondary School Mathematics*. Reston, VA: NCTM, 1970. (33rd Yearbook). This yearbook contains sections about preparing plans for teaching algebra.

Plan, Algebra I. Oak Lawn, IL: Plan Products, 1983. Provides the complete introductory algebra curriculum advocated by the School Mathematics Study Group. The teacher's kit includes placement tests, achievement tests, and duplicating masters.

The Plastigraph. Bronx, NY: Academic Industries, 1983. A board graph, coated on both sides with flexible mylar plastic, is designed for teachers of high school mathematics. The axes are prenumbered to save valuable time in preparing lessons.

Rasmussen, Peter, *Key to Algebra*. Hayward, CA: Activity Resources, 1975. A set of small pamphlets that provide practice in basic algebraic skills.

Quadratics. Chicago: LaPine Scientific Company, 1983. Includes six cassettes with worksheets—quadratic formula, nature of roots, role of a, b, c in $f(x) = ax^2 + bx + c$.

Quadratic Equations. Chicago: LaPine Scientific Company, 1983. Includes three filmstrips and three cassettes—solving quadratic equations by factoring, by completing the square, by the quadratic formula.

Rectangular Coordinates Stamp. Chicago: LaPine Scientific Company, 1983. A rubber stamp measuring 3 x 3 inches, ideal for tests and other handouts.

School Science and Mathematics Association, *School Science and Mathematics*. Bowling Green, OH: SSMA. This monthly journal is published nine times a year and includes pedagogy and research in mathematics education useful for secondary and postsecondary teachers.

Addresses of Producers of Resources

Academic Industries, Inc.
P.O. Box 428
Baychester Station
Bronx, NY 10469

Activity Resources Company, Inc.
P.O. Box 4875
Hayward, CA 94540

Addison-Wesley
1 Jacob Way
Reading, MA 01867

Allyn and Bacon, Inc.
7 Wells Ave.
Newton, MA 02159

APPLE Computer, Inc.
10260 Bandley Drive
Cupertino, CA 95014

Classroom Computer News
Box 266
Cambridge, MA 02138

Commodore, Inc.
390 Reed Street
Santa Clara, CA 95050

The Computing Teacher
University of Oregon
Eugene, OR 97403

CONDUIT
P.O. Box 388
Iowa City, IA 52244

Coronet Films
65 East South Water Street
Chicago, IL 60601

Creative Publications
P.O. Box 10328
Palo Alto, CA 94303

Dale Seymour Publications
P.O. Box 10888
Palo Alto, CA 94303

Doubleday and Company, Inc.
501 Franklin Ave.
Garden City, NY 10014

Dover Publications
180 Varick Street
New York, NY 10014

EDUCAT Publishers, Inc.
P.O. Box 2891
Clinton, IA 52735

Educational Computer
Box 535
Cupertino, CA 95015

Electronic Education
1311 Executive Center Drive
Tallahassee, FL 32301

ERIC Clearinghouse for Science, Mathematics, and
    Environmental Education
College of Education
The Ohio State University
1200 Chambers Road, Third Floor
Columbus, OH 43212

Film Associates of California
11559 Santa Monica Boulevard
Los Angeles, CA 90025

W. H. Freeman and Company
660 Market Street
San Francisco, CA 94104

Gamco Industries, Inc.
Box 310 P
Big Springs, TX 79720

Harper and Row, Publishers
10 East 53rd Street
New York, NY 10022

Harvard University Press
79 Garden Street
Cambridge, MA 02138

Holt, Rinehart, and Winston
383 Madison Avenue
New York, NY 10017

Incider Magazine
80 Pine Street
Peterborough, NH 03458

Key Curriculum Project
P.O. Box 2304-N
Berkeley, CA 94702

LaPine Scientific Company
Department D 4 3 2
6009 South Knox Avenue
Chicago, IL 60629

Lano Company
4741 West Liberty Street
Ann Arbor, MI 48103

McGraw-Hill
330 W. 42nd Street
New York, NY 10036

The Math Group, Inc.
396 East 79th Street
Suite 1C
Minneapolis, MN 55420

MATH HOUSE
Department G-6
Division of MOSAIC MEDIA, INC.
P.O. Box 711
Glen Ellyn, IL 60137

Math-Master Labs
Box 1911
Big Spring, TX 79720

The Micro Center
Box 6
Pleasantville, NY 10570

Midwest Publications
P.O. Box 448
Pacific Grove, CA 93950

Minnesota Educational Computing Corporation
2520 Broadway Drive
St. Paul, MN 55113

MIT Press
28 Carleton Street
Cambridge, MA 02142

Modern Learning Aids
16 Spear Street
San Francisco, CA 94105

National Council of Teachers of Mathematics
1906 Association Drive
Reston, VA 22091

Nibble Magazine
Box 325
Lincoln, MA 01773

Opportunities for Learning, Inc.
8950 Lurline
Chatsworth, CA 91311

Plan Products
Department 771
WESTINGHOUSE LEARNING CORPORATION
5005 West 110th Street
Oak Lawn, IL 60453

Prentice-Hall, Inc.
Englewood Cliffs, NJ 07632

Prindle, Weber, and Schmidt, Inc.
20 Provident Street
Statler Office Building
Boston, MA 02116

Radio Shack
1400 One Tandy Center
Fort Worth, TX 76102

Random House, Inc.
201 E. 50th Street
New York, NY 10022

Research Council for Diagnostic and
   Prescriptive Mathematics
School of Education
University of California
Berkeley, CA 94720

School Science and Mathematics
126 Life Science Building
Bowling Green State University
Bowling Green, OH 43403

Scott, Foresman and Company
1900 East Lake Avenue
Glenview, IL 60025

The Skills Group
Communications Park
Box 100
White Plains, NY 10602

Sunburst Communications
39 Washington Avenue
Pleasantville, NY 10570

Teachers Publishing Company
23 Leroy Avenue
Darien, CT 06820

Texas Instruments, Inc.
P.O. Box 22013
Dallas, TX 75221

University of Chicago Press
5801 Ellis Avenue
Chicago, IL 60637

Van Nostrand Reinhold Company
450 West 33rd
New York, NY 10010

W. B. Saunders
West Washington Square
Philadelphia, PA 19105

Wff'N Proof Publishers
P.O. Box 71
New Haven, CT 06501

APPENDIX B

Sample Answers (for Selected Reproduction Pages)

Reproduction Page 37

1. 52
2. 96
3. $5a + 5c$
4. $4ab$
5. 6
6. 25
7. 14
8. 90
9. 23
10. 36

1. $A = 15$
2. $A = 12$
3. $t = \frac{9}{2}$
4. $V = \frac{32}{3}$
5. $P = 32$
6. $C = 100$
7. $S = 48\pi$
8. $A = 117x$
9. $d = 150$
10. $A = 70x$

Reproduction Page 38

1. a) Distributive (of multiplication over addition)
   b) Identity property of addition
   c) Identity property of multiplication
   d) Associative (of addition)

2. a) 70
   b) 108
   c) 90
   d) 24
   e) 12
   f) 2255

Reproduction Page 46

1. $x = 55$
2. $x = 25$
3. $x = 2$
4. $x = 2$
5. $x = 2$

6. $x = 25$
7. $x = 27$
8. $F = 40$
9. $y = 2$
10. $x = 3$

Reproduction Page 48

1. $x = 1$
2. $y = 2$
3. $x = 42$
4. $x = 3$
5. $y = \dfrac{-5}{4}$

6. $x = \dfrac{7}{3}$
7. $y = 1$
8. $x = \dfrac{12}{5}$
9. $y = \dfrac{8}{25}$
10. $x = -2$

Reproduction Page 53

1. $-1 < x \leqslant 2$
2. $0 \leqslant x < \dfrac{3}{4}$
3. $5 \leqslant x < 8$
4. $-1 \leqslant x \leqslant 10$
5. $-1 \leqslant x \leqslant 10$
6. $-1 < x < 3$

$\Big\}$ Graph each

7. a) y is between 3 and 9, including 9.
   b) Graph
   c) $y > 3$ and $y \leqslant 9$
8. a) $2y$ is between 6 and 18, including 18.
   b) Graph
   c) $2y > 6$ and $2y \leqslant 18$
9. a) x is between negative 3 and positive 3.
   b) Graph
   c) $x > -3$ and $x < +3$
10. a) The absolute value of x is between 0 and 3, including 0.
    b) Graph
    c) $|x| \geqslant 0$ and $|x| < 3$

Reproduction Page 56

1. y-int. 6
   slope –1
2. y-int. –1
   slope $\dfrac{1}{4}$
3. y-int. 0
   slope 32
4. no y-int.
   slope undefined
5. y-int. 6
   slope 0

6. y-int. –1
   slope 1
7. y-int. $\dfrac{5}{2}$
   slope $\dfrac{-1}{2}$
8. y-int. $\dfrac{5}{2}$
   slope $\dfrac{-1}{2}$
9. y-int. 7
   slope –2
10. y-int. 6
    slope 1

A. 4. and 5. represent lines.
B. 7. and 8. are the same line.

Reproduction Page 57

1. Solution set $\{(1,-2)\}$, independent
2. Solution set $\{(1,-1)\}$, independent
3. Solution set $\{\varnothing\}$, inconsistent
4. Infinitely many solutions, dependent
5. Solution set $\{(-3,-1)\}$, independent

1. $x + y = 1$
   $x + y = 2$
2. $x - 5 = y$
   $2x + 1 = y$
3. $x + y = 7$
   $3x + 3y = 21$

Reproduction Page 59

1. Solution set $\left\{\left(\frac{9}{2}, -3\right)\right\}$

2. Solution set $\left\{\left(\frac{43}{29}, \frac{93}{29}\right)\right\}$

3. Solution set $\left\{\left(\frac{71}{17}, \frac{55}{17}\right)\right\}$

4. Solution set $\{(-8, 22)\}$
5. Infinitely many solutions
6. Solution set $\{(2, 0)\}$

Reproduction Page 62

A. 1. 16
    2. 531,441
    3. 4096
    4. 5,764,801
B. 1. 16
    2. 531,441
    3. 4096
    4. 5,764,801

C. 1. $3^6 = 729$
    2. $2^{10} = 1024$
    3. $7^6 = 117,649$
    4. $4^6 = 4096$
    5. x^4
    6. a^{12}
    7. $x^4 y^6$
    8. $a^{12} b^6$
    9. $5^0 = 1$
   10. 576

Reproduction Page 68

A. 1. $x^2 - 2x - 15$
    2. $2a^2 + 11a + 15$
    3. $x^2 - 16$
    4. $4a^2 + 12a + 9$
    5. $20 + x - x^2$
    6. $3x^2 - 14x - 5$
    7. $4x^2 - 49$
    8. $16x^2 - 24xy + 9y^2$
    9. $x^2 + 8x - 20$
   10. $2x^2 + 7x - 15$

B. 3. $x^2 - 5x + 6$
    6. $x^2 + 2x + 1$
    9. $a^2 + 5a + 6$
   12. $x^2 - 7x - 8$
   15. $6x^2 + 11x - 10$
   18. $4x^2 - 25$

Reproduction Page 72

1. $(3x + 6)(x + 3)$
2. $-(x + 11)(x + 1)$
3. $(x - y)(x + y)(x^2 + y^2)$
4. $(x - 1)(x + 1)(x - 3)(x + 3)$
5. $2(x + 1)(x + 4)$
6. $(m - 2)(m + 2)(m^2 + 4)$
7. $(x - 1)(x + 1)(x - 4)(x + 4)$
8. $3x(2x - 1)(x + 1)$
9. $2a(3b + 5c)(3b - 5c)$

10. $25(a - 2b)(a + 2b)$
11. $p(p - 1)(p + 1)(p^2 + 7)$
12. $4(x - 2)(x - 2)(x - 2)(x - 2)$
13. $9x^2(y - 2)(y + 2)$
14. $x(x + 1)(x - 5)$
15. $x(x + 4)$
16. $x(3x - 4)(x + 1)$
17. $3(2x + 3)(x - 1)$
18. $(a - 3b)(a + 3b)(a^2 + 9b^2)$

Reproduction Page 77

	A. $x = 1$	$x = 2$	$x = 3$		B. Exclude $x =$
1.	-1	0	$\frac{1}{3}$		1. 0
2.	$\frac{4}{3}$	1	$\frac{4}{5}$		2. -2

3.	$-\dfrac{3}{2}$	-4	UNDEF.	3.	3
4.	$-\dfrac{3}{2}$	-4	UNDEF.	4.	3, -3
5.	$-\dfrac{1}{3}$	0	$\dfrac{1}{5}$	5.	-2
6.	-1	4	3	6.	$\dfrac{3}{2}$
7.	$\dfrac{-5}{4}$	$\dfrac{-11}{7}$	-2	7.	9
8.	-1	-1	-1	8.	6
9.	-1	-1	-1	9.	$\dfrac{4}{5}$
10.	-3	UNDEF.	5	10.	2

Reproduction Page 88

A.   *Opposite (–a)*

-2

$-x$

$\dfrac{1}{2}$

$-(x-3)$ or $(3-x)$

$\dfrac{-x}{2}$

$\dfrac{-3}{x-4}$ or $\dfrac{3}{4-x}$

$\dfrac{-(x-2)}{3x}$ or $\dfrac{(2-x)}{3x}$

$\dfrac{-(2x-3)}{2x+3}$ or $\dfrac{3-2x}{2x+3}$

$\dfrac{-2(x-3)}{x+1}$ or $\dfrac{2(3-x)}{x+1}$

$--\dfrac{1}{x}+2$ or $\dfrac{1}{x}-2$

Check: $a + (-a) \overset{?}{=} 0$

$2 + (-2) = 0$

$x + (-x) = 0$

$-\dfrac{1}{2} + \left(\dfrac{1}{2}\right) = 0$

$(x-3) + (3-x) = 0$

$\dfrac{x}{2} + \left(\dfrac{-x}{2}\right) = 0$

$\dfrac{3}{x-4} + \left(\dfrac{3}{4-x}\right) = \dfrac{3}{x-4} + \dfrac{-3}{x-4} = 0$

$\dfrac{(x-2)}{3x} + \left(\dfrac{(2-x)}{3x}\right) = 0$

$\dfrac{2x-3}{2x+3} + \left(\dfrac{3-2x}{2x+3}\right) = 0$

$\dfrac{2(x-3)}{x+1} + \left(\dfrac{2(3-x)}{x+1}\right) = 0$

$\dfrac{-1}{x} + 2 + \dfrac{1}{x} - 2 = 0$

B.   1. $\dfrac{x+2}{3} + \dfrac{(-2)}{3}$

2. $\dfrac{b^2}{b+1} + \dfrac{(-1)}{b+1}$

3. $\dfrac{3a+2b}{3b} + \dfrac{(-a-2b)}{6a}$

4. $\dfrac{2x-1}{4} + \dfrac{(1-x)}{8}$

5. $\dfrac{4}{3r} + \dfrac{(-r-2)}{r}$

6. $\dfrac{3x-2}{4x} + \dfrac{(-3x-1)}{6x}$

7. $\dfrac{2z}{z-1} + \dfrac{(-3z)}{z+1}$

8. $\dfrac{5a}{a^2-9} + \dfrac{(-4)}{a+3}$

9. $\dfrac{y-5}{4y} + \dfrac{(1-3y)}{y}$

10. $\dfrac{2}{m-2} + \dfrac{(-2)}{m-2}$

11. $\dfrac{x-2}{3x} + \dfrac{(2x-1)}{5x}$

12. $4x + \dfrac{(5-2x)}{3}$

Reproduction Page 93

1. $a = 6$
2. $x = 10$
3. $x = -6$
4. $\{\emptyset\}$

5. $a = 2$
6. $b = \dfrac{-1}{2}$

7. Solution set $\{(2,3)\}$,

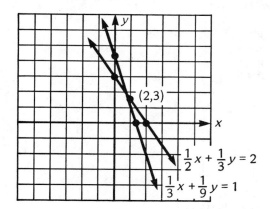

8. Solution set $\{(-4,-6)\}$,

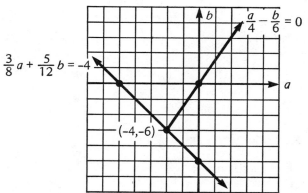

Reproduction Page 105

Slope

1. 2
2. $\frac{3}{2}$
3. 2
4. 2
5. 4
6. $\frac{1}{2}$
7. –2

8. Undefined
9. 0
10. (Not a linear function)
11. (Not a linear function)
12. (Not a linear function
13. $\frac{1}{12}$
14. (Not a linear function)
15. Undefined

No. (10, 11, 12, and 14 are not.)
3. and 4. are equations for the *same line*.
6. and 7. are equations for lines which are *perpendicular* to each other.

Reproduction Page 109

1. Solution set $\{(4,-2)\}$
2. Infinitely many solutions
3. Solution set $\{(2,7)\}$

4. Solution set $\{(0,0)\}$
5. No solutions

Reproduction Page 111

1. Addition; C = 883 stamps
2. Multiplication; F = 15 outfits
3. Subtraction; f = 11 freethrows
4. a. Division; P = 22 miles/gallon
   b. Multiplication; C = $25.27
   c. Multiplication, division; x = 16.54 miles
5. Multiplication, subtraction, division; n = 16 nickels

6. Multiplication; I = $180.00
7. Multiplication; J = $2\frac{1}{4}$ hours
8. Multiplication, subtraction; $n \geqslant 3$ years
9. Multiplication, subtraction; A = 46.94 sq. meters
10. Addition, division; a = 142

Reproduction Page 113

1. $C = -40$
2. $P = 34$
   $I = 12$
3. $a = 25$
   $b = 13$

4. $x = 104.5$
   $y = 115.5$
5. $x = 4$
   $y = 3$
   $z = 5$

Reproduction Page 117

1. Inconsistent
2. Inconsistent
3. $S = 5, A = 1$
4. 7

5. Moe, Larry, Curly,
   $150 $75 $90
   Moe, Larry, Curly,
   $60 $120 $135

Reproduction Page 119

1. $(x - 2)(x + 3)$
2. $(4y + 3)(3y + 2)$
3. $b(b - 5)$
4. $(x + 3)^2$
5. $(y - 4)(y + 4)$

6. $(3x - 1)(4x + 2)$
7. $(y - 1)(y - 3)(y + 1)(y + 3)$
8. $a(a + 2)(a - 2)$
9. $(3y - 5)(y + 7)$
10. $(4t - 6)(t + 5)$

Reproduction Page 122

1. $x = \frac{9}{2}, \frac{5}{2}$
2. $x = \frac{21}{4}, \frac{9}{4}$
3. $x = \frac{5}{4}, \frac{-1}{4}$
4. $x = \frac{1}{16}, \frac{-9}{16}$
5. $x = \frac{19}{9}, \frac{-7}{9}$

6. $p = \frac{16}{9}, \frac{-4}{9}$
7. $y = \frac{9}{16}, \frac{-1}{16}$
8. $x = 8, -2$
9. $x = 52, -46$
10. $n = \frac{53}{16}, \frac{-45}{16}$

Reproduction Page 128

	(b)	(c)		(b)	(c)
1.	(2,0)	$x = 2$	9.	(1, 1)	$x = 1$
2.	(0,3)	$x = 0$	10.	(-1,0)	$x = -1$
3.	(-3,2)	$x = -3$	11.	(-1,0)	$x = -1$
4.	(0,-4)	$x = 0$	12.	(-1,-4)	$x = -1$
5.	(3,-4)	$x = 3$	13.	(0,9)	$x = 0$
6.	(-1,0)	$x = -1$	14.	$\left(\frac{-3}{4}, \frac{-121}{8}\right)$	$x = \frac{-3}{4}$
7.	(0,-3)	$x = 0$	15.	(-1,-3)	$x = -1$
8.	(-2,-5)	$x = -2$			

APPENDIX **C**

Reproduction Pages

The pages that follow have been provided to facilitate the reproducing of exercises, sample compositions, and materials needed for activities suggested in the preceding pages. Each page is perforated to make removal from this book easier. Once removed, a page can be used in several ways:

1. *For projection with an opaque projector.* No further preparation is necessary if the page is to be used with an opaque projector. Simply insert it in the projector and the page can be viewed by the entire class.

2. *For projection with an overhead projector.* The Reproduction Page must be converted to a transparency for use on an overhead projector. Overlay the Reproduction Page with a blank transparency and run both of them through a copying machine.

3. *For duplication with a spirit duplicator.* A master can be made from the Reproduction Page by overlaying it with a special heat sensitive spirit master and running both through a copying machine. The spirit master can then be used to reproduce 50 to 100 copies on paper.

DAILY DOZEN QUIZZES

NAME _____ SCORE _____

1. $\frac{3}{4} + \frac{1}{4}$ _____
2. $\frac{3}{4} - \frac{1}{4}$ _____
3. $\frac{3}{4} \cdot \frac{1}{4}$ _____
4. $\frac{3}{4} \div \frac{1}{4}$ _____
5. $\frac{1}{2} + \frac{1}{3}$ _____
6. $\frac{1}{2} - \frac{1}{3}$ _____
7. $\frac{1}{2} \cdot \frac{1}{3}$ _____
8. $\frac{1}{2} \div \frac{1}{3}$ _____
9. $2 + \frac{1}{4}$ _____
10. $2 - \frac{1}{4}$ _____
11. $2 \cdot \frac{1}{4}$ _____
12. $2 \div \frac{1}{4}$ _____

NAME _____ SCORE _____

1. $\frac{3}{8} + \frac{1}{8}$ _____
2. $\frac{3}{8} - \frac{1}{8}$ _____
3. $\frac{3}{8} \cdot \frac{1}{8}$ _____
4. $\frac{3}{8} \div \frac{1}{8}$ _____
5. $\frac{1}{2} + \frac{1}{4}$ _____
6. $\frac{1}{2} - \frac{1}{4}$ _____
7. $\frac{1}{2} \cdot \frac{1}{4}$ _____
8. $\frac{1}{2} \div \frac{1}{4}$ _____
9. $2 + \frac{1}{2}$ _____
10. $2 - \frac{1}{2}$ _____
11. $2 \cdot \frac{1}{2}$ _____
12. $2 \div \frac{1}{2}$ _____

NAME _____ SCORE _____

1. $\frac{3}{10} + \frac{1}{10}$ _____
2. $\frac{3}{10} - \frac{1}{10}$ _____
3. $\frac{3}{10} \cdot \frac{1}{10}$ _____
4. $\frac{3}{10} \div \frac{1}{10}$ _____
5. $\frac{2}{5} + \frac{1}{3}$ _____
6. $\frac{2}{5} - \frac{1}{3}$ _____
7. $\frac{2}{5} \cdot \frac{1}{3}$ _____
8. $\frac{2}{5} \div \frac{1}{3}$ _____
9. $5 + \frac{2}{5}$ _____
10. $5 - \frac{2}{5}$ _____
11. $5 \cdot \frac{2}{5}$ _____
12. $5 \div \frac{2}{5}$ _____

NAME _____ SCORE _____

1. $\frac{5}{12} + \frac{5}{12}$ _____
2. $\frac{5}{12} - \frac{5}{12}$ _____
3. $\frac{5}{12} \cdot \frac{5}{12}$ _____
4. $\frac{5}{12} \div \frac{5}{12}$ _____
5. $\frac{5}{6} + \frac{1}{3}$ _____
6. $\frac{5}{6} - \frac{1}{3}$ _____
7. $\frac{5}{6} \cdot \frac{1}{3}$ _____
8. $\frac{5}{6} \div \frac{1}{3}$ _____
9. $3 + \frac{2}{3}$ _____
10. $3 - \frac{2}{3}$ _____
11. $3 \cdot \frac{2}{3}$ _____
12. $3 \div \frac{2}{3}$ _____

Copyright © 1984 by Allyn and Bacon, Inc. Reproduction of this material is restricted to use with *A Guidebook for Teaching Algebra*, by Terry A. Goodman, John Bernard, Martin P. Cohen, and Joanne E. Meldon.

DAILY DOZEN QUIZZES

NAME _____ SCORE _____

1. $2\frac{1}{2} + \frac{1}{2}$ _____
2. $2\frac{1}{2} - \frac{1}{2}$ _____
3. $2\frac{1}{2} \cdot \frac{1}{2}$ _____
4. $2\frac{1}{2} \div \frac{1}{2}$ _____
5. $\frac{3}{4} + \frac{2}{3}$ _____
6. $\frac{3}{4} - \frac{2}{3}$ _____
7. $\frac{3}{4} \cdot \frac{2}{3}$ _____
8. $\frac{3}{4} \div \frac{2}{3}$ _____
9. $2\frac{1}{3} + 2$ _____
10. $2\frac{1}{3} - 2$ _____
11. $2\frac{1}{3} \cdot 2$ _____
12. $2\frac{1}{3} \div 2$ _____

NAME _____ SCORE _____

1. $2\frac{3}{5} + \frac{2}{5}$ _____
2. $2\frac{3}{5} - \frac{2}{5}$ _____
3. $2\frac{3}{5} \cdot \frac{2}{5}$ _____
4. $2\frac{3}{5} \div \frac{2}{5}$ _____
5. $\frac{5}{6} + \frac{2}{3}$ _____
6. $\frac{5}{6} - \frac{2}{3}$ _____
7. $\frac{5}{6} \cdot \frac{2}{3}$ _____
8. $\frac{5}{6} \div \frac{2}{3}$ _____
9. $3\frac{3}{4} + 2$ _____
10. $3\frac{3}{4} - 2$ _____
11. $3\frac{3}{4} \cdot 2$ _____
12. $3\frac{3}{4} \div 2$ _____

NAME _____ SCORE _____

1. $3\frac{1}{2} + 2\frac{1}{2}$ _____
2. $3\frac{1}{2} - 2\frac{1}{2}$ _____
3. $3\frac{1}{2} \cdot 2\frac{1}{2}$ _____
4. $3\frac{1}{2} \div 2\frac{1}{2}$ _____
5. $2\frac{1}{2} + \frac{3}{4}$ _____
6. $2\frac{1}{2} - \frac{3}{4}$ _____
7. $2\frac{1}{2} \cdot \frac{3}{4}$ _____
8. $2\frac{1}{2} \div \frac{3}{4}$ _____
9. $3 + 2\frac{1}{3}$ _____
10. $3 - 2\frac{1}{3}$ _____
11. $3 \cdot 2\frac{1}{3}$ _____
12. $3 \div 2\frac{1}{3}$ _____

NAME _____ SCORE _____

1. $2\frac{1}{8} + 1\frac{3}{8}$ _____
2. $2\frac{1}{8} - 1\frac{3}{8}$ _____
3. $2\frac{1}{8} \cdot 1\frac{3}{8}$ _____
4. $2\frac{1}{8} \div 1\frac{3}{8}$ _____
5. $3\frac{1}{6} + 1\frac{2}{3}$ _____
6. $3\frac{1}{6} - 1\frac{2}{3}$ _____
7. $3\frac{1}{6} \cdot 1\frac{2}{3}$ _____
8. $3\frac{1}{6} \div 1\frac{2}{3}$ _____
9. $1\frac{3}{4} + 2$ _____
10. $2 - 1\frac{3}{4}$ _____
11. $1\frac{2}{3} \cdot \frac{4}{5}$ _____
12. $2 \div 2$ _____

Copyright © 1984 by Allyn and Bacon, Inc. Reproduction of this material is restricted to use with *A Guidebook for Teaching Algebra,* by Terry A. Goodman, John Bernard, Martin P. Cohen, and Joanne E. Meldon.

DAILY DOZEN QUIZZES

NAME _____ SCORE _____

1. $\frac{3}{8} + \frac{1}{2}$ _____

2. $2 - \frac{3}{4}$ _____

3. $\frac{2}{5} \div 5$ _____

4. $1\frac{2}{5} - \frac{1}{10}$ _____

5. $\frac{5}{12} + \frac{1}{12}$ _____

6. $2 \div 4$ _____

7. $2\frac{1}{2} \cdot 6$ _____

8. $\frac{3}{4} + 1\frac{2}{3}$ _____

9. $1\frac{2}{5} \div 7$ _____

10. $4\frac{1}{6} - \frac{2}{3}$ _____

11. $\frac{3}{8} \cdot \frac{2}{5}$ _____

12. $2 \cdot \frac{3}{4}$ _____

NAME _____ SCORE _____

1. $\frac{4}{5} + \frac{1}{3}$ _____

2. $3 - \frac{2}{5}$ _____

3. $\frac{3}{8} \div 3$ _____

4. $2\frac{3}{4} - \frac{1}{2}$ _____

5. $\frac{3}{8} + \frac{3}{8}$ _____

6. $3 \div 9$ _____

7. $5\frac{1}{3} \cdot 3$ _____

8. $\frac{3}{8} + 1\frac{3}{4}$ _____

9. $2\frac{1}{7} \div 5$ _____

10. $8\frac{1}{3} - \frac{5}{6}$ _____

11. $\frac{4}{9} \cdot \frac{3}{5}$ _____

12. $\frac{3}{8} \cdot 4$ _____

NAME _____ SCORE _____

1. $6 \div 8$ _____

2. $\frac{5}{9} - \frac{1}{6}$ _____

3. $\frac{3}{5} \cdot \frac{2}{7}$ _____

4. $3 - 1\frac{2}{3}$ _____

5. $5\frac{1}{2} \div \frac{1}{2}$ _____

6. $\frac{7}{8} + \frac{5}{8}$ _____

7. $2\frac{1}{2} \cdot 3\frac{1}{5}$ _____

8. $3\frac{1}{3} - 2\frac{4}{9}$ _____

9. $\frac{3}{4} + \frac{2}{5}$ _____

10. $\frac{3}{7} \div 9$ _____

11. $2\frac{1}{2} + 3\frac{3}{4}$ _____

12. $\frac{5}{8} \cdot 4$ _____

NAME _____ SCORE _____

1. $\frac{3}{4} \cdot \frac{2}{5}$ _____

2. $\frac{5}{6} \div 5$ _____

3. $1\frac{3}{5} + 2\frac{3}{10}$ _____

4. $5 - 1\frac{2}{3}$ _____

5. $4 \div 6$ _____

6. $\frac{3}{4} + \frac{2}{5}$ _____

7. $4\frac{2}{3} \cdot \frac{3}{7}$ _____

8. $6 \div 2\frac{2}{3}$ _____

9. $\frac{3}{8} + \frac{7}{8}$ _____

10. $1\frac{1}{2} - \frac{3}{4}$ _____

11. $\frac{11}{12} - \frac{3}{4}$ _____

12. $6 \cdot \frac{5}{6}$ _____

Copyright © 1984 by Allyn and Bacon, Inc. Reproduction of this material is restricted to use with *A Guidebook for Teaching Algebra,* by Terry A. Goodman, John Bernard, Martin P. Cohen, and Joanne E. Meldon.

DAILY DOZEN QUIZZES

NAME _____ SCORE _____

1. 2 + (-8)   _____
2. 2 - (-8)   _____
3. 2(-8)   _____
4. $\frac{2}{-8}$ _____
5. -6 + 4   _____
6. -6 - 4   _____
7. -6 · 4   _____
8. $\frac{-6}{4}$ _____
9. -3 + (-6)   _____
10. -3 - (-6)   _____
11. -3(-6)   _____
12. $\frac{-3}{-6}$ _____

NAME _____ SCORE _____

1. 3 + (-2)   _____
2. 3 - (-2)   _____
3. 3(-2)   _____
4. $\frac{3}{-2}$ _____
5. -7 + 5   _____
6. -7 - 5   _____
7. -7 · 5   _____
8. $\frac{-7}{5}$ _____
9. -4 + (-8)   _____
10. -4 - (-8)   _____
11. -4(-8)   _____
12. $\frac{-4}{-8}$ _____

NAME _____ SCORE _____

1. 9 + (-12)   _____
2. 9 - (-12)   _____
3. 9(-12)   _____
4. $\frac{9}{-12}$ _____
5. -6 + 2   _____
6. -6 - 2   _____
7. -6 · 2   _____
8. $\frac{-6}{2}$ _____
9. -8 + (-6)   _____
10. -8 - (-6)   _____
11. -8(-6)   _____
12. $\frac{-8}{-6}$ _____

NAME _____ SCORE _____

1. 12 + (-3)   _____
2. 12 - (-3)   _____
3. 12(-3)   _____
4. $\frac{12}{-3}$ _____
5. -2 + 8   _____
6. -2 - 8   _____
7. -2 · 8   _____
8. $\frac{-2}{8}$ _____
9. -5 + (-5)   _____
10. -5 - (-5)   _____
11. -5(-5)   _____
12. $\frac{-5}{-5}$ _____

Copyright © 1984 by Allyn and Bacon, Inc. Reproduction of this material is restricted to use with *A Guidebook for Teaching Algebra*, by Terry A. Goodman, John Bernard, Martin P. Cohen, and Joanne E. Meldon.

DAILY DOZEN QUIZZES

NAME _____ SCORE _____

1. -5 + 8 _____
2. $\frac{-2}{6}$ _____
3. 3 + (-7) _____
4. 2(-4) _____
5. -5 - 8 _____
6. $\frac{6}{-2}$ _____
7. -3 + (-5) _____
8. $\frac{-8}{-3}$ _____
9. -5 · 3 _____
10. 3 - (-7) _____
11. (-4)(-6) _____
12. 3 - 8 _____

NAME _____ SCORE _____

1. 2 + (-8) _____
2. 8(-2) _____
3. $\frac{-12}{-5}$ _____
4. -3 + 7 _____
5. -3(-4) _____
6. 5 - (-8) _____
7. $\frac{-3}{6}$ _____
8. -4 - (-6) _____
9. -2 - 7 _____
10. $\frac{8}{-2}$ _____
11. 2 - 7 _____
12. -2 · 7 _____

NAME _____ SCORE _____

1. 6 - (-8) _____
2. -2 - 9 _____
3. 4(-12) _____
4. 5 + (-10) _____
5. $\frac{-6}{-8}$ _____
6. 4 - 12 _____
7. -2 + 9 _____
8. $\frac{12}{-3}$ _____
9. -2 · 9 _____
10. -6 - (-8) _____
11. -2(-8) _____
12. $\frac{-2}{10}$ _____

NAME _____ SCORE _____

1. -4 · 6 _____
2. 3 + (-5) _____
3. $\frac{8}{-4}$ _____
4. (-4)(-5) _____
5. -4 - 6 _____
6. 4 - 6 _____
7. $\frac{-4}{6}$ _____
8. 6 - (-11) _____
9. $\frac{-10}{-2}$ _____
10. -4 + 6 _____
11. 3(-5) _____
12. -8 - (-2) _____

Copyright © 1984 by Allyn and Bacon, Inc. Reproduction of this material is restricted to use with *A Guidebook for Teaching Algebra*, by Terry A. Goodman, John Bernard, Martin P. Cohen, and Joanne E. Meldon.

DAILY DOZEN QUIZZES

NAME _____ SCORE _____

1. 2 - 6 - 4   _____
2. -4 + 5 - 2   _____
3. -8 - 2 - 3   _____
4. 8 - 5 + 5   _____
5. -3 + 7 + 2   _____
6. 2 - 6 - 2 + 4   _____
7. -8 + 5 - 3 + 6   _____
8. 2(-3)(-4)   _____
9. (-2)(-3)(-4)   _____
10. -2 - 3 - 4   _____
11. (-1)(-4)(-5)(-2) _____
12. -4 + 8 - 6 - 2   _____

NAME _____ SCORE _____

1. 8 - 6 - 4   _____
2. -7 + 5 - 2   _____
3. -6 - 2 - 4   _____
4. 2 - 6 + 4   _____
5. -8 + 1 + 5   _____
6. 8 - 10 + 2 - 3   _____
7. -4 + 7 - 9 + 2   _____
8. 8(-2)(-5)   _____
9. (-8)(-2)(-5)   _____
10. -8 - 2 - 5   _____
11. 6 - 8 - 2 + 5   _____
12. (-2)(-1)(-4)(-2) _____

NAME _____ SCORE _____

1. 3 - 8 + 4   _____
2. -6 - 2 + 5   _____
3. -8 - 3 - 2   _____
4. 6 - 8 - 2   _____
5. -5 + 11 - 2   _____
6. -3 + 7 - 5 + 1   _____
7. 9 - 12 + 7 - 2   _____
8. 6(-3)(-4)   _____
9. (-6)(-3)(-4)   _____
10. -6 - 3 - 4   _____
11. (-6)(-2)(-1)(-3) _____
12. 9 - 2 - 12 + 6   _____

NAME _____ SCORE _____

1. 4 - 3 + 3   _____
2. -2 - 3 - 4   _____
3. -2 + 5 - 4   _____
4. 8 - 4 - 4   _____
5. -6 - 2 + 5   _____
6. -6 + 2 + 5   _____
7. 8 - 4 + 2 - 9   _____
8. 3(-5)(-4)   _____
9. (-3)(-5)(-4)   _____
10. -3 - 5 - 4   _____
11. (-8)(-4)(-1)(-2) _____
12. -3 - 4 + 7 - 2   _____

Copyright © 1984 by Allyn and Bacon, Inc. Reproduction of this material is restricted to use with *A Guidebook for Teaching Algebra*, by Terry A. Goodman, John Bernard, Martin P. Cohen, and Joanne E. Meldon.

DAILY DOZEN QUIZZES

NAME _____ SCORE _____

1. $2 + 3 \cdot 4$ _____
2. $5 + 2(-3)$ _____
3. $4 - 7 \cdot 2$ _____
4. $5 - 8 + 4$ _____
5. $2 \cdot 8 + 3$ _____
6. $2 \cdot 3^2$ _____
7. $-5 + 4^2$ _____
8. $2 - 4(-3)$ _____
9. $2^3 + 5$ _____
10. $(-2)^3$ _____
11. $2 \cdot 3^2 + 10$ _____
12. $6 - 3 \cdot 2^2$ _____

NAME _____ SCORE _____

1. $6 + 2 \cdot 5$ _____
2. $8 + 2(-4)$ _____
3. $7 - 2 \cdot 3$ _____
4. $2 - 7 - 3$ _____
5. $5 \cdot 6 - 2$ _____
6. $3 \cdot 4^2$ _____
7. $-6 + 3^2$ _____
8. $10 - 2(-3)$ _____
9. $(-2)^3 + 7$ _____
10. 2^4 _____
11. $4 - 3 \cdot 2^2$ _____
12. $5 + 3(-2)^3$ _____

NAME _____ SCORE _____

1. $7 + 3 \cdot 5$ _____
2. $3 + 2(-4)$ _____
3. $5 - 4 \cdot 3$ _____
4. $6 - 8 + 1$ _____
5. $2 \cdot 3 + 4$ _____
6. $2 \cdot 6^2$ _____
7. $-6 + 2^3$ _____
8. $15 - 7(-2)$ _____
9. $(-2)^3 - 2$ _____
10. $(-3)^2$ _____
11. $2 \cdot 5^2 - 6$ _____
12. $4 + 3 \cdot 2^2$ _____

NAME _____ SCORE _____

1. $3 + 7 \cdot 2$ _____
2. $5 + 3(-4)$ _____
3. $6 - 5 \cdot 2$ _____
4. $4 - 5 + 2$ _____
5. $9 \cdot 6 - 5$ _____
6. $7 \cdot 3^2$ _____
7. $-4 + 3^2$ _____
8. $3 - 5(-6)$ _____
9. $(-2)^3 + 2$ _____
10. 4^3 _____
11. $13 - 3 \cdot 5^2$ _____
12. $-16 - 5 \cdot 2^3$ _____

Copyright © 1984 by Allyn and Bacon, Inc. Reproduction of this material is restricted to use with *A Guidebook for Teaching Algebra*, by Terry A. Goodman, John Bernard, Martin P. Cohen, and Joanne E. Meldon.

DAILY DOZEN QUIZZES

NAME _____ SCORE _____

$a = 2 \quad b = 3$

1. $a + 2b$ _____
2. $3a - b$ _____
3. $ab + 2$ _____
4. $5a \cdot 2b$ _____
5. $a^2 + a$ _____
6. $4ab$ _____
7. $a(b + 3)$ _____
8. $4ab - 3b$ _____
9. $-2a - b$ _____
10. $3a^2 + 4$ _____
11. $2 + 3b$ _____
12. $6 - 2b^2$ _____

NAME _____ SCORE _____

$a = -2 \quad b = 3$

1. $a + 2b$ _____
2. $3a - b$ _____
3. $ab + 2$ _____
4. $5a \cdot 2b$ _____
5. $a^2 + a$ _____
6. $4ab$ _____
7. $a(b + 3)$ _____
8. $4ab - 3b$ _____
9. $-2a - b$ _____
10. $3a^2 + 4$ _____
11. $2 + 3b$ _____
12. $6 - 2b^2$ _____

NAME _____ SCORE _____

$a = -2 \quad b = -3$

1. $a + 2b$ _____
2. $3a - b$ _____
3. $ab + 2$ _____
4. $5a \cdot 2b$ _____
5. $a^2 + a$ _____
6. $4ab$ _____
7. $a(b + 3)$ _____
8. $4ab - 3b$ _____
9. $-2a - b$ _____
10. $3a^2 + 4$ _____
11. $2 + 3b$ _____
12. $6 - 2b^2$ _____

NAME _____ SCORE _____

$a = 2 \quad b = -3$

1. $a + 2b$ _____
2. $3a - b$ _____
3. $ab + 2$ _____
4. $5a \cdot 2b$ _____
5. $a^2 + a$ _____
6. $4ab$ _____
7. $a(b + 3)$ _____
8. $4ab - 3b$ _____
9. $-2a - b$ _____
10. $3a^2 + 4$ _____
11. $2 + 3b$ _____
12. $6 - 2b^2$ _____

Copyright © 1984 by Allyn and Bacon, Inc. Reproduction of this material is restricted to use with *A Guidebook for Teaching Algebra*, by Terry A. Goodman, John Bernard, Martin P. Cohen, and Joanne E. Meldon.

DAILY DOZEN QUIZZES

NAME _____ SCORE _____

$a = 3 \quad b = 1$

1. $2a + b$ _____
2. $a^2 - b$ _____
3. $3ab$ _____
4. $2a^2 - 4$ _____
5. $5 - 3b^2$ _____
6. $a^2 + a$ _____
7. $4 + 2a^2$ _____
8. $a^3 + b^3$ _____
9. $ab + b^2$ _____
10. $5ab + 7$ _____
11. $-2a - b$ _____
12. $-3a^2 - 4b$ _____

NAME _____ SCORE _____

$a = -3 \quad b = 1$

1. $2a + b$ _____
2. $a^2 + b$ _____
3. $3ab$ _____
4. $2a^2 - 4$ _____
5. $5 - 3b^2$ _____
6. $a^2 + a$ _____
7. $4 + 2a^2$ _____
8. $a^3 + b^3$ _____
9. $ab + b^2$ _____
10. $5ab + 7$ _____
11. $-2a - b$ _____
12. $-3a^2 - 4b$ _____

NAME _____ SCORE _____

$a = -3 \quad b = -1$

1. $2a + b$ _____
2. $a^2 - b$ _____
3. $3ab$ _____
4. $2a^2 - 4$ _____
5. $5 - 3b^2$ _____
6. $a^2 + a$ _____
7. $4 + 2a^2$ _____
8. $a^3 + b^3$ _____
9. $ab + b^2$ _____
10. $5ab + 7$ _____
11. $-2a - b$ _____
12. $-3a^2 - 4b$ _____

NAME _____ SCORE _____

$a = 3 \quad b = -1$

1. $2a + b$ _____
2. $a^2 - b$ _____
3. $3ab$ _____
4. $2a^2 - 4$ _____
5. $5 - 3b^2$ _____
6. $a^2 + a$ _____
7. $4 + 2a^2$ _____
8. $a^3 + b^3$ _____
9. $ab + b^2$ _____
10. $5ab + 7$ _____
11. $-2a - b$ _____
12. $-3a^2 - 4b$ _____

Copyright © 1984 by Allyn and Bacon, Inc. Reproduction of this material is restricted to use with *A Guidebook for Teaching Algebra,* by Terry A. Goodman, John Bernard, Martin P. Cohen, and Joanne E. Meldon.

DAILY DOZEN QUIZZES

NAME _____ SCORE _____
TRUE or FALSE

1. $|-5| = 3$ _____
2. $-(-4) = 4$ _____
3. $2(3x) = (2 \cdot 3)(2 \cdot x)$ _____
4. $8 + 5 = 5 + 8$ _____
5. $-|-7| = 7$ _____
6. $-(5x - 1) = -5x + 1$ _____
7. $2(3 - x) = 6 - x$ _____
8. $-5 > -4$ _____
9. $2x + 5x = 7x^2$ _____
10. $(-1)^{17} = -1$ _____
11. $-\dfrac{2}{-5} = \dfrac{2}{5}$ _____
12. $2 - x = x - 2$ _____

NAME _____ SCORE _____
TRUE or FALSE

1. $|+3| = -3$ _____
2. $-(4 + x) = -4 + x$ _____
3. $2(3a) = (2 \cdot 3)a$ _____
4. $3 - 7 = 7 - 3$ _____
5. $-(-5) = 5$ _____
6. $-|-5| = 5$ _____
7. $2(x - 4) = 2x - 4$ _____
8. $-2 < -3$ _____
9. $x + 2x = 2x$ _____
10. $(-1)^{18} = 1$ _____
11. $\dfrac{-3}{5} = -\dfrac{3}{5}$ _____
12. $x + 4 = 4 + x$ _____

NAME _____ SCORE _____
TRUE or FALSE

1. $2(4a) = (2 \cdot 4)(2 \cdot a)$ _____
2. $a + b = b + a$ _____
3. $2(x - 6) = 2x - 12$ _____
4. $-|-3| = -3$ _____
5. $-(-3) = -3$ _____
6. $-2 > -10$ _____
7. $(-1)^{27} = 1$ _____
8. $x + 4x = 5x^2$ _____
9. $x - 2 = 2 - x$ _____
10. $-(-3x + 4) = 3x + 4$ _____
11. $\dfrac{2x}{2x} = 0$ _____
12. $x \cdot x = 2x$ _____

NAME _____ SCORE _____
TRUE or FALSE

1. $x + x = x^2$ _____
2. $|-7| = 7$ _____
3. $-3 > -4$ _____
4. $2 - x = -(x - 2)$ _____
5. $-(-5) = 5$ _____
6. $2(3 - x) = 6 - 2x$ _____
7. $2(3x) = 6 \cdot 2x$ _____
8. $x \cdot x = 2x$ _____
9. $(-1)^{36} = 1$ _____
10. $-|-6| = -6$ _____
11. $\dfrac{x}{x} = 1$ _____
12. $(-3)(-4) = -12$ _____

Copyright © 1984 by Allyn and Bacon, Inc. Reproduction of this material is restricted to use with *A Guidebook for Teaching Algebra*, by Terry A. Goodman, John Bernard, Martin P. Cohen, and Joanne E. Meldon.

DAILY DOZEN QUIZZES

NAME _____ SCORE _____

1. $a^3 \cdot a^4$ _____
2. $(a^2)^3$ _____
3. $\dfrac{a^4}{a^3}$ _____
4. $(2a)^3$ _____
5. $a^2 \cdot a^2$ _____
6. $a^2 + a^2$ _____
7. $a^2 - a^2$ _____
8. $\dfrac{a^2}{a^2}$ _____
9. $a^{-3} \cdot a^7$ _____
10. $(2a^3)^2$ _____
11. $\dfrac{a^7}{a^4}$ _____
12. $(a^2 b^3)^4$ _____

NAME _____ SCORE _____

1. $x^2 \cdot x^5$ _____
2. $(x^2)^5$ _____
3. $\dfrac{x^5}{x^2}$ _____
4. $(2x)^3$ _____
5. $x^3 \cdot x^3$ _____
6. $x^3 + x^3$ _____
7. $x^3 - x^3$ _____
8. $\dfrac{x^3}{x^3}$ _____
9. $x^5 \cdot x^{-3}$ _____
10. $(2x^2)^3$ _____
11. $\dfrac{x^8}{x}$ _____
12. $(xy^2)^3$ _____

NAME _____ SCORE _____

1. $c^4 \cdot c^5$ _____
2. $(c^4)^5$ _____
3. $x^2 + x^2$ _____
4. $\dfrac{a^3}{a}$ _____
5. $(2b)^3$ _____
6. $x^3 \cdot x^5$ _____
7. $x^5 - x^5$ _____
8. $\left(\dfrac{a}{2}\right)^3$ _____
9. $b^{-3} \cdot b^3$ _____
10. $(a^2 b)^4$ _____
11. $(-2x^2)^3$ _____
12. $a^2 \cdot a^3 \cdot b^4$ _____

NAME _____ SCORE _____

1. $(x^2)^3$ _____
2. $x^4 - x^4$ _____
3. $b^2 \cdot b^3$ _____
4. $\dfrac{x^4}{x^4}$ _____
5. $a^{-2} \cdot a^2$ _____
6. $\left(\dfrac{b}{c^2}\right)^3$ _____
7. $a^2 + a^2$ _____
8. $(ax^3)^2$ _____
9. $\dfrac{x^5}{x^2}$ _____
10. $a^2 \cdot a \cdot b^2$ _____
11. $(-2a)^3$ _____
12. $x^4 \cdot x^4$ _____

Copyright © 1984 by Allyn and Bacon, Inc. Reproduction of this material is restricted to use with *A Guidebook for Teaching Algebra*, by Terry A. Goodman, John Bernard, Martin P. Cohen, and Joanne E. Meldon.

DAILY DOZEN QUIZZES

NAME _____ SCORE _____

1. $a + a$ _____
2. $a - a$ _____
3. $a \cdot a$ _____
4. $\dfrac{a}{a}$ _____
5. $2x + x$ _____
6. $2x - x$ _____
7. $2x \cdot x$ _____
8. $\dfrac{2x}{x}$ _____
9. $8b + 2b$ _____
10. $2a \cdot 3a$ _____
11. $2a - 5a$ _____
12. $\dfrac{3a}{3}$ _____

NAME _____ SCORE _____

1. $x + x$ _____
2. $x - x$ _____
3. $x \cdot x$ _____
4. $\dfrac{x}{x}$ _____
5. $3c + c$ _____
6. $3c - c$ _____
7. $2x \cdot x$ _____
8. $\dfrac{3c}{c}$ _____
9. $2d \cdot 3d$ _____
10. $3b - 7b$ _____
11. $3a + 5a$ _____
12. $\dfrac{8x}{8x}$ _____

NAME _____ SCORE _____

1. $b - b$ _____
2. $\dfrac{b}{b}$ _____
3. $b + b$ _____
4. $b \cdot b$ _____
5. $8a - a$ _____
6. $8a \cdot a$ _____
7. $8a + a$ _____
8. $\dfrac{8a}{a}$ _____
9. $2d + 3d$ _____
10. $5c \cdot 2c$ _____
11. $8x - 6x$ _____
12. $\dfrac{3a}{a}$ _____

NAME _____ SCORE _____

1. $c - c$ _____
2. $c \cdot c$ _____
3. $c + c$ _____
4. $\dfrac{c}{c}$ _____
5. $2x + x$ _____
6. $2x \cdot x$ _____
7. $\dfrac{2x}{x}$ _____
8. $2x - x$ _____
9. $9b \cdot b$ _____
10. $-2b - 10b$ _____
11. $-\dfrac{4x}{2x}$ _____
12. $5a + 2a$ _____

Copyright © 1984 by Allyn and Bacon, Inc. Reproduction of this material is restricted to use with *A Guidebook for Teaching Algebra*, by Terry A. Goodman, John Bernard, Martin P. Cohen, and Joanne E. Meldon.

DAILY DOZEN QUIZZES

NAME _____ SCORE _____

1. $-2a - 4a$ _____
2. $2x \cdot 3$ _____
3. $c + 2c$ _____
4. $-8x + 8x$ _____
5. $\dfrac{x}{x}$ _____
6. $2a - 5a$ _____
7. $(-2a)(-4a)$ _____
8. $3(-4x)$ _____
9. $-6x + 8x$ _____
10. $\dfrac{-6x}{3x}$ _____
11. $2a \cdot a$ _____
12. $x + x$ _____

NAME _____ SCORE _____

1. $3a - 7a$ _____
2. $(-3x)(-6x)$ _____
3. $\dfrac{-8x}{x}$ _____
4. $-2a + 5a$ _____
5. $5 \cdot 2a$ _____
6. $b + b$ _____
7. $-3x - 6x$ _____
8. $2(-5a)$ _____
9. $\dfrac{a}{a}$ _____
10. $-2x + 2x$ _____
11. $b \cdot 3b$ _____
12. $2b + b$ _____

NAME _____ SCORE _____

1. $-5x + 5x$ _____
2. $(-4b)(-8b)$ _____
3. $c + c$ _____
4. $3a(-4)$ _____
5. $x + 3x$ _____
6. $4(-3x)$ _____
7. $\dfrac{-6x}{-6x}$ _____
8. $a - 6a$ _____
9. $-6x + 10x$ _____
10. $\dfrac{c}{c}$ _____
11. $5a \cdot a$ _____
12. $-4b - 8b$ _____

NAME _____ SCORE _____

1. $\dfrac{a}{a}$ _____
2. $a \cdot 5a$ _____
3. $-b - 5b$ _____
4. $-3x + 9x$ _____
5. $\dfrac{-8a}{2a}$ _____
6. $-x + x$ _____
7. $(-4a)(-5)$ _____
8. $c - 4c$ _____
9. $c(-4c)$ _____
10. $2a + a$ _____
11. $(-b)(-5b)$ _____
12. $t + t$ _____

Copyright © 1984 by Allyn and Bacon, Inc. Reproduction of this material is restricted to use with *A Guidebook for Teaching Algebra*, by Terry A. Goodman, John Bernard, Martin P. Cohen, and Joanne E. Meldon.

DAILY DOZEN QUIZZES

NAME _____ SCORE _____

1. $3ab - 8ab$ _____
2. $2a \cdot 3b$ _____
3. $\dfrac{12ab}{4b}$ _____
4. $-2ax - ax$ _____
5. $(-3ax)(-2a)$ _____
6. $-3x^2 + 5x^2$ _____
7. $a^2 + a^2$ _____
8. $3x^2(4x)$ _____
9. $\dfrac{12a^2b}{6ab}$ _____
10. $6x^2 + x^2$ _____
11. $-2ab + 3ab + ab$ _____
12. $3a(-2c)(4b)$ _____

NAME _____ SCORE _____

1. $x^2 + x^2$ _____
2. $ax - 8ax$ _____
3. $5b(2b^2)$ _____
4. $2ab - 12ab$ _____
5. $a^2 + 5a^2$ _____
6. $\dfrac{-6x^2}{3x}$ _____
7. $5a(-4b)$ _____
8. $\dfrac{8ax}{-2x}$ _____
9. $3ab(-2a)$ _____
10. $-6ab + 4ab$ _____
11. $(-2a)(-4c)(-3b)$ _____
12. $-6x^2 - 2x^2 - x^2$ _____

NAME _____ SCORE _____

1. $\dfrac{-6ab}{-3a}$ _____
2. $x^2 + x^2$ _____
3. $-5a^2 + 5a^2$ _____
4. $3xy - 3xy$ _____
5. $4c(-3c^2)$ _____
6. $bc + bc$ _____
7. $\dfrac{3x^2}{3x}$ _____
8. $(-2x)(-8y)$ _____
9. $-2ab - ab$ _____
10. $a^2 + a^2 - 8a^2$ _____
11. $(-4ab)(-2b)$ _____
12. $(-2x)(4x)(-3x)$ _____

NAME _____ SCORE _____

1. $-3xy - xy$ _____
2. $a^2 + a^2 - 2a^2$ _____
3. $(-3b)(2a)$ _____
4. $\dfrac{-12x^2}{3x}$ _____
5. $2x^2 + 3x^2$ _____
6. $-5a(-2a^2)$ _____
7. $2bc - 8bc$ _____
8. $-3a^2 + a^2$ _____
9. $(-3b)(-2a)(-5b)$ _____
10. $x^3 + x^3$ _____
11. $(3ax)(-4x^2)$ _____
12. $\dfrac{-8ac}{-8c}$ _____

Copyright © 1984 by Allyn and Bacon, Inc. Reproduction of this material is restricted to use with *A Guidebook for Teaching Algebra*, by Terry A. Goodman, John Bernard, Martin P. Cohen, and Joanne E. Meldon.

DAILY DOZEN QUIZZES

NAME _____ SCORE _____

SIMPLIFY

1. $3a - 5 - 6a$ _____
2. $2 - 3a + 7a$ _____
3. $-2x + 5 + x$ _____
4. $x^2 + 6x + 3x^2$ _____
5. $2a - b - 6a$ _____
6. $3a + 2ab - 3a$ _____
7. $x^2 - 2x - 5x$ _____
8. $ab + ab + a$ _____
9. $3 - 2a - 8$ _____
10. $3x - 4x^2 - 2x^2$ _____
11. $-2 - 7 + 3a$ _____
12. $7b + 2a - 5a$ _____

NAME _____ SCORE _____

SIMPLIFY

1. $2a - 5 - 7a$ _____
2. $3 - 2x + 7x$ _____
3. $-6x + 5 + x$ _____
4. $a^2 + 6a + 4a^2$ _____
5. $13a - b - 6a$ _____
6. $3a + 2ax - 3a$ _____
7. $x^2 - 2x - 6x$ _____
8. $ac + ac + a$ _____
9. $8 - 3a - 2$ _____
10. $2x + 4x^2 - 2x^2$ _____
11. $-3 - 5 + 3a$ _____
12. $3b + 2a - a$ _____

NAME _____ SCORE _____

SIMPLIFY

1. $4a - 2b - 6b$ _____
2. $2 - 8 + a$ _____
3. $3x - x^2 - x^2$ _____
4. $-5 + 2a - 8$ _____
5. $xy + xy + x$ _____
6. $x^2 - 3x + x^2$ _____
7. $3b - 2ab - 3b$ _____
8. $-2a - b - 6a$ _____
9. $2x^2 + 5x - 8x^2$ _____
10. $-3x - 2 + x$ _____
11. $ab - ac - 3ab$ _____
12. $2a - 3a - 5a$ _____

NAME _____ SCORE _____

SIMPLIFY

1. $7 + a - 9$ _____
2. $2 + 3 - 5a$ _____
3. $3a + 2b - 8a$ _____
4. $3y - 12y + x$ _____
5. $2 - 3a + 5a$ _____
6. $x^2 + 3x - x^2$ _____
7. $2a + 7a^2 - 3a^2$ _____
8. $3x - 9 - x$ _____
9. $3ab + ab + ac$ _____
10. $-2 - 6x - 8$ _____
11. $3x^2 - 2x + x^2$ _____
12. $3ab + 4ba + 5$ _____

Copyright © 1984 by Allyn and Bacon, Inc. Reproduction of this material is restricted to use with *A Guidebook for Teaching Algebra,* by Terry A. Goodman, John Bernard, Martin P. Cohen, and Joanne E. Meldon.

DAILY DOZEN QUIZZES

NAME _____ SCORE _____

1. $x + 2 = 6$ _____
2. $x - 2 = 6$ _____
3. $2x = 6$ _____
4. $\frac{x}{2} = 6$ _____
5. $3 + x = 9$ _____
6. $3 - x = 9$ _____
7. $3x = 9$ _____
8. $\frac{x}{3} = 9$ _____
9. $x + 4 = -8$ _____
10. $x - 4 = -8$ _____
11. $4x = -8$ _____
12. $\frac{x}{4} = -8$ _____

NAME _____ SCORE _____

1. $x + 4 = 6$ _____
2. $x - 4 = 6$ _____
3. $4x = 6$ _____
4. $\frac{x}{4} = 6$ _____
5. $2 + x = 14$ _____
6. $2 - x = 14$ _____
7. $2x = 14$ _____
8. $\frac{x}{2} = 14$ _____
9. $x + 3 = -3$ _____
10. $x - 3 = -3$ _____
11. $3x = -3$ _____
12. $\frac{x}{3} = -3$ _____

NAME _____ SCORE _____

1. $x + (-2) = 6$ _____
2. $x - (-2) = 6$ _____
3. $-2x = 6$ _____
4. $\frac{x}{-2} = 6$ _____
5. $-4 + x = 10$ _____
6. $-4 - x = 10$ _____
7. $-4x = 10$ _____
8. $\frac{x}{-4} = 10$ _____
9. $x + (-3) = -12$ _____
10. $x - (-3) = -12$ _____
11. $-3x = -12$ _____
12. $\frac{x}{-3} = -12$ _____

NAME _____ SCORE _____

1. $x + (-5) = 2$ _____
2. $x - (-5) = 2$ _____
3. $-5x = 2$ _____
4. $\frac{x}{-5} = 2$ _____
5. $-6 + x = -4$ _____
6. $-6 - x = -4$ _____
7. $-6x = -4$ _____
8. $\frac{x}{-6} = -4$ _____
9. $x + (-4) = -2$ _____
10. $x - (-4) = -2$ _____
11. $-4x = -2$ _____
12. $\frac{x}{-4} = -2$ _____

Copyright © 1984 by Allyn and Bacon, Inc. Reproduction of this material is restricted to use with *A Guidebook for Teaching Algebra*, by Terry A. Goodman, John Bernard, Martin P. Cohen, and Joanne E. Meldon.

DAILY DOZEN QUIZZES

NAME _____ SCORE _____

1. $x + 3 = 1$
2. $2x = 6$
3. $x - 8 = 4$
4. $\frac{x}{2} = 6$
5. $-4x = -6$
6. $x - 8 = -2$
7. $5 + x = 6$
8. $\frac{x}{2} = 2$
9. $x + 6 = -5$
10. $-4x = -12$
11. $3 - x = -9$
12. $x - 6 = -8$

NAME _____ SCORE _____

1. $x + 7 = 2$
2. $3x = 12$
3. $x - 2 = 5$
4. $\frac{x}{3} = 6$
5. $-3 + x = -5$
6. $-3x = -3$
7. $x - 2 = -8$
8. $\frac{x}{2} = 0$
9. $x + 6 = -2$
10. $5 - x = -5$
11. $-8x = -2$
12. $x - 8 = -2$

NAME _____ SCORE _____

1. $x + 7 = -2$
2. $x - 5 = -8$
3. $\frac{x}{2} = 1$
4. $2x = 2$
5. $3 + x = -4$
6. $-3x = -4$
7. $-2 + x = -6$
8. $\frac{x}{-3} = 2$
9. $x - (-4) = 6$
10. $-6x = 0$
11. $4 - x = -9$
12. $\frac{x}{2} = 2$

NAME _____ SCORE _____

1. $3 + x = -4$
2. $x - 6 = -9$
3. $\frac{x}{-2} = -3$
4. $4x = 0$
5. $2 + x = -5$
6. $-2x = -6$
7. $-8 + x = -8$
8. $\frac{x}{-3} = -6$
9. $x - (-5) = -2$
10. $-x = 3$
11. $-3 - x = -7$
12. $\frac{x}{-2} = 2$

Copyright © 1984 by Allyn and Bacon, Inc. Reproduction of this material is restricted to use with *A Guidebook for Teaching Algebra*, by Terry A. Goodman, John Bernard, Martin P. Cohen, and Joanne E. Meldon.

DAILY DOZEN QUIZZES

NAME _____ SCORE _____

1. $-x = -2$
2. $4 - x = -2$
3. $x + 3 = 0$
4. $-5 + x = -3$
5. $-4x = 2$
6. $x - 7 = 3$
7. $\frac{x}{2} = 6$
8. $x + \frac{1}{2} = 3$
9. $\frac{1}{3}x = 2$
10. $x - \frac{3}{4} = \frac{2}{3}$
11. $\frac{3}{2} - x = -\frac{1}{2}$
12. $x - \frac{1}{2} = -\frac{2}{3}$

NAME _____ SCORE _____

1. $-x = 6$
2. $x - 4 = -2$
3. $\frac{x}{3} = -9$
4. $-6 + x = -8$
5. $x + \frac{1}{3} = 2$
6. $\frac{2}{3}x = 6$
7. $8 - x = -2$
8. $x + \frac{2}{5} = \frac{7}{10}$
9. $x - 3 = 0$
10. $\frac{2}{3} - x = \frac{1}{3}$
11. $-5x = 2$
12. $-2x = \frac{1}{2}$

NAME _____ SCORE _____

1. $5 - x = -2$
2. $-3x = 12$
3. $\frac{x}{-4} = -2$
4. $x + 7 = 0$
5. $x - \frac{1}{2} = \frac{3}{4}$
6. $x - (-4) = -6$
7. $-x = -6$
8. $x + \frac{3}{4} = \frac{1}{8}$
9. $\frac{1}{4}x = \frac{1}{2}$
10. $-10 + x = -2$
11. $\frac{3}{4} - x = -\frac{1}{4}$
12. $\frac{x}{\frac{2}{3}} = 6$

NAME _____ SCORE _____

1. $-12 + x = -2$
2. $\frac{1}{3}x = 12$
3. $-x = 0$
4. $x - 5 = -7$
5. $\frac{2}{3}x = 0$
6. $\frac{x}{-2} = -\frac{1}{4}$
7. $6 - x = -9$
8. $x + \frac{2}{3} = 4$
9. $-6x = 4$
10. $x - \frac{1}{2} = 2\frac{1}{3}$
11. $\frac{x}{3} = 1$
12. $x - 8 = 0$

Copyright © 1984 by Allyn and Bacon, Inc. Reproduction of this material is restricted to use with *A Guidebook for Teaching Algebra*, by Terry A. Goodman, John Bernard, Martin P. Cohen, and Joanne E. Meldon.

DAILY DOZEN QUIZZES

NAME _____ SCORE _____

1. $2x + 5 = 3$ _____
2. $3x - 4 = 2$ _____
3. $6 + 2x = 8$ _____
4. $10 - 3x = -2$ _____
5. $3x + 2x = 10$ _____
6. $5x - x = -8$ _____
7. $3 = 3x + 5$ _____
8. $5 = 4x + x$ _____
9. $3x + 4 = -8$ _____
10. $-3 = 2x + x$ _____
11. $4x - 1 = 1$ _____
12. $6 - 2x = 7$ _____

NAME _____ SCORE _____

1. $4x + 7 = 3$ _____
2. $5x - 6 = 4$ _____
3. $5 + 3x = -7$ _____
4. $7 - 2x = 1$ _____
5. $2x + 4x = 12$ _____
6. $2x - 6x = -16$ _____
7. $8 = 2x - 10$ _____
8. $12 = 3x - x$ _____
9. $4 = 3x - 2$ _____
10. $-7 = x - 4x$ _____
11. $8x - 2x = 0$ _____
12. $-8 = 3x - 9$ _____

NAME _____ SCORE _____

1. $5x + 2 = 12$ _____
2. $3x - 5 = -11$ _____
3. $4 + 3x = 1$ _____
4. $8 - 6x = -4$ _____
5. $5x + x = 18$ _____
6. $x - 3x = -4$ _____
7. $-6 = 3x - 3$ _____
8. $-16 = 2x + 6x$ _____
9. $5x + x = 12$ _____
10. $3x + 4 = -9$ _____
11. $4 - 5x = -6$ _____
12. $-6 = 2 - 3x$ _____

NAME _____ SCORE _____

1. $3x + 5 = 11$ _____
2. $4x - 3 = -7$ _____
3. $8 + 2x = 0$ _____
4. $6 - 4x = 2$ _____
5. $x + 3x = -12$ _____
6. $5x - x = 0$ _____
7. $-8 = 2x + 4$ _____
8. $-10 = 3x - x$ _____
9. $2x + 7 = 1$ _____
10. $4 - 5x = -3$ _____
11. $12x + 5 = 7$ _____
12. $-9 = 4x - 6x$ _____

Copyright © 1984 by Allyn and Bacon, Inc. Reproduction of this material is restricted to use with *A Guidebook for Teaching Algebra*, by Terry A. Goodman, John Bernard, Martin P. Cohen, and Joanne E. Meldon.

DAILY DOZEN QUIZZES

NAME _____ SCORE _____

1. $2x + 3 = 4x$ _____
2. $5x = 2x + 9$ _____
3. $2x + 3 = 4$ _____
4. $4x + 5x = 9$ _____
5. $2x + 5 = x - 4$ _____
6. $4 + 3x = 3x - 6$ _____
7. $\frac{x}{2} + 4 = 6$ _____
8. $3 - 2x = 8 - x$ _____
9. $3x - 5x = -7$ _____
10. $7x - 8 = 5x - 8$ _____
11. $4x + 5 = 6x + 5$ _____
12. $9 - 2x = 3 - 3x$ _____

NAME _____ SCORE _____

1. $5x + 2 = 8x$ _____
2. $4x = 3x - 7$ _____
3. $5x + 2 = 8$ _____
4. $2x - 8x = -12$ _____
5. $3x - 7 = 2x - 8$ _____
6. $5 - 2x = 8 - 3x$ _____
7. $\frac{x}{3} - 2 = 7$ _____
8. $7x + 12 = 6x - 4$ _____
9. $2x - 8x = -12$ _____
10. $4 + 3x = 8x + 4$ _____
11. $7 - 2x = 7 - 8x$ _____
12. $2x - 4 = 3x - 5$ _____

NAME _____ SCORE _____

1. $3x - 4 = -6$ _____
2. $4 + 2x = 6 + x$ _____
3. $\frac{x}{5} + 3 = -2$ _____
4. $2x + 8 = 3x - 4$ _____
5. $3x - 4 = 6x$ _____
6. $3x - 5 = 8x - 5$ _____
7. $7 - 5x = 6x$ _____
8. $3x + 2 = 2 - 7x$ _____
9. $3x = 2x - 8$ _____
10. $9x = 2 - 3x$ _____
11. $-2x - 5x = -14$ _____
12. $6x - 8x = 0$ _____

NAME _____ SCORE _____

1. $2x - 5x = -6$ _____
2. $6x = 9x - 12$ _____
3. $3x - 5 = 8 + 2x$ _____
4. $2x + 7 = 3x - 12$ _____
5. $5x - 9 = -4x - 9$ _____
6. $2x - 4 = 6$ _____
7. $3 + \frac{x}{4} = -8$ _____
8. $2x + 12 = 12 - 6x$ _____
9. $6x + 5 = 4x$ _____
10. $3x = 4x - 2$ _____
11. $2 + 3x = 2x - 12$ _____
12. $-6x - x = 7$ _____

Copyright © 1984 by Allyn and Bacon, Inc. Reproduction of this material is restricted to use with *A Guidebook for Teaching Algebra*, by Terry A. Goodman, John Bernard, Martin P. Cohen, and Joanne E. Meldon.

DAILY DOZEN QUIZZES

NAME _____ SCORE _____

TRANSLATE

1. 2 less than x _____
2. $\frac{1}{2}$ of x _____
3. x increased by 5 _____
4. 6 more than x _____
5. The sum of x and 3 _____
6. The product of x and 2 _____
7. Twice x _____
8. x decreased by 5 _____
9. The ratio of x to 4 _____
10. 6 divided by x _____
11. 9 subtracted from x _____
12. The square of x _____

NAME _____ SCORE _____

TRANSLATE

1. 3 less than x _____
2. $\frac{1}{5}$ of x _____
3. x increased by 6 _____
4. 5 more than x _____
5. The sum of x and 4 _____
6. The product of x and 3 _____
7. Double x _____
8. x decreased by 6 _____
9. The ratio of x to 5 _____
10. x divided by 2 _____
11. 6 subtracted from x _____
12. The square of x _____

NAME _____ SCORE _____

TRANSLATE

1. x increased by 7 _____
2. 2 more than x _____
3. Twice x _____
4. 5 less than x _____
5. x decreased by 4 _____
6. The product of x and 5 _____
7. 3 subtracted from x _____
8. $\frac{2}{3}$ of x _____
9. x divided by 3 _____
10. The sum of x and 7 _____
11. The square of x _____
12. The ratio of x to 9 _____

NAME _____ SCORE _____

TRANSLATE

1. The sum of x and 5 _____
2. $\frac{1}{3}$ of x _____
3. x divided by 8 _____
4. The ratio of 3 to x _____
5. x increased by 2 _____
6. 4 subtracted from x _____
7. 3 more than x _____
8. The double of x _____
9. The square of x _____
10. 8 less than x _____
11. The product of x and 6 _____
12. x decreased by 2 _____

Copyright © 1984 by Allyn and Bacon, Inc. Reproduction of this material is restricted to use with *A Guidebook for Teaching Algebra*, by Terry A. Goodman, John Bernard, Martin P. Cohen, and Joanne E. Meldon.

DAILY DOZEN QUIZZES

NAME _____ SCORE _____
GRAPH THE SOLUTION SET

1. $x + 2 > 3$ ←——————→ 1
2. $x - 4 < 5$ ←——————→
3. $x + 5 \geqslant 7$ ←——————→
4. $3 - x < 4$ ←——————→
5. $2x \geqslant -6$ ←——————→
6. $-3x \geqslant -6$ ←——————→
7. $\frac{x}{2} < 4$ ←——————→
8. $x - 5 \geqslant -8$ ←——————→
9. $\frac{x}{-3} > 2$ ←——————→
10. $4 + x \geqslant -3$ ←——————→
11. $-3x \geqslant 0$ ←——————→
12. $2 - x < -3$ ←——————→

NAME _____ SCORE _____
GRAPH THE SOLUTION SET

1. $x + 3 < 4$ ←——————→ 1
2. $x - 5 > 2$ ←——————→
3. $-3x \leqslant 6$ ←——————→
4. $2 + x < 4$ ←——————→
5. $\frac{x}{2} \geqslant -3$ ←——————→
6. $x + 3 < -2$ ←——————→
7. $2 - x \leqslant 5$ ←——————→
8. $3x > 3$ ←——————→
9. $x - 5 > -2$ ←——————→
10. $\frac{x}{-3} \geqslant -1$ ←——————→
11. $5 - x > 0$ ←——————→
12. $x - 3 \geqslant -3$ ←——————→

NAME _____ SCORE _____
GRAPH THE SOLUTION SET

1. $\frac{x}{2} \geqslant 4$ ←——————→
2. $x + 2 < 4$ ←——————→
3. $-3x < 6$ ←——————→
4. $x - 5 > -2$ ←——————→
5. $\frac{x}{-3} > -1$ ←——————→
6. $3 + x \leqslant 0$ ←——————→
7. $2 < 2x$ ←——————→
8. $3 > x + 1$ ←——————→
9. $-5 \leqslant 2 - x$ ←——————→
10. $-3 > \frac{x}{2}$ ←——————→
11. $6 < -3x$ ←——————→
12. $x + 2 \geqslant 2$ ←——————→

NAME _____ SCORE _____
GRAPH THE SOLUTION SET

1. $2 > x + 3$ ←——————→
2. $x - 4 > 6$ ←——————→
3. $-3x \geqslant 0$ ←——————→
4. $-7 < x - 2$ ←——————→
5. $x + 5 > 2$ ←——————→
6. $\frac{x}{4} > -1$ ←——————→
7. $3 < 2x$ ←——————→
8. $-2x \leqslant 5$ ←——————→
9. $6 > -2x$ ←——————→
10. $3 \leqslant x + 4$ ←——————→
11. $x - 5 < -2$ ←——————→
12. $-2 \leqslant 2 - x$ ←——————→

Copyright © 1984 by Allyn and Bacon, Inc. Reproduction of this material is restricted to use with *A Guidebook for Teaching Algebra*, by Terry A. Goodman, John Bernard, Martin P. Cohen, and Joanne E. Meldon.

DAILY DOZEN QUIZZES

NAME _____ SCORE _____

IDENTIFY THE SLOPE

1. $y = 2x - 5$ _____
2. $y = x + 3$ _____
3. $y = 4 - 3x$ _____
4. $2x + 5 = y$ _____
5. $y = \frac{x}{2} + 4$ _____
6. $y = 3$ _____
7. $3 - 4x = y$ _____
8. $y = 4x$ _____
9. $2x + y = 6$ _____
10. $4x - 2y = 12$ _____
11. $x - 3y = 6$ _____
12. $x - 3 = y$ _____

NAME _____ SCORE _____

IDENTIFY THE SLOPE

1. $y = 3x - 4$ _____
2. $y = x - 2$ _____
3. $y = 5 + 2x$ _____
4. $3x - 4 = y$ _____
5. $y = \frac{x}{3} + 5$ _____
6. $y = -2$ _____
7. $2 - 4x = y$ _____
8. $y = -3x$ _____
9. $x + 2y = 6$ _____
10. $6x - 3y = 3$ _____
11. $x - 2y = -6$ _____
12. $x - 2 = y$ _____

NAME _____ SCORE _____

IDENTIFY THE SLOPE

1. $x + 2y = 4$ _____
2. $x + 2 = y$ _____
3. $y = 3x + 5$ _____
4. $y = 4 - x$ _____
5. $3x + y = -3$ _____
6. $y = 6$ _____
7. $y = \frac{x}{2} + 7$ _____
8. $x - 3 = y$ _____
9. $y = -2x$ _____
10. $y = -2$ _____
11. $2x - 8y = 12$ _____
12. $x = y - 4$ _____

NAME _____ SCORE _____

IDENTIFY THE SLOPE

1. $y = -2$ _____
2. $x + y = 6$ _____
3. $y = 3x - 4$ _____
4. $y = 2 + 3x$ _____
5. $2x - y = 4$ _____
6. $y = x$ _____
7. $6x + 2y = 2$ _____
8. $y = 3 - 2x$ _____
9. $y = 0$ _____
10. $2x - 3y = 6$ _____
11. $x = y - 3$ _____
12. $2x = y + 8$ _____

Copyright © 1984 by Allyn and Bacon, Inc. Reproduction of this material is restricted to use with *A Guidebook for Teaching Algebra*, by Terry A. Goodman, John Bernard, Martin P. Cohen, and Joanne E. Meldon.

DAILY DOZEN QUIZZES

NAME _____ SCORE _____
IDENTIFY THE *y*-INTERCEPT AND SLOPE

1. $y = 2x - 5$
2. $y = x + 3$
3. $y = 4 - 3x$
4. $2x + 5 = y$
5. $y = \frac{x}{2} + 4$
6. $y = 3$
7. $3 - 4x = y$
8. $y = 4x$
9. $2x + y = 6$
10. $4x - 2y = 12$
11. $x - 3y = 6$
12. $x - 3 = y$

NAME _____ SCORE _____
IDENTIFY THE *y*-INTERCEPT AND SLOPE

1. $y = 3x - 4$
2. $y = x - 2$
3. $y = 5 + 2x$
4. $3x - 4 = y$
5. $y = \frac{x}{3} + 5$
6. $y = -2$
7. $2 - 4x = y$
8. $y = -3x$
9. $x + 2y = 6$
10. $6x - 3y = 3$
11. $x - 2y = -6$
12. $x - 2 = y$

NAME _____ SCORE _____
IDENTIFY THE *y*-INTERCEPT AND SLOPE

1. $x + 2y = 4$
2. $x + 2 = y$
3. $y = 3x + 5$
4. $y = 4 - x$
5. $3x + y = -3$
6. $y = 6$
7. $y = \frac{x}{2} + 7$
8. $x - 3 = y$
9. $y = -2x$
10. $y = -2$
11. $2x - 8y = 12$
12. $x = y - 4$

NAME _____ SCORE _____
IDENTIFY THE *y*-INTERCEPT AND SLOPE

1. $y = -2$
2. $x + y = 6$
3. $y = 3x - 4$
4. $y = 2 + 3x$
5. $2x - y = 4$
6. $y = x$
7. $6x + 2y = 2$
8. $y = 3 - 2x$
9. $y = 0$
10. $2x - 3y = 6$
11. $x = y - 3$
12. $2x = y + 8$

Copyright © 1984 by Allyn and Bacon, Inc. Reproduction of this material is restricted to use with *A Guidebook for Teaching Algebra*, by Terry A. Goodman, John Bernard, Martin P. Cohen, and Joanne E. Meldon.

DAILY DOZEN QUIZZES

NAME _____ SCORE _____
IDENTIFY THE x-INTERCEPT AND y-INTERCEPT

1. $y = 2x - 5$
2. $y = x + 3$
3. $y = 4 - 3x$
4. $2x + 5 = y$
5. $y = \frac{x}{2} + 4$
6. $y = 3$
7. $3 - 4x = y$
8. $y = 4x$
9. $2x + y = 6$
10. $4x - 2y = 12$
11. $x - 3y = 6$
12. $x - 3 = y$

NAME _____ SCORE _____
IDENTIFY THE x-INTERCEPT AND y-INTERCEPT

1. $y = 3x - 4$
2. $y = x - 2$
3. $y = 5 + 2x$
4. $3x - 4 = y$
5. $y = \frac{x}{3} + 5$
6. $y = -2$
7. $2 - 4x = y$
8. $y = -3x$
9. $x + 2y = 6$
10. $6x - 3y = 3$
11. $x - 2y = -6$
12. $x - 2 = y$

NAME _____ SCORE _____
IDENTIFY THE x-INTERCEPT AND y-INTERCEPT

1. $x + 2y = 4$
2. $x + 2 = y$
3. $y = 3x + 5$
4. $y = 4 - x$
5. $3x + y = -3$
6. $y = 6$
7. $y = \frac{x}{2} + 7$
8. $x - 3 = y$
9. $y = -2x$
10. $y = -2$
11. $2x - 8y = 12$
12. $x = y - 4$

NAME _____ SCORE _____
IDENTIFY THE x-INTERCEPT AND y-INTERCEPT

1. $y = -2$
2. $x + y = 6$
3. $y = 3x - 4$
4. $y = 2 + 3x$
5. $2x - y = 4$
6. $y = x$
7. $6x + 2y = 2$
8. $y = 3 - 2x$
9. $y = 0$
10. $2x - 3y = 6$
11. $x = y - 3$
12. $2x = y + 8$

Copyright © 1984 by Allyn and Bacon, Inc. Reproduction of this material is restricted to use with *A Guidebook for Teaching Algebra*, by Terry A. Goodman, John Bernard, Martin P. Cohen, and Joanne E. Meldon.

DAILY DOZEN QUIZZES

NAME _____ SCORE _____

SIMPLIFY

1. $(a + 3b) + (2a - 5b)$ _____
2. $(a + 3b) - (2a - 5b)$ _____
3. $(x + 2)(a - 4)$ _____
4. $\dfrac{2x + 6}{2}$ _____
5. $(2x - 5y) + (x - 2y)$ _____
6. $(2x - 5y) - (x - 2y)$ _____
7. $(2x - 5y)(x - 2y)$ _____
8. $\dfrac{2x - 5}{2}$ _____
9. $(a^2 - 3) + (a^2 + 3)$ _____
10. $(a^2 - 3) - (a^2 + 3)$ _____
11. $(a^2 - 3)(a^2 + 3)$ _____
12. $\dfrac{2a^2 + 6a}{2a}$ _____

NAME _____ SCORE _____

SIMPLIFY

1. $(3a - 4) + (7 - 2a)$ _____
2. $(3a - 4) - (7 - 2a)$ _____
3. $(x - 3)(x + 3)$ _____
4. $\dfrac{x - 3}{x - 3}$ _____
5. $(x - 5) + (x + 2)$ _____
6. $(x - 5) - (x + 2)$ _____
7. $(x - 5)(x + 2)$ _____
8. $\dfrac{x - 5}{5 - x}$ _____
9. $(2a + 3) + (a - 5)$ _____
10. $(2a + 3) - (a - 5)$ _____
11. $(2a + 3)(a - 5)$ _____
12. $\dfrac{2a - 6}{2}$ _____

NAME _____ SCORE _____

SIMPLIFY

1. $(a + 3) + (2 + a)$ _____
2. $(a + 3) - (2 + a)$ _____
3. $(a + 3)(2 + a)$ _____
4. $\dfrac{a + 3}{3 + a}$ _____
5. $(2a - b) + (b - 5a)$ _____
6. $(2a - b) - (b - 5a)$ _____
7. $\dfrac{2a - b}{b - 2a}$ _____
8. $(2x + 3)^2$ _____
9. $(2 - 5a) - (7 - 6a)$ _____
10. $(x - 2a)(x - 3a)$ _____
11. $\dfrac{2x + 6}{6}$ _____
12. $\dfrac{x + 4}{x + 4}$ _____

NAME _____ SCORE _____

SIMPLIFY

1. $(3x - 2) + (x - 4)$ _____
2. $(3x - 2) - (x - 4)$ _____
3. $(3x - 2)(x - 4)$ _____
4. $(3x - 2)^2$ _____
5. $\dfrac{3x - 2}{3x - 2}$ _____
6. $(8x^2 - 2x) - (x^2 - 2x)$ _____
7. $\dfrac{3x - 2}{2 - 3x}$ _____
8. $(x - 3)(x + 3)$ _____
9. $\dfrac{3x - 2}{3}$ _____
10. $(2a^2 - 3a) + (a^2 - a)$ _____
11. $\dfrac{2x - 3}{x}$ _____
12. $\dfrac{3x + 2}{x + 3x}$ _____

Copyright © 1984 by Allyn and Bacon, Inc. Reproduction of this material is restricted to use with *A Guidebook for Teaching Algebra*, by Terry A. Goodman, John Bernard, Martin P. Cohen, and Joanne E. Meldon.

DAILY DOZEN QUIZZES

NAME _____ SCORE _____
FACTOR
1. $x^2 - 4$ _____
2. $x^2 - 4x$ _____
3. $x^2 - 4x - 5$ _____
4. $x^2 - 4x + 4$ _____
5. $x^2 - 5x + 4$ _____
6. $x^2 - 6x + 5$ _____
7. $x^2 - 4a^2$ _____
8. $x^2 - 4ax + 4a^2$ _____
9. $4 - x^2$ _____
10. $4 - 4x + x^2$ _____
11. $4 + 4x + x^2$ _____
12. $4 - 3x - x^2$ _____

NAME _____ SCORE _____
FACTOR
1. $x^2 - 9x$ _____
2. $x^2 - 9$ _____
3. $x^2 - 5x + 6$ _____
4. $x^2 - 7x + 6$ _____
5. $x^2 + 5x - 6$ _____
6. $x^2 - 5x - 6$ _____
7. $x^2 + 7x + 6$ _____
8. $x^2 + 5xy - 14y^2$ _____
9. $14 + 9x + x^2$ _____
10. $14 - 9x + x^2$ _____
11. $-9x + x^2$ _____
12. $9 - x^2$ _____

NAME _____ SCORE _____
FACTOR
1. $x^2 - 1$ _____
2. $x^2 - x$ _____
3. $x^2 - x - 6$ _____
4. $x^2 - 5x + 6$ _____
5. $1 - x^2$ _____
6. $x^2 + 5xy + 6y^2$ _____
7. $x - x^2$ _____
8. $2x - 6$ _____
9. $2x^2 - 6x$ _____
10. $2x^2 - 7x + 3$ _____
11. $x^2 - 6x + 9$ _____
12. $x^2 - 6x$ _____

NAME _____ SCORE _____
FACTOR
1. $2x^2 - 2x$ _____
2. $x^2 - 25$ _____
3. $3 - 3a$ _____
4. $a^2 - a - 12$ _____
5. $a^2 + 6a + 9$ _____
6. $9 - x^2$ _____
7. $a^2 + 2ab + b^2$ _____
8. $3x^2 - 6x$ _____
9. $3x^2 - x - 2$ _____
10. $3x^2 - x$ _____
11. $6 + 5a + a^2$ _____
12. $x^2 + x - 6$ _____

Copyright © 1984 by Allyn and Bacon, Inc. Reproduction of this material is restricted to use with *A Guidebook for Teaching Algebra*, by Terry A. Goodman, John Bernard, Martin P. Cohen, and Joanne E. Meldon.

DAILY DOZEN QUIZZES

NAME _____ SCORE _____
SOLVE FOR x

1. $x - 2 = 0$ _____
2. $x + 3 = 0$ _____
3. $2 - a = 0$ _____
4. $x - 1 = 0$ _____
5. $5 + b = 0$ _____
6. $2a - 1 = 0$ _____
7. $3x + 2 = 0$ _____
8. $2 - a = 0$ _____
9. $3b - 1 = 0$ _____
10. $2 - 5x = 0$ _____
11. $2a + 3 = 0$ _____
12. $1 - 4x = 0$ _____

NAME _____ SCORE _____
SOLVE FOR x

1. $x + 5 = x$ _____
2. $x - 3 = 0$ _____
3. $4 + x = 0$ _____
4. $5 - x = 0$ _____
5. $2x + 1 = 0$ _____
6. $x - 2 = 0$ _____
7. $3x - 2 = 0$ _____
8. $2 + 3x = 0$ _____
9. $x + 1 = 0$ _____
10. $4 - 2x = 0$ _____
11. $2a + 3 = 0$ _____
12. $4 - x = 0$ _____

NAME _____ SCORE _____
SOLVE FOR x

1. $x - 7 = 0$ _____
2. $2 + x = 0$ _____
3. $x + 5 = 0$ _____
4. $3x - 1 = 0$ _____
5. $2 + 3x = 0$ _____
6. $6 - 2x = 0$ _____
7. $4x + 4 = 0$ _____
8. $x - 2 = 0$ _____
9. $2x + 5 = 0$ _____
10. $5 - x = 0$ _____
11. $3x + 1 = 0$ _____
12. $6 - 2x = 0$ _____

NAME _____ SCORE _____
SOLVE FOR x

1. $5 + x = 0$ _____
2. $x - 3 = 0$ _____
3. $x + 2 = 0$ _____
4. $2x - 1 = 0$ _____
5. $4 - x = 0$ _____
6. $7x + 2 = 0$ _____
7. $2x - 3 = 0$ _____
8. $6 - 2x = 0$ _____
9. $8 + x = 0$ _____
10. $x - \frac{1}{2} = 0$ _____
11. $2x + 1 = 0$ _____
12. $4x - 5 = 0$ _____

Copyright © 1984 by Allyn and Bacon, Inc. Reproduction of this material is restricted to use with *A Guidebook for Teaching Algebra,* by Terry A. Goodman, John Bernard, Martin P. Cohen, and Joanne E. Meldon.

DAILY DOZEN QUIZZES

NAME _____ SCORE _____
FACTOR

1. $x^2 + 3x = 0$ _____
2. $x^2 - 4x = 0$ _____
3. $x^2 - 4 = 0$ _____
4. $x^2 - 6x + 9 = 0$ _____
5. $x^2 + 8x - 9 = 0$ _____
6. $x^2 + 2x - 9 = 0$ _____
7. $x^2 - 11x + 24 = 0$ _____
8. $x^2 - x - 72 = 0$ _____
9. $x^2 + 6x - 7 = 0$ _____
10. $6x - 2x^2 = 0$ _____
11. $9 - 10x + x^2 = 0$ _____
12. $3x^2 + 8x - 3 = 0$ _____

NAME _____ SCORE _____
FACTOR

1. $x^2 - 5x = 0$ _____
2. $x^2 + 4x = 0$ _____
3. $x^2 + 4x - 5 = 0$ _____
4. $x^2 - 25 = 0$ _____
5. $2x^2 - 8x = 0$ _____
6. $x^2 - x - 6 = 0$ _____
7. $x^2 + 3x - 10 = 0$ _____
8. $x^2 + 3x = 0$ _____
9. $x^2 - 10x + 25 = 0$ _____
10. $x^2 + 2x + 1 = 0$ _____
11. $15 - 8x + x^2 = 0$ _____
12. $16 - x^2 = 0$ _____

NAME _____ SCORE _____
FACTOR

1. $x^2 + 2x - 15 = 0$ _____
2. $x^2 + 2x = 0$ _____
3. $x^2 - 16 = 0$ _____
4. $x^2 - 8x + 16 = 0$ _____
5. $x^2 - 8x - 20 = 0$ _____
6. $2x^2 + 5x + 3 = 0$ _____
7. $2x^2 - 6x = 0$ _____
8. $5 - 4x - x^2 = 0$ _____
9. $x^2 - 8x + 12 = 0$ _____
10. $10 + 3x - x^2 = 0$ _____
11. $3x - x^2 = 0$ _____
12. $x^2 + x = 0$ _____

NAME _____ SCORE _____
FACTOR

1. $x^2 + 6x + 9 = 0$ _____
2. $x^2 + 6x = 0$ _____
3. $x^2 - 9 = 0$ _____
4. $x^2 - x - 6 = 0$ _____
5. $2x^2 - 9x + 7 = 0$ _____
6. $x^2 - 4x + 4 = 0$ _____
7. $81 - x^2 = 0$ _____
8. $81x - x^2 = 0$ _____
9. $81x - 3x^2 = 0$ _____
10. $6x^2 - 7x - 5 = 0$ _____
11. $4 - 36x^2 = 0$ _____
12. $4x^2 + x - 3 = 0$ _____

Copyright © 1984 by Allyn and Bacon, Inc. Reproduction of this material is restricted to use with *A Guidebook for Teaching Algebra*, by Terry A. Goodman, John Bernard, Martin P. Cohen, and Joanne E. Meldon.

DAILY DOZEN QUIZZES

NAME _____ SCORE _____

SOLVE FOR x

1. $x^2 + 3x = 0$ _____

2. $x^2 - 4x = 0$ _____

3. $x^2 - 4 = 0$ _____

4. $x^2 - 6x + 9 = 0$ _____

5. $x^2 - 10x = 0$ _____

6. $x^2 + 8x - 9 = 0$ _____

7. $x^2 - 11x + 24 = 0$ _____

8. $x^2 - x - 72 = 0$ _____

9. $x^2 + 6x - 7 = 0$ _____

10. $6x - 2x^2 = 0$ _____

11. $9 - 10x + x^2 = 0$ _____

12. $3x^2 + 8x - 3 = 0$ _____

NAME _____ SCORE _____

SOLVE FOR x

1. $x^2 - 5x = 0$ _____

2. $x^2 + 5x = 0$ _____

3. $x^2 + 4x - 5 = 0$ _____

4. $x^2 - 25 = 0$ _____

5. $2x^2 - 8x = 0$ _____

6. $x^2 - x - 6 = 0$ _____

7. $x^2 + 3x - 10 = 0$ _____

8. $x^2 + 3x = 0$ _____

9. $x^2 - 10x + 25 = 0$ _____

10. $x^2 + 2x + 1 = 0$ _____

11. $15 - 8x + x^2 = 0$ _____

12. $16 - x^2 = 0$ _____

NAME _____ SCORE _____

SOLVE FOR x

1. $x^2 + 2x - 15 = 0$ _____

2. $x^2 + 2x = 0$ _____

3. $x^2 - 16 = 0$ _____

4. $x^2 - 8x + 16 = 0$ _____

5. $x^2 - 8x - 20 = 0$ _____

6. $2x^2 + 5x + 3 = 0$ _____

7. $2x^2 - 6x = 0$ _____

8. $5 - 4x - x^2 = 0$ _____

9. $x^2 - 8x + 12 = 0$ _____

10. $10 + 3x - x^2 = 0$ _____

11. $3x - x^2 = 0$ _____

12. $x^2 + x = 0$ _____

NAME _____ SCORE _____

SOLVE FOR x

1. $x^2 + 6x + 9 = 0$ _____

2. $x^2 + 6x = 0$ _____

3. $x^2 - 9 = 0$ _____

4. $x^2 - x - 6 = 0$ _____

5. $2x^2 - 9x + 7 = 0$ _____

6. $x^2 - 4x + 4 = 0$ _____

7. $81 - x^2 = 0$ _____

8. $81x - x^2 = 0$ _____

9. $81x - 3x^2 = 0$ _____

10. $6x^2 - 7x - 5 = 0$ _____

11. $4 - 36x^2 = 0$ _____

12. $4x^2 + x - 3 = 0$ _____

Copyright © 1984 by Allyn and Bacon, Inc. Reproduction of this material is restricted to use with *A Guidebook for Teaching Algebra*, by Terry A. Goodman, John Bernard, Martin P. Cohen, and Joanne E. Meldon.

DAILY DOZEN QUIZZES

NAME _____ SCORE _____

IDENTIFY A, B, C

1. $2x^2 - 3x + 5 = 0$ $\quad\underline{\ 2\ }\ \underline{\ -3\ }\ \underline{\ 5\ }$
2. $x^2 + 6x - 1 = 0$ _____ _____ _____
3. $x^2 - x + 4 = 0$ _____ _____ _____
4. $x - 2x^2 + 3 = 0$ _____ _____ _____
5. $4 - 5x + x^2 = 0$ _____ _____ _____
6. $x^2 - 2x = 0$ _____ _____ _____
7. $x^2 + 4 = 0$ _____ _____ _____
8. $3 + x^2 = 0$ _____ _____ _____
9. $2x - x^2 = 0$ _____ _____ _____
10. $x^2 - x - 7 = 0$ _____ _____ _____
11. $2x + 5 + x^2 = 0$ _____ _____ _____
12. $9x^2 - 7x = 4$ _____ _____ _____

NAME _____ SCORE _____

IDENTIFY A, B, C

1. $3x^2 - 5x + 1 = 0$ $\quad\underline{\ 3\ }\ \underline{\ -5\ }\ \underline{\ 1\ }$
2. $x^2 + 3x + 4 = 0$ _____ _____ _____
3. $x^2 - x - 2 = 0$ _____ _____ _____
4. $a - 3a^2 + 5 = 0$ _____ _____ _____
5. $2 - 3b - b^2 = 0$ _____ _____ _____
6. $x^2 + 5x = 0$ _____ _____ _____
7. $4 + x^2 = 0$ _____ _____ _____
8. $x^2 - 2x + 3 = 0$ _____ _____ _____
9. $2 + x^2 - x = 0$ _____ _____ _____
10. $x^2 + 7 = 2x$ _____ _____ _____
11. $x^2 - 4x = 1$ _____ _____ _____
12. $x^2 - 9 = 0$ _____ _____ _____

NAME _____ SCORE _____

IDENTIFY A, B, C

1. $3x^2 - 5x - 2 = 0$ $\quad\underline{\ 3\ }\ \underline{\ -5\ }\ \underline{\ -2\ }$
2. $2x^2 + x - 7 = 0$ _____ _____ _____
3. $x^2 - 3x + 1 = 0$ _____ _____ _____
4. $x^2 - 9 = 0$ _____ _____ _____
5. $4x + x^2 = 0$ _____ _____ _____
6. $2x - 9 = x^2$ _____ _____ _____
7. $3 - 4x - x^2 = 0$ _____ _____ _____
8. $2 + x^2 = 0$ _____ _____ _____
9. $3x^2 - 4 = x$ _____ _____ _____
10. $x^2 + 7x = -5$ _____ _____ _____
11. $x^2 - 4x - 1 = 0$ _____ _____ _____
12. $2 - 3x = -x^2$ _____ _____ _____

NAME _____ SCORE _____

IDENTIFY A, B, C

1. $2x^2 + 3x + 5 = 0$ $\quad\underline{\ 2\ }\ \underline{\ 3\ }\ \underline{\ 5\ }$
2. $9 + x^2 - 4x = 0$ _____ _____ _____
3. $x^2 + 6x = 0$ _____ _____ _____
4. $9 - x^2 = 0$ _____ _____ _____
5. $9 + x^2 = 7x$ _____ _____ _____
6. $x^2 + 4x = -2$ _____ _____ _____
7. $x^2 - x = 5$ _____ _____ _____
8. $2 = 3x - x^2$ _____ _____ _____
9. $x^2 - 4x = 0$ _____ _____ _____
10. $3 - x - x^2 = 0$ _____ _____ _____
11. $2 - 3x = x^2$ _____ _____ _____
12. $x^2 = 3x$ _____ _____ _____

Copyright © 1984 by Allyn and Bacon, Inc. Reproduction of this material is restricted to use with *A Guidebook for Teaching Algebra*, by Terry A. Goodman, John Bernard, Martin P. Cohen, and Joanne E. Meldon.

DAILY DOZEN QUIZZES

NAME _____ SCORE _____

1. $\dfrac{1}{x} + \dfrac{1}{x}$ _____
2. $\dfrac{1}{x} - \dfrac{1}{x}$ _____
3. $\dfrac{1}{x} \cdot \dfrac{1}{x}$ _____
4. $\dfrac{1}{x} \div \dfrac{1}{x}$ _____
5. $\dfrac{2}{x} + \dfrac{1}{x}$ _____
6. $\dfrac{2}{x} - \dfrac{1}{x}$ _____
7. $\dfrac{2}{x} \cdot \dfrac{1}{x}$ _____
8. $\dfrac{2}{x} \div \dfrac{1}{x}$ _____
9. $\dfrac{1}{a} + \dfrac{1}{x}$ _____
10. $\dfrac{1}{a} - \dfrac{1}{x}$ _____
11. $\dfrac{1}{a} \cdot \dfrac{1}{x}$ _____
12. $\dfrac{1}{a} \div \dfrac{1}{x}$ _____

NAME _____ SCORE _____

1. $\dfrac{2}{a} + \dfrac{4}{a}$ _____
2. $\dfrac{2}{a} - \dfrac{4}{a}$ _____
3. $\dfrac{2}{a} \cdot \dfrac{4}{a}$ _____
4. $\dfrac{2}{a} \div \dfrac{4}{a}$ _____
5. $\dfrac{3}{a} + \dfrac{2}{x}$ _____
6. $\dfrac{3}{a} - \dfrac{2}{x}$ _____
7. $\dfrac{3}{a} \cdot \dfrac{2}{x}$ _____
8. $\dfrac{3}{a} \div \dfrac{2}{x}$ _____
9. $2 + \dfrac{1}{x}$ _____
10. $2 \cdot \dfrac{1}{x}$ _____
11. $2 \div \dfrac{1}{x}$ _____
12. $2 - \dfrac{1}{x}$ _____

NAME _____ SCORE _____

1. $\dfrac{6}{c} + \dfrac{2}{c}$ _____
2. $\dfrac{6}{c} - \dfrac{2}{c}$ _____
3. $\dfrac{6}{c} \cdot \dfrac{2}{c}$ _____
4. $\dfrac{6}{c} \div \dfrac{2}{c}$ _____
5. $\dfrac{3}{x} \cdot x$ _____
6. $\dfrac{3}{x} + x$ _____
7. $\dfrac{3}{x} \div x$ _____
8. $\dfrac{2}{c} + \dfrac{3}{b}$ _____
9. $\dfrac{3}{2} + \dfrac{4}{x}$ _____
10. $\dfrac{3}{2} \cdot \dfrac{4}{x}$ _____
11. $2 \div \dfrac{1}{x}$ _____
12. $\dfrac{3}{a} - \dfrac{5}{b}$ _____

NAME _____ SCORE _____

1. $\dfrac{1}{2a} + \dfrac{1}{2a}$ _____
2. $\dfrac{1}{2a} - \dfrac{1}{2a}$ _____
3. $\dfrac{1}{2a} \cdot \dfrac{1}{2a}$ _____
4. $\dfrac{1}{2a} \div \dfrac{1}{2a}$ _____
5. $\dfrac{3}{2x} + \dfrac{1}{x}$ _____
6. $\dfrac{3}{2x} - \dfrac{1}{x}$ _____
7. $\dfrac{3}{2x} \cdot \dfrac{1}{x}$ _____
8. $\dfrac{3}{2x} \div \dfrac{1}{x}$ _____
9. $\dfrac{1}{4a} + \dfrac{1}{2a}$ _____
10. $\dfrac{1}{4a} \cdot \dfrac{1}{2a}$ _____
11. $a + \dfrac{3}{x}$ _____
12. $2 - \dfrac{a}{x}$ _____

Copyright © 1984 by Allyn and Bacon, Inc. Reproduction of this material is restricted to use with *A Guidebook for Teaching Algebra*, by Terry A. Goodman, John Bernard, Martin P. Cohen, and Joanne E. Meldon.

DAILY DOZEN QUIZZES

NAME _____ SCORE _____
CLEAR FRACTIONS

1. $\frac{1}{2}x + 3 = 4$ $x + 6 = 8$

2. $\frac{x}{4} + \frac{1}{3} = 2$

3. $2t = \frac{3}{4}$

4. $3x - \frac{1}{2} = \frac{2}{3}$

5. $2 - \frac{a}{3} = \frac{1}{6}$

6. $\frac{c}{2} + \frac{3}{5} = 1$

7. $3 - \frac{4x}{5} = \frac{1}{5}$

8. $\frac{2}{3}x + \frac{1}{6} = 4$

9. $2a - \frac{3}{8} = \frac{1}{6}$

10. $\frac{3}{4} - \frac{2}{3}x = \frac{x}{2}$

11. $4 - \frac{3}{5}x = \frac{7}{10}$

12. $5 = \frac{2x}{3} - \frac{1}{5}$

NAME _____ SCORE _____
CLEAR FRACTIONS

1. $\frac{x}{4} - 2 = \frac{1}{2}$ $x - 8 = 2$

2. $\frac{1}{3}x - \frac{2}{3} = 1$

3. $2a = \frac{1}{3}$

4. $2x - \frac{1}{5} = \frac{3}{10}$

5. $5 - \frac{c}{2} = \frac{5}{6}$

6. $\frac{x}{9} + \frac{2}{3} = 1$

7. $4 - \frac{2x}{5} = \frac{1}{3}$

8. $\frac{3}{4}x - \frac{1}{6} = 2$

9. $2b - \frac{7}{8} = 0$

10. $\frac{2}{3}a + \frac{a}{2} = \frac{5}{6}$

11. $\frac{5}{18} - \frac{2a}{3} = \frac{1}{6}$

12. $2 = \frac{1}{2}x - \frac{2x}{3}$

NAME _____ SCORE _____
CLEAR FRACTIONS

1. $\frac{x}{5} - \frac{2}{3} = 4$ $3x - 10 = 60$

2. $\frac{1}{2}x + 3 = \frac{1}{6}$

3. $3c = \frac{2}{5} - 1$

4. $\frac{3x}{4} - \frac{1}{2} = 5$

5. $\frac{a}{2} - \frac{1}{3} = \frac{1}{6}$

6. $\frac{5b}{3} + 2 = \frac{2b}{4}$

7. $x - \frac{2}{3} = \frac{4}{7}$

8. $3 - \frac{1}{2} = \frac{x}{2}$

9. $\frac{4x}{5} - \frac{2x}{3} = \frac{7}{15}$

10. $2x - \frac{1}{4} = 2\frac{1}{4}$

11. $\frac{3}{4}x + 1 = 0$

12. $\frac{x}{2} - \frac{1}{3}x = \frac{5}{6}$

NAME _____ SCORE _____
CLEAR FRACTIONS

1. $x - \frac{2}{5} = \frac{3}{10}$ $10x - 4 = 3$

2. $\frac{1}{2}x + 3 = \frac{2}{3}$

3. $4a = \frac{3}{5}$

4. $\frac{x}{3} - \frac{1}{2} = 4$

5. $\frac{2c}{5} + \frac{1}{2} = 3$

6. $2 - \frac{x}{3} = \frac{3}{4}$

7. $a - \frac{2}{3} = \frac{5}{6}$

8. $\frac{2a}{5} + \frac{1}{2} = 1$

9. $3 + \frac{3}{8} = \frac{1}{5}x$

10. $\frac{2}{3}x + \frac{3x}{4} = 0$

11. $9 - \frac{a}{2} = \frac{5}{3}$

12. $\frac{2x}{5} + \frac{1}{3}x = \frac{1}{2}$

Copyright © 1984 by Allyn and Bacon, Inc. Reproduction of this material is restricted to use with *A Guidebook for Teaching Algebra*, by Terry A. Goodman, John Bernard, Martin P. Cohen, and Joanne E. Meldon.

DAILY DOZEN QUIZZES

NAME _____ SCORE _____

EVALUATE WHEN $x = 2$

1. $f(x) = 2x + 3$ _____
2. $f(x) = 7x - 1$ _____
3. $f(x) = x^2$ _____
4. $f(x) = |x|$ _____
5. $f(x) = x + 5$ _____
6. $f(x) = x^2 + x + 3$ _____
7. $f(x) = 2x^2$ _____
8. $f(x) = |x - 2|$ _____
9. $f(x) = 3x^2 - 4$ _____
10. $f(x) = x^2 + 3x$ _____
11. $f(x) = -x + 5$ _____
12. $f(x) = -\frac{1}{2}x + 3$ _____

NAME _____ SCORE _____

EVALUATE WHEN $x = 0$

1. $f(x) = 3x - 4$ _____
2. $f(x) = 8 + 9x$ _____
3. $f(x) = x^2 + 3$ _____
4. $f(x) = |x - 2|$ _____
5. $f(x) = 5 - x$ _____
6. $f(x) = x^2 + 3x - 4$ _____
7. $f(x) = 3x^2$ _____
8. $f(x) = |x + 7|$ _____
9. $f(x) = 14 - 6x^2$ _____
10. $f(x) = x^2 + 5x$ _____
11. $f(x) = -x - 7$ _____
12. $f(x) = 2 - x + x^2$ _____

NAME _____ SCORE _____

EVALUATE WHEN $x = -5$

1. $f(x) = 3x + 2$ _____
2. $f(x) = 7x - 8$ _____
3. $f(x) = x^2 - 4$ _____
4. $f(x) = |x + 3|$ _____
5. $f(x) = x^2 - 2x$ _____
6. $f(x) = -3x^2$ _____
7. $f(x) = |x|$ _____
8. $f(x) = 4 - 2x$ _____
9. $f(x) = -x + 7$ _____
10. $f(x) = x^2 - x$ _____
11. $f(x) = 2 - |x|$ _____
12. $f(x) = 3x^2 - 7$ _____

NAME _____ SCORE _____

EVALUATE WHEN $x = \frac{1}{2}$

1. $f(x) = 2x + 5$ _____
2. $f(x) = 7x - 3$ _____
3. $f(x) = x^2$ _____
4. $f(x) = |x - 3|$ _____
5. $f(x) = x + 4$ _____
6. $f(x) = x^2 + 2x$ _____
7. $f(x) = 3x^2$ _____
8. $f(x) = 10 - 6x$ _____
9. $f(x) = x^2 + 8x - 3$ _____
10. $f(x) = -x - 2$ _____
11. $f(x) = -\frac{1}{2}x + 1$ _____
12. $f(x) = \frac{2}{3}x - x^2$ _____

Copyright © 1984 by Allyn and Bacon, Inc. Reproduction of this material is restricted to use with *A Guidebook for Teaching Algebra*, by Terry A. Goodman, John Bernard, Martin P. Cohen, and Joanne E. Meldon.

DAILY DOZEN QUIZZES

NAME _____ SCORE _____

$$f(x) = 3x - 2$$

1. $x = 2$ $f(x) =$ _____
2. $x = -3$ $f(x) =$ _____
3. $x = 0$ $f(x) =$ _____
4. $x = \dfrac{1}{3}$ $f(x) =$ _____
5. $x = 6$ $f(x) =$ _____
6. $x = -8$ $f(x) =$ _____
7. $x = 1$ $f(x) =$ _____
8. $x = -1$ $f(x) =$ _____
9. $x = \dfrac{2}{3}$ $f(x) =$ _____
10. $x = -\dfrac{1}{3}$ $f(x) =$ _____
11. $x = \dfrac{4}{3}$ $f(x) =$ _____
12. $x = -5$ $f(x) =$ _____

NAME _____ SCORE _____

$$y = f(x) = x^2 - 3$$

1. $x = 2$ $y =$ _____
2. $x = 3$ $y =$ _____
3. $x = -1$ $y =$ _____
4. $x = 0$ $y =$ _____
5. $x = -2$ $f(x) =$ _____
6. $x = 4$ $y =$ _____
7. $x = 5$ $f(x) =$ _____
8. $x = -3$ $f(x) =$ _____
9. $x = \dfrac{1}{2}$ $y =$ _____
10. $x = 1$ $y =$ _____
11. $x = \dfrac{4}{3}$ $y =$ _____
12. $x = \dfrac{5}{2}$ $y =$ _____

NAME _____ SCORE _____

$$y = f(x) = 3x^2 + 1$$

1. $x = 0$ $y =$ _____
2. $x = 1$ $y =$ _____
3. $x = 2$ $y =$ _____
4. $x = 3$ $f(x) =$ _____
5. $x = -1$ $y =$ _____
6. $x = -2$ $y =$ _____
7. $x = -3$ $f(x) =$ _____
8. $x = \dfrac{1}{3}$ $f(x) =$ _____
9. $x = \dfrac{2}{3}$ $y =$ _____
10. $x = -\dfrac{1}{3}$ $y =$ _____
11. $x = \dfrac{4}{3}$ $f(x) =$ _____
12. $x = -5$ $y =$ _____

NAME _____ SCORE _____

$$y = f(x) = x^2 - 3x$$

1. $x = 4$ $y =$ _____
2. $x = -2$ $y =$ _____
3. $x = -1$ $y =$ _____
4. $x = 0$ $y =$ _____
5. $x = 1$ $y =$ _____
6. $x = 2$ $y =$ _____
7. $x = 3$ $y =$ _____
8. $x = \dfrac{1}{3}$ $y =$ _____
9. $x = \dfrac{2}{3}$ $y =$ _____
10. $x = -\dfrac{1}{3}$ $y =$ _____
11. $x = \dfrac{5}{3}$ $y =$ _____
12. $x = -7$ $y =$ _____

Copyright © 1984 by Allyn and Bacon, Inc. Reproduction of this material is restricted to use with *A Guidebook for Teaching Algebra*, by Terry A. Goodman, John Bernard, Martin P. Cohen, and Joanne E. Meldon.

DAILY DOZEN QUIZZES

NAME _____ SCORE _____

Does the FUNCTION contain the given point?

1. $y = 2x - 3$; $(2,1)$ _____YES_____
2. $y = 3x + 4$; $(-1,7)$ _____
3. $f(x) = 2x + 6$; $(0,6)$ _____
4. $f(x) = 6x^2$; $(2,144)$ _____
5. $y = x^2$; $(3,6)$ _____
6. $y = 3x + 4$; $(1,7)$ _____
7. $f(x) = 3 - x$; $(-1,4)$ _____
8. $f(x) = 2x + 6$; $(2,28)$ _____
9. $y = x + x$; $(3,9)$ _____
10. $y = |x|$; $(-4,4)$ _____
11. $y = x - x^2$; $(1,0)$ _____
12. $f(x) = 3x^2$; $(-1,-3)$ _____

NAME _____ SCORE _____

Does the FUNCTION contain the given point?

1. $f(x) = 3x - 1$; $(-2,-5)$ _____NO_____
2. $f(x) = -2x$; $(5,3)$ _____
3. $y = 2x - 5$; $(-1,5)$ _____
4. $f(x) = x^2 - 3$; $(1,-2)$ _____
5. $f(x) = 4x^2$; $(3,144)$ _____
6. $y = x^2 - x$; $(-2,8)$ _____
7. $y = 2x$; $(0,0)$ _____
8. $y = x^2 + 5$; $(-1,6)$ _____
9. $f(x) = |x - 3|$; $(1,-2)$ _____
10. $y = \frac{x}{2} + 5$; $(6,5\frac{1}{2})$ _____
11. $y = -3 + x^2$; $(-1,-2)$ _____
12. $f(x) = x(x - 1)$; $(4,12)$ _____

NAME _____ SCORE _____

Does the FUNCTION contain the given point?

1. $y = 2x + 5$; $(1,7)$ _____YES_____
2. $y = x^2 - 3$; $(-1,-4)$ _____
3. $f(x) = |x|$; $(-3,3)$ _____
4. $f(x) = 4 - 3x$; $(-1,3)$ _____
5. $f(x) = 3x^2$; $(2,36)$ _____
6. $y = x^2 - x$; $(-1,2)$ _____
7. $f(x) = 3x - 12$; $(-2,-18)$ _____
8. $y = 3 - 8x^2$; $(-1,11)$ _____
9. $y = |2x - 3|$; $(1,1)$ _____
10. $y = 3x^2 - 7$; $(2,5)$ _____
11. $y = 8 - 2x$; $(5,30)$ _____
12. $y = 3$; $(1,3)$ _____

NAME _____ SCORE _____

Does the FUNCTION contain the given point?

1. $y = 3x - 4$; $(1,-1)$ _____YES_____
2. $y = x^2 + 5$; $(0,7)$ _____
3. $y = 5x$; $(1,5)$ _____
4. $y = |5 - x|$; $(8,-3)$ _____
5. $y = 4x^2$; $(0,0)$ _____
6. $y = x - x^2$; $(1,0)$ _____
7. $y = 2x^2$; $(4,64)$ _____
8. $y = -2x - 5$; $(0,5)$ _____
9. $y = 3 - 4x$; $(1,1)$ _____
10. $y = x^2 + 3x$; $(-1,-2)$ _____
11. $y = 2 - x$; $(3,1)$ _____
12. $y = 4$; $(2,4)$ _____

Copyright © 1984 by Allyn and Bacon, Inc. Reproduction of this material is restricted to use with *A Guidebook for Teaching Algebra*, by Terry A. Goodman, John Bernard, Martin P. Cohen, and Joanne E. Meldon.

SOLVE FOR AN UNKNOWN QUANTITY

Find each value

1. $8 \cdot 6 + 4$ _____

2. $(3 + 9) \cdot 8$ _____

3. $5 \cdot (a + c)$ _____

4. $4 \cdot a \cdot b$ _____

5. $6(1 + 7) \div 8$ _____

6. $25 - 7 \cdot 0$ _____

7. $19 - 1 \cdot 5$ _____

8. $(19 - 1) \cdot 5$ _____

9. $9 + 6 + 8$ _____

10. $12 + 4 \cdot 6$ _____

Find the given unknown quantity in each formula.

1. $A = \frac{1}{2}bh$ $b = 3,$ $h = 10$ Solve for A _____

2. $A = \frac{1}{2}h(b + c)$ $b = 7,$ $c = 5,$ $h = 2$ Solve for A _____

3. $t = \frac{d}{r}$ $d = 9,$ $r = 2$ Solve for t _____

4. $V = \frac{4}{3}\pi r^3$ $r = 2$ Solve for V _____

5. $P = 2(l + w)$ $l = 9,$ $w = 7$ Solve for P _____

6. $C = \frac{5}{9}(F - 32)$ $F = 212$ Solve for C _____

7. $S = 2\pi rh + 2\pi r^2$ $r = 2,$ $h = 10$ Solve for S _____

8. $A = lxw$ $l = 13,$ $w = 9$ Solve for A _____

9. $d = rt$ $r = 50,$ $t = 3$ Solve for d _____

10. $A = bxh$ $b = 10,$ $h = 7$ Solve for A _____

Copyright © 1984 by Allyn and Bacon, Inc. Reproduction of this material is restricted to use with *A Guidebook for Teaching Algebra,* by Terry A. Goodman, John Bernard, Martin P. Cohen, and Joanne E. Meldon.

ALGEBRAIC PROPERTIES OF WHOLE NUMBERS

Use the properties you have been studying to help you with the following:

1. Name the property illustrated by each.

   a) $6 \cdot (40 + 4) = (6 \cdot 40) + (6 \cdot 4)$ _____

   b) $(4 - 4) + 7 = 7$ _____

   c) $1 \cdot (57 \cdot 68) = 57 \cdot 68$ _____

   d) $26 + (38 + 49) = (26 + 38) + 49$ _____

2. Simplify the following.

   a) $(2 + 67) + 1 =$ _____

   b) $12 \cdot (3 + 6) =$ _____

   c) $9(4) + 9(6) =$ _____

   d) $30 - (12 - 6) =$ _____

   e) $(30 - 12) - 6 =$ _____

   f) $11(205) =$ _____

Copyright © 1984 by Allyn and Bacon, Inc. Reproduction of this material is restricted to use with *A Guidebook for Teaching Algebra*, by Terry A. Goodman, John Bernard, Martin P. Cohen, and Joanne E. Meldon.

ABSOLUTE VALUE

1. When we want to indicate that we are only interested in distance, we use this symbol | |.

   |5| means the distance of 5 from 0 on the number line. Then

   |5| = _____

   How about |−2| = _____ ? That's right |−2| = 2

   Try these:

   a) |6| = _____   d) |−75| = _____

   b) |−4| = _____   e) |−17| = _____

   c) |12| = _____   f) |342| = _____

2. Notice,

   |3| = _____

   |−3| = _____

   and 3 + (−3) = _____

   3 and −3 are additive _____ but their distances from 0 are _____

   _____ .

3. Consider the following:

   −3 tells us two things

   A) The − tells us direction or sign.

   B) The 3 tells us distance or absolute value.

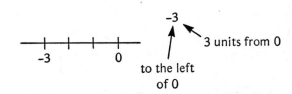

   a) −6 _____ units to the _____ of 0

   b) −9 _____ units to the _____ of 0

   c) 8 _____ units to the _____ of 0

   d) −x _____ units to the _____ of 0

   e) 2Y _____ units to the _____ of 0

Copyright © 1984 by Allyn and Bacon, Inc. Reproduction of this material is restricted to use with *A Guidebook for Teaching Algebra*, by Terry A. Goodman, John Bernard, Martin P. Cohen, and Joanne E. Meldon.

MULTIPLICATION OF INTEGERS

1. Consider the following:

decreasing by 1

$3 \cdot 3 = 9$ ⟵—— decreasing by 3

$3 \cdot 2 = 6$

$3 \cdot 1 = 3$

$3 \cdot 0 = 0$

$3 \cdot -1 = $ _____

If we consider the pattern, then we have $3 \cdot -1 = $ _____ .

Notice, we may also consider $3 \cdot -1$ as $-1 + -1 + -1 = $ _____ .

Thus, the product of a positive integer and a negative integer is a _____ integer.

Try these:

a) $6 \cdot -5 = $ _____   d) $3(-4 + 2) = $ _____

b) $-5 \cdot 3 = $ _____   e) $-7 \cdot 3 = $ _____

c) $14 \cdot -3 = $ _____   f) $-a \cdot 4 = $ _____

2. Complete this pattern:

decreasing by 1

$-3 \cdot 3 = -9$ ⟵—— *increasing* by 3

$-3 \cdot 2 = -6$

$-3 \cdot 1 = -1$

$-3 \cdot 0 = 0$

$-3 \cdot -1 = $ _____

Following the pattern, we have $-3 \cdot -1 = $ _____ .

In general, $-a \cdot -b = $ _____

3. Consider the following:

$3(-2 + 2) = $

If we add first and then multiply, we have $3(-2 + 2) = 3 \cdot 0 = 0$

Now, let's multiply first and then add:

$3(-2 + 2) = 3(-2) + (3 \cdot 2)$

$= 3(-2) + 6$

We now can say $3(-2 + 2) = 0 = 3(-2) + 6$.

So $3(-2)$ must be "acting" like _____ .

4. Use a similar argument to show $-4(-3) = 12$.

Copyright © 1984 by Allyn and Bacon, Inc. Reproduction of this material is restricted to use with *A Guidebook for Teaching Algebra*, by Terry A. Goodman, John Bernard, Martin P. Cohen, and Joanne E. Meldon.

IRRATIONAL NUMBERS

Remember a number S is irrational if it cannot be expressed as $\frac{m}{n}$ where m and n are integers.

1. Which of the following are irrational numbers?

   a) $\sqrt{81}$ _____   d) $\sqrt{100}$ _____

   b) $\sqrt{7}$ _____   e) $\sqrt{13}$ _____

   c) $\sqrt{\frac{9}{4}}$ _____   f) $\sqrt{8}$ _____

2. Replace t with the smallest possible whole number to make a true statement.

   a) $3 < \sqrt{14} < t$ _____   c) $8 < \sqrt{75} < t$ _____

   b) $14 < \sqrt{220} < t$ _____   d) $9 < \sqrt{91} < t$ _____

3. Complete the following diagram to indicate the relationships among the following (reals, rationals, irrationals, integers, wholes).

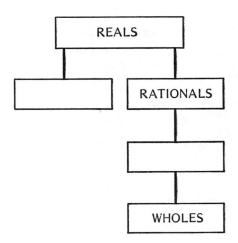

Copyright © 1984 by Allyn and Bacon, Inc. Reproduction of this material is restricted to use with *A Guidebook for Teaching Algebra,* by Terry A. Goodman, John Bernard, Martin P. Cohen, and Joanne E. Meldon.

DECIMAL APPROXIMATIONS FOR IRRATIONAL NUMBERS

Suppose we want to write $\sqrt{2}$ as a decimal. We know

$$1 < \sqrt{2} < \underline{\hspace{6cm}} \text{ (whole number)}$$

Now, let's "fit" $\sqrt{2}$ to one decimal place

$1.4 < \sqrt{2} < 1.5$ How do we know?
$1.4 \times 1.4 = 1.96$
$1.5 \times 1.5 = 2.25$

We can continue and find
$1.41 < \sqrt{2} < 1.42$
$1.414 < \sqrt{2} < 1.415$

Use your calculator to find the following:

1. $\sqrt{100} = \underline{\hspace{4cm}}$
2. $\sqrt{75} \ = \underline{\hspace{4cm}}$
3. $\sqrt{17} \ = \underline{\hspace{4cm}}$
4. $\sqrt{51} \ = \underline{\hspace{4cm}}$

Why would the notation $\sqrt{7}$ be more convenient than the decimal notation?

Copyright © 1984 by Allyn and Bacon, Inc. Reproduction of this material is restricted to use with *A Guidebook for Teaching Algebra*, by Terry A. Goodman, John Bernard, Martin P. Cohen, and Joanne E. Meldon.

SIMPLIFYING ALGEBRAIC EXPRESSIONS

Simplify each of the following algebraic expressions. Use properties when possible. If unsure, check by evaluating both the original expression and the new one for several values of the variable.

1. $(25x + 2) - 2$

2. $(7 + 2x) - 2x$

3. $(9 - 2x) + 9$

4. $(2x - 17) + 17$

5. $\dfrac{7x}{7}$

6. $-9\left(\dfrac{5x}{-9}\right)$

7. $(8x - 1) + 1$

8. $(x + 8) - x$

9. $3\left(\dfrac{x - 2}{3}\right)$

10. $\dfrac{(x - 2)(x + 2)}{(x - 2)}; \; x \neq 2$

11. $(3 - 5x) + 5x$

12. $8x - (2 + 3x)$

13. $11 - 3(x + 2)$

14. $(13x - 5) - 13x$

15. $3x + (5 - 4x)$

16. $x - 2(x + 2)$

17. $7x - 5(7x - 5)$

18. $6x - 11(2x + 3)$

19. $9(8 - 7x) - 6x + 5$

20. $5(6x - 7) - 8(x - 9)$

Copyright © 1984 by Allyn and Bacon, Inc. Reproduction of this material is restricted to use with *A Guidebook for Teaching Algebra*, by Terry A. Goodman, John Bernard, Martin P. Cohen, and Joanne E. Meldon.

EQUATIONS AND INEQUALITIES

Indicate whether or not the given item is acceptable as an equation or inequality, relating properly formed algebraic expressions. Be prepared to discuss your reasons.

1. $x - \dfrac{x-6}{5} = 2(x+2)$

2. $\dfrac{x^2}{x} = 2$

3. $= \pi r^2$

4. $a(b+c) = ab + c$

5. $a + b = b + a$

6. $4 + 5 \geqslant 6 + 3$

7. $21 + 2w =$

8. $8 - = 4 + (2 +$

9. $\dfrac{1}{x} + \dfrac{1}{y} - \dfrac{1}{7}$

10. $x - 1 = x + 1$

11. $-2 \leqslant 3 - 1$

12. $(((4) - (x)) = (7))$

13. $x \in (x + 1)$

14. $x^2 + 2 = 3x - 1$

15. $-x = x^2 + y$

16. $x > 2y$

17. $|x - 6| < 1$

18. $f(x) = 2x + 1$

19. $^2x = x_2$

20. $\sqrt[3]{x} = \sqrt{x}$

Copyright © 1984 by Allyn and Bacon, Inc. Reproduction of this material is restricted to use with *A Guidebook for Teaching Algebra,* by Terry A. Goodman, John Bernard, Martin P. Cohen, and Joanne E. Meldon.

ORDER OF OPERATIONS

For each equation determine the order of operations that lead to the result on the right. Then, solve the equation by undoing the operations in reverse order.

1. $7(x - 3) = 42$

2. $\dfrac{x + 7}{5} = 3$

3. $2(x + 5) = 13$

4. $\dfrac{2x - 5}{7} = 3$

5. $\left(\dfrac{x}{2}\right) + 9 = 12$

6. $\left(\dfrac{x}{10}\right) - 2 = 5$

7. $5x + 3 = 0$

8. $8x - 7 = -2$

9. $3(x + 8) - 7 = 2$

10. $\dfrac{x - 2}{3} = -5$

11. $* \, 3(5 + x) = 17$

12. $9 - x = 4$

13. $3 = \dfrac{25 - x}{7}$

14. $\dfrac{x^2 + 1}{2} = 4$

---

*Problems 11–14 offer some new challenges not found in the first 10.

Copyright © 1984 by Allyn and Bacon, Inc. Reproduction of this material is restricted to use with *A Guidebook for Teaching Algebra*, by Terry A. Goodman, John Bernard, Martin P. Cohen, and Joanne E. Meldon.

USING ISOLATION PROCEDURES

Practice using isolation procedures as you solve the following equations.

1. $100 - x = 45$

2. $x + (25 + 14) = 64$

3. $15 + 2x = 19$

4. $5(17 - x) = 75$

5. $\dfrac{9 - 2x}{5} = 1$

6. $22\dfrac{1}{2} = \dfrac{70 - x}{2}$

7. $\dfrac{2(3 + x)}{5} = 12$

8. $\dfrac{-40}{9} = \dfrac{5}{9}(32 - F)$; Solve for F

9. $5(19 - 2y) = 75$

10. $22 - 3(24 - 11x) = 49$

Copyright © 1984 by Allyn and Bacon, Inc. Reproduction of this material is restricted to use with *A Guidebook for Teaching Algebra,* by Terry A. Goodman, John Bernard, Martin P. Cohen, and Joanne E. Meldon.

ATTRACTION, COLLECTION, AND ISOLATION

Practice using the strategies for removing parentheses, attraction, collection, and isolation. Think about the properties and algebraic processes that are used for each of these.

1. $11x + 3 + 2x = 55$

2. $45 = 7x + (9 - 3x)$

3. $(17 - 2x) + 3x = 17$

4. $4y + 2(y + 3) = 51$

5. $18 = 5x + 3(x - 2)$

6. $8x - (6 - x) = 57$

7. $11 = x(9 - y) + 3y$

8. $37 = 5(4-3x) - 2x$

9. $7y - 2(y - 2) = 24$

10. $2x - 4(x - 3) - x = 21$

Copyright © 1984 by Allyn and Bacon, Inc. Reproduction of this material is restricted to use with *A Guidebook for Teaching Algebra,* by Terry A. Goodman, John Bernard, Martin P. Cohen, and Joanne E. Meldon.

SOLVING EQUATIONS

Concentrate on the strategies and balance operations as you solve each of the following equations.

1. $\dfrac{x+5}{3} = 2$

2. $12y = 3y + 18$

3. $\dfrac{2}{3}x = 14 - \dfrac{1}{3}x$

4. $3(5 + 2x) = 11x$

5. $17y = 8 + 9(y - 2)$

6. $5x + 2 = 9 - 2x$

7. $9 - 5y = 2(y + 1)$

8. $16 - 3x = 2(x + 2)$

9. $23 - 7(6y + 1) = 8y + 15$

10. $x^2 + 3x = x^2 - 6$

Copyright © 1984 by Allyn and Bacon, Inc. Reproduction of this material is restricted to use with *A Guidebook for Teaching Algebra,* by Terry A. Goodman, John Bernard, Martin P. Cohen, and Joanne E. Meldon.

SOLVING FOR INDICATED VARIABLES

Solve the formula or equation for the indicated variable. Note: Because of the x's on the right, number 1 has not yet been solved for x.

1. $x = w - xy$; for x

2. $d = rt$; for r

3. $I = prt$; for t

4. $A = p + prt$; for p

5. $F = \frac{9}{5}C + 32$; for C

6. $P = 2(l + w)$; for w

7. $A = \frac{1}{2}bh$; for b

8. $y = mx + b$; for b

9. $y = mx + b$; for m

10. $F + V - E = 2$; for E

Copyright © 1984 by Allyn and Bacon, Inc. Reproduction of this material is restricted to use with *A Guidebook for Teaching Algebra*, by Terry A. Goodman, John Bernard, Martin P. Cohen, and Joanne E. Meldon.

FINDING ERRORS

1. Continue evaluating each equation in the "solution" using $x = 2$ to find the error.

"Solution"	Statement when $x = 2$
1. $5 + 3(x - 1) = 12 + 2x$	$8 = 16$
2. $5 + 3x - 3 = 12 + 2x$	$\underline{\quad ? \quad} = 16$
3. $3x + 2 = 12 + 2x$	
4. $5x + 2 = 12$	
5. $5x = 10$	
6. $x = 2$	

For each of the following use the same method as in number 1 to find the errors.

2. $3x - 4(x - 1) = 25$
$3x - 4x - 4 = 25$
$-1x - 4 = 25$
$-1x = 29$
$x = 29$

3. $16 - 3x = 2(x + 2)$
$16 - 3x = 2x + 4$
$16 - 1x = 4$
$-1x = -12$
$x = -11$

Copyright © 1984 by Allyn and Bacon, Inc. Reproduction of this material is restricted to use with *A Guidebook for Teaching Algebra*, by Terry A. Goodman, John Bernard, Martin P. Cohen, and Joanne E. Meldon.

USING NUMBER LINES

Using a number line to represent the real number domain of the variable, graph the solution set for each of the following inequalities. (Apply the reversibility principle when needed.)

1. $x \leqslant -2$

2. $-2 > x$

3. $x \leqslant 0$ (x is negative)

4. $x > 0$ (x is positive)

5. $y \geqslant 0$ (y is nonnegative)

6. $y \leqslant 0$ (y is nonpositive)

7. $z > -\frac{1}{2}$

8. $\frac{1}{2} \leqslant x$

9. $3.1 \leqslant y$

10. $\pi < z$

Copyright © 1984 by Allyn and Bacon, Inc. Reproduction of this material is restricted to use with *A Guidebook for Teaching Algebra,* by Terry A. Goodman, John Bernard, Martin P. Cohen, and Joanne E. Meldon.

SOLVING INEQUALITIES

Use the properties of inequality and solution strategies to solve the following inequalities.

1. $\dfrac{x+5}{3} \geqslant 2$

2. $12y \leqslant 3y + 18$

3. $\dfrac{2}{3}x < 14 - \dfrac{1}{3}x$

4. $3(5 + 2x) > 11x$

5. $17y \leqslant 8 + 9(y - 2)$

6. $5x + 2 < 9 - 2x$

7. $9 - 5y > 2(y + 1)$

8. $16 - 3x \geqslant 2(x + 2)$

9. $23 - 7(6y + 1) \geqslant 8y + 15$

10. $x^2 + 3x < x^2 - 6$

Copyright © 1984 by Allyn and Bacon, Inc. Reproduction of this material is restricted to use with *A Guidebook for Teaching Algebra*, by Terry A. Goodman, John Bernard, Martin P. Cohen, and Joanne E. Meldon.

DOUBLE INEQUALITIES

For numbers 1–6, write the double inequality having the same meaning as the given compound sentence. Also graph the solution set.

1. $x > -1$ and $x \leqslant 2$

2. $x < \dfrac{3}{4}$ and $x \geqslant 0$

3. $5 \leqslant x$ and $x < 8$

4. $10 \geqslant x$ and $-1 \leqslant x$

5. $10 \geqslant x$ and $-x \leqslant 1$

6. $2x < 6$ and $x + 2 > 1$

For numbers 7–10, you are given a double inequality
a. Write, in words, the corresponding meaning
b. Graph the solution set
c. Indicate the compound *and*-sentence having the same meaning.

7. $3 < y \leqslant 9$

8. $6 < (2y) \leqslant 18$

9. $-3 < x < +3$

10. $0 \leqslant |x| < 3$

Copyright © 1984 by Allyn and Bacon, Inc. Reproduction of this material is restricted to use with *A Guidebook for Teaching Algebra,* by Terry A. Goodman, John Bernard, Martin P. Cohen, and Joanne E. Meldon.

DOUBLE INEQUALITIES

When possible, solve the given double inequality using the simultaneous approach on all three members. Otherwise change to the corresponding single inequalities to solve. In each case, graph the solution set on a number line.

1. $19 < 2x - 3 \leqslant 25$

2. $\frac{1}{2} \leqslant \frac{x+1}{2} \leqslant 5$

3. $19 < 3 - 2x < 25$

4. $\frac{1}{2} \leqslant \frac{1-x}{2} < 5$

5. $3 - x < 1 + x < 4 - x$

6. $2x > 3x > 6$

7. $x + 1 < x + 2 < 3$

8. $-3 \leqslant 2x - 25 \leqslant +3$

9. $-3 \leqslant 25 - 2x \leqslant +3$

10. $0 \leqslant |x| < +3$

Copyright © 1984 by Allyn and Bacon, Inc. Reproduction of this material is restricted to use with *A Guidebook for Teaching Algebra,* by Terry A. Goodman, John Bernard, Martin P. Cohen, and Joanne E. Meldon.

ABSOLUTE VALUE INEQUALITIES

Solve each of the following absolute value inequalities and sketch a graph of its solution set.

1. $|x| < 100$

2. $|x - 8| < 3$

3. $|-6x| < 12$

4. $|x + 3| \leqslant 2$

5. $|5x + 1| \leqslant 6$

6. $|7x| \geqslant 7$

7. $|5x - 2| > 10$

8. $|-4x| \geqslant \dfrac{1}{2}$

9. $|7 - 3x| > 20$

10. $|8 + 4x| < 3.2$

Copyright © 1984 by Allyn and Bacon, Inc. Reproduction of this material is restricted to use with *A Guidebook for Teaching Algebra,* by Terry A. Goodman, John Bernard, Martin P. Cohen, and Joanne E. Meldon.

METHODS OF SOLVING SYSTEMS: GRAPHING

Instructions: *Graph each of the following equations. You should use graph paper.*

1. $y + x = 6$

2. $3x - 12y = 12$

3. $y = 32x$

4. $x = 4$

5. $y = 6$

6. $x - y = 1$

7. $2x + 4y = 10$

8. $x + 2y = 5$

9. $7 - y = 2x$

10. $-x = 6 - y$

A. Do equations 4 and 5 represent points or lines? _____

B. Compare the graphs of equations 7 and 8.
   What do you notice? _____
   _____
   _____

Copyright © 1984 by Allyn and Bacon, Inc. Reproduction of this material is restricted to use with *A Guidebook for Teaching Algebra,* by Terry A. Goodman, John Bernard, Martin P. Cohen, and Joanne E. Meldon.

METHODS OF SOLVING SYSTEMS: GRAPHING

Instructions: *Solve each system (pair) of equations by graphing and state whether it is independent, dependent, or inconsistent.*

1. $3x - 2y = 7$
   $2x - 3y = 8$ _____

2. $y = -x$
   $y = 3x - 4$ _____

3. $2x + 3y = 6$
   $8x + 12y = 1$ _____

4. $y = 2x - 6$
   $3y = 6x - 18$ _____

5. $x + y = -4$
   $y - 2x = 5$ _____

Write a system of linear equations which has:

1. No solution   _____

2. One solution   _____

3. An infinite number of solutions   _____

Copyright © 1984 by Allyn and Bacon, Inc. Reproduction of this material is restricted to use with *A Guidebook for Teaching Algebra,* by Terry A. Goodman, John Bernard, Martin P. Cohen, and Joanne E. Meldon.

SOLVING SYSTEMS OF INEQUALITIES: GRAPHING

Instructions: *Solve the following system of linear inequalities by graphing. Check with a test point. Use graph paper.*

1. $y < -x + 3$
   $y \leqslant 2x + 3$

2. $y > 2$
   $x > 2$

3. $2y + 3 < 3$
   $\quad y \geqslant x$

4. $\quad x + y \leqslant 8$
   $-3x + 3y > 1$

5. $\quad x < y$
   $-y < 2$
   $x - y > 5$

6. Write a system of linear inequalities which describes the shaded region below.

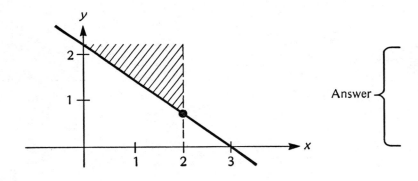

Answer $\left\{ \rule{0pt}{40pt} \right.$

Copyright © 1984 by Allyn and Bacon, Inc. Reproduction of this material is restricted to use with *A Guidebook for Teaching Algebra,* by Terry A. Goodman, John Bernard, Martin P. Cohen, and Joanne E. Meldon.

SOLVING LINEAR EQUATIONS

Instructions: *Solve the following systems of equations by whichever method is convenient. Check your solutions.*

1. $2x + y = 6$
   $2x - y = 12$

2. $5x - 2y = 1$
   $3x - 7y = -18$

3. $3x + 2y = 19$
   $4x - 3y = 7$

4. $2p + q = 16$
   $3p + 1 = -2$

5. $2a - 3b = 7$
   $4a - 6b = 14$

6. $x - 2 = y$
   $x + y = 2$

Copyright © 1984 by Allyn and Bacon, Inc. Reproduction of this material is restricted to use with *A Guidebook for Teaching Algebra*, by Terry A. Goodman, John Bernard, Martin P. Cohen, and Joanne E. Meldon.

POWER TO THE POWERS

Mr. Jones makes you the following offer. If you will water his garden for 10 days, he will pay you in one of two ways. With the first way, he will pay you 1¢ on the first day, 3¢ on the second day, 9¢ on the third day, and so on. Your other option is to take a total pay of $500.00. Complete the following table to help you decide.

Day	Wages for Day	Total for Days So Far
1	1¢	1¢
2	3¢	4
3	9¢ = 3 · 3	13
4	27¢ = (3 · 3) · 3	40
5	_____	_____
6	_____	_____
7	_____	_____
8	_____	_____
9	_____	_____
10	_____	_____

Copyright © 1984 by Allyn and Bacon, Inc. Reproduction of this material is restricted to use with *A Guidebook for Teaching Algebra*, by Terry A. Goodman, John Bernard, Martin P. Cohen, and Joanne E. Meldon.

EXPONENTIAL EXPRESSIONS

A. Fill in the following table:

Number	Base	Exponent	Meaning	Value of Given Power
5^3	5	3	$5 \cdot 5 \cdot 5$	125
2^4				
1^7				
$(-2)^5$				
$(-3)^4$				
			$x \cdot x \cdot x \cdot x \cdot x$	
	-1	6		
	2			32

B. Complete the following:

Given	Factored Form	Let $x = 3$ and $y = 2$	Value of Given
$2x^3$	$2 \cdot x \cdot x \cdot x$	$2 \cdot 3 \cdot 3 \cdot 3$	54
$(2x)^3$			
xy^2			
$3x^2y$			
$(xy)^2$			
$(-3)^3x^2$			
$(-4x)^3$			

C. Write each of the following in factored form: then evaluate when $a = -2$ and $b = 3$

1. $2ab$
2. $3a^2$
3. $(5b)^2$
4. $-3a^2b$
5. $-3ab^2$

6. $(-3ab)^2$
7. $(-2a)^2$
8. $(-2a)^3$
9. a^4b^2
10. $5ab^3$

Copyright © 1984 by Allyn and Bacon, Inc. Reproduction of this material is restricted to use with *A Guidebook for Teaching Algebra,* by Terry A. Goodman, John Bernard, Martin P. Cohen, and Joanne E. Meldon.

WORKING WITH EXPONENTS

A. Use your calculator, if necessary, to find each of the following:

1. $(2^2)^2 = $ _____   (Remember! Parentheses tell us what
2. $(3^3)^4 = $ _____   operation to do first.)
3. $(4^2)^3 = $ _____
4. $(7^2)^4 = $ _____

B. Again, use your calculator to find:

1. $2^2 \cdot 2^2 \qquad\quad = 2^4 \;=$ _____
2. $3^3 \cdot 3^3 \cdot 3^3 \cdot 3^3 = 3^{12} =$ _____
3. $4^2 \cdot 4^2 \cdot 4^2 \qquad = 4^6 \;=$ _____
4. $7^2 \cdot 7^2 \cdot 7^2 \cdot 7^2 = 7^8 \;=$ _____

C. Now, compare your answers for A1 and B1, A2 and B2, etc. What seems to be happening? To see if you have found the pattern, do the following.

1. $(3^2)^3 \quad = 3^2 \cdot 3^2 \cdot 3^2 \qquad = 3^\square =$ _____
2. $(2^5)^2 \quad = 2^5 \cdot 2^5 \qquad\qquad = 2^\square =$ _____
3. $(7^3)^4 \quad = 7^3 \cdot 7^3 \cdot 7^3 \cdot 7^3 = 7^\square =$ _____
4. $(4^2)^3 \quad = 4^\square =$ _____
5. $(x^2)^2 \quad = x^\square =$ _____
6. $(a^4)^3 \quad = a^\square =$ _____
7. $(x^2 y^3)^2 = x^2 y^3 \cdot x^2 y^3 = x^2 \cdot x^2 \cdot y^3 \cdot y^3 = x^\square \cdot y^\square$
8. $(a^4 b^2)^3 = a^\square \cdot b^\square$
9. $(5^4)^0 \quad =$ _____
10. $3^2 \cdot 4^3 =$ _____

Remember, we can operate using only exponents, if we have the same base (look at C10!!!)
    You can check your answers above by substituting values.

Example:

$$(x^2 y^3)^2 = x^4 y^6$$

Let $x = 2$
$\quad\;\; y = 3$

Then, $(x^2 y^3)^2 = (2^2 3^2)^2 = (4 . 27)^2 = (108)^2 = 11{,}664$
$$\text{checks!}$$

and $x^4 \cdot y^6 = 2^4 \cdot 3^6 = 16 \cdot 729 = 11{,}664$

Copyright © 1984 by Allyn and Bacon, Inc. Reproduction of this material is restricted to use with *A Guidebook for Teaching Algebra,* by Terry A. Goodman, John Bernard, Martin P. Cohen, and Joanne E. Meldon.

DIVISION USING EXPONENTS

1. Complete the following table:

Problem	Calculate Using Your Calculator	Exponential Form Using Division Rule
$\dfrac{2^4}{2^4}$	1	2^0
$\dfrac{3^2}{3^2}$		
$\dfrac{5^6}{5^6}$		
$\dfrac{4^{10}}{4^{10}}$		

Again, it appears that $a^0 = $ _____

This fits what we already know about a number divided by itself.

2. Complete this table:

Problem	Using Your Calculator	Exponential Form Using Division Rule
$\dfrac{2^2}{2^4}$	$2^2 \div 2^4 = .25 = \dfrac{1}{4}$	$\dfrac{2^2}{2^4} = 2^{2-4} = 2^{-2}$
$\dfrac{5^3}{5^4}$	$5^3 \div 5^4 = .2 = \dfrac{1}{5}$	$\dfrac{5^3}{5^4} = 5^{3-4} = 5^{-1}$
$\dfrac{2^3}{2^6}$		
$\dfrac{4^1}{4^3}$		
$\dfrac{10^3}{10^7}$		

In order to make our two answers for each of the problems be consistent we should define

$2^{-2} = $ _____ (in exponential form)

In general, we say $a^{-x} = \dfrac{1}{a^x}$

What is $\dfrac{1}{a^{-x}}$? _____

Copyright © 1984 by Allyn and Bacon, Inc. Reproduction of this material is restricted to use with *A Guidebook for Teaching Algebra*, by Terry A. Goodman, John Bernard, Martin P. Cohen, and Joanne E. Meldon.

ADDING POLYNOMIALS

Consider the following example:

$$346 \quad = \quad 300 + 40 + 6$$
$$\underline{+ 251} \quad = \quad \underline{200 + 50 + 1}$$
$$597 \qquad\quad 500 + 90 + 7$$

A. Rewrite this using exponents:

$$300 + 40 + 6 \quad = \quad 3 \cdot 10^2 + 4 \cdot \underline{} + 6$$
$$\underline{+ 200 + 50 + 1} \quad \overset{=}{} \quad \underline{2 \cdot \underline{} + 5 \cdot 10^1 + 1}$$
$$500 + 90 + 7 \qquad\quad 5 \cdot 10^2 + 9 \cdot \underline{} + 7$$

B. Now, suppose we let $x = 10$. Then we will have:

$$300 + 40 + 6 \quad = \quad 3x^2 + 4 \underline{} + 6$$
$$\underline{+ 200 + 50 + 1} \qquad \underline{2\underline{} + 5 \underline{} + 1}$$
$$500 + 90 + 7 \qquad\quad 5x^2 + 9 \underline{} + 7$$

C. Use this model to add the following. Think of x as 10.

    1. $3x^2 + 5x + 2$
       $\underline{9x^2 + 7x + 5}$

    2. $9x^2 + 7x + 7$
       $\underline{3x^2 + 2x + 1}$

    3. $8x^2 + 14x + 9$
       $\underline{4x^2 + 3x + 1}$

    4. $7x^3 + 3x^2 + 4x + 2$
       $\underline{3x^3 + 9x^2 + 2x + 6}$

    5. $(3x^2 + 4x + 7) + (2x^2 + 5x + 2) = \underline{\hspace{4cm}}$
    6. $(17x^2 + 9) + (3x^2 + 6x + 4) = \underline{\hspace{4cm}}$
    7. $(6x^2 + 3x + 4) + (x^2 + 2x) = \underline{\hspace{4cm}}$
    8. $(x^3 + 4x^2 + 3x + 7) + (3x^3 + 2x^2 + 5x + 1) = \underline{\hspace{4cm}}$

D. Check 1, 2, and 3 above using $x = 10$.

   Example:

$$2x^2 + 3x + 4$$
$$\underline{+ 3x^2 + 6x + 3}$$
$$5x^2 + 9x + 7$$

Let $x = 10$. Then we have:

$$(2 \cdot 10^2 + 3 \cdot 10 + 4) + (3.10^2 + 6 \cdot 10 + 3)$$
$$= (200 + 30 + 4) + (300 + 60 + 3)$$
$$= 500 + 90 + 7$$

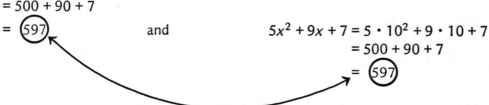

$$= \widehat{597} \qquad\qquad \text{and} \qquad\qquad 5x^2 + 9x + 7 = 5 \cdot 10^2 + 9 \cdot 10 + 7$$
$$= 500 + 90 + 7$$
$$= \widehat{597}$$

Copyright © 1984 by Allyn and Bacon, Inc. Reproduction of this material is restricted to use with *A Guidebook for Teaching Algebra,* by Terry A. Goodman, John Bernard, Martin P. Cohen, and Joanne E. Meldon.

ADDING POLYNOMIALS: PREREQUISITE SKILLS

A. "Add" the following:

$-6 + 4 =$ _____ $-2 - 7 =$ _____ $0 - 8 =$ _____ $-2 - 4 =$ _____

$-2 - 3 =$ _____ $-3 + 8 =$ _____ $8 - 2 =$ _____ $-2 + 8 =$ _____

$3 - 5 =$ _____ $-6 + 6 =$ _____ $-7 + 1 =$ _____ $5 - 7 =$ _____

B. "Add" the following:

8	-5	6	1	5	-4	-4
$\underline{-2}$	$\underline{-3}$	$\underline{-9}$	$\underline{-4}$	$\underline{-5}$	$\underline{-9}$	$\underline{9}$

C. "Add" the following; if they are not like terms, state so.

1. $-2x + 5x$ _____   4. $-2x + 3x^2$ _____   7. $x^2 + x^2$ _____

2. $-3x^2 - 2x^2$ _____   5. $3ab - 8ab$ _____   8. $-5c^3 - c^3$ _____

3. $8ab + ab$ _____   6. $ab + ac$ _____   9. $a^2b + 3ab$ _____

D. Write each of the following in "simple form"

1. $2 - 3b + a$ _____   6. $2 - x$ _____

2. $x^2 + 5 - 2x$ _____   7. $3c + a - 2$ _____

3. $a + a^2 - 3$ _____   8. $5x - x^2 + 1$ _____

4. $-2b - 3 + b^2$ _____   9. $2x^2 - 3y^2 + 5xy$ _____

5. $6x - 5 - 2y$ _____   10. $3 - 4x^2 + x^3 - x$ _____

E. Match each pair of like terms in the proper order (problem 1. is done for you)

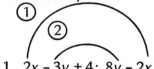

1. $2x - 3y + 4;\ 8y - 2x$ _____

2. $4a - 3 + 5b;\ 2b - a - 1$ _____

3. $x^2 - 2x - 5;\ x^2 + 6 - 4x$ _____

4. $3a^2 - 2 - ab;\ 6ab + a^2 + 7$ _____

Answer When You Add

Copyright © 1984 by Allyn and Bacon, Inc. Reproduction of this material is restricted to use with *A Guidebook for Teaching Algebra,* by Terry A. Goodman, John Bernard, Martin P. Cohen, and Joanne E. Meldon.

SUBTRACTING POLYNOMIALS

A. Complete each of the following: Answers must be in "Simple Form"

   1. $(2x + 5) - (3x - 7)$
       $= ($ $) + ($ $)$

   2. $(x^2 - 5x + 1) - (x^2 - 2x - 7)$
       $= ($ $) + ($ $)$

   3. $(7x + 2y - 3) - (2x + y - 5)$
       $= ($ $) + ($ $)$

   4. $(3a - 4a^2 + 2) - (6a^2 - 5a + 4)$
       $= ($ $) + ($ $)$

   5. $(x^2 + 3x - 4) - (6 - x^2 + x)$
       $= ($ $) + ($ $)$

   6. $(8 - 2x + x^2) - (4x - 2x^2)$
       $= ($ $) + ($ $)$

B. Subtract the following:

$3x^2 + 2x - 8$
$\underline{x^2 - 5x + 3}$

$8x - 7$
$\underline{8x - 2}$

$9x - 6y + 5$
$\underline{x - y + 2}$

$8x - 3y + 12$
$\underline{9x - 3y + 19}$

$2x + 5y$
$\underline{x - 4y - 3}$

$18x^2 - 2x + 6$
$\underline{10x^2 - x + 6}$

C. Check your answers in part A above by letting $x = 2$.

    Step I: Substitute 2 for x in each of the given parentheses and find each number.

    Step II: Subtract the 2 resulting numbers.

    Step III: Substitute 2 into the answer and find the number.

                Does it match the answer in Step II?

Copyright © 1984 by Allyn and Bacon, Inc. Reproduction of this material is restricted to use with *A Guidebook for Teaching Algebra*, by Terry A. Goodman, John Bernard, Martin P. Cohen, and Joanne E. Meldon.

MULTIPLYING POLYNOMIALS

A. Complete the following chart:

Given		Their Sum	Their Product
-2	-5		
-3	8		
$2x$	$-3x$		
$4a$	5		
$-x^2$	$-2x^2$		
$-3b$	$7a$		

B. Remove the parentheses:

$2(3x - 4)$ _____ $3a(2a - 1)$ _____

$-4(x + 5)$ _____ $x^2(x + 2)$ _____

$x(x - 2)$ _____ $-3ab(a^2 - 4)$ _____

$-(2x - 7)$ _____ $(7a - 4)$ _____

C. Complete the following:

1. $(2a + 3)(4b - 5) = 2a() + ()$

   $=$

   $=$ [ ]

2. $(a + 2b)(c - 3d) = a() + 2b()$

   $=$

   $=$ [ ]

3. $(x - 2a)(3x + 5) = x() - 2a()$

   $=$

   $=$ [ ]

4. $(2a - 1)(4b + 3) = 2a() - 1()$

   $=$

   $=$ [ ]

Copyright © 1984 by Allyn and Bacon, Inc. Reproduction of this material is restricted to use with *A Guidebook for Teaching Algebra*, by Terry A. Goodman, John Bernard, Martin P. Cohen, and Joanne E. Meldon.

MENTAL MULTIPLICATION

A. Complete the following chart:

Given	F	O	I	L	Trinomial Answer
1. $(x + 3)(x - 5)$					
2. $(2a + 5)(a + 3)$					
3. $(x - 4)(x + 4)$					
4. $(2a + 3)(2a + 3)$					
5. $(4 + x)(5 - x)$					
6. $(3x + 1)(x - 5)$					
7. $(2x - 7)(2x + 7)$					
8. $(4x - 3y)(4x - 3y)$					
9. $(x + 10)(x - 2)$					
10. $(2x - 3)(x + 5)$					

Be sure to record the
Signs of these terms

B. Do the multiplication mentally and record only the answer.

1. $(x + 3)(x - 5)$ _____
2. $(x + 2)(x + 2)$ _____
3. $(x - 2)(x - 3)$ _____
4. $(x - 5)(x - 8)$ _____
5. $(x + 3)(x - 6)$ _____
6. $(x + 1)(x + 1)$ _____
7. $(2x + 1)(x + 3)$ _____
8. $(2x - 4)(x - 5)$ _____
9. $(a + 2)(a + 3)$ _____
10. $(x - 5y)(x + 2y)$ _____

11. $(2x - 3)(2x - 3)$ _____
12. $(x - 8)(x + 1)$ _____
13. $(x - 4)(x + 4)$ _____
14. $(2x + 3)(x - 8)$ _____
15. $(3x - 2)(2x + 5)$ _____
16. $(x^2 - 4)(x^2 + 6)$ _____
17. $(ab - 2)(ab - 7)$ _____
18. $(2x - 5)(2x + 5)$ _____
19. $(x - y)(x - y)$ _____
20. $(x^2 + 3y)(x^2 - 3y)$ _____

Copyright © 1984 by Allyn and Bacon, Inc. Reproduction of this material is restricted to use with *A Guidebook for Teaching Algebra*, by Terry A. Goodman, John Bernard, Martin P. Cohen, and Joanne E. Meldon.

THE DISTRIBUTIVE LAW

A. Use the Distributive Law to multiply the following:
1. $5(x + y) = 5x + 5y$
2. $12(3 + 5) = 12 \cdot 3 + 12 \cdot 5$
3. $a(b + c) =$ _____
4. $5x(x^2 - 3x + 2) =$ _____
5. $x(x + 4) =$ _____
6. $s^2(s - 7) =$ _____
7. $y^3(y^2 + y - 4) =$ _____

B. Factor the following polynomials by using the Distributive Law in reverse.
1. $7x + 7y = 7(x + y)$
2. $9x - 3y =$ _____
3. $3x - 6nx =$ _____
4. $3x^3 + 6x^2 - 9x = 3x($ _____ + _____ - _____ $)$
5. $30x + 25x =$ _____ $(6x + 5)$
6. $a^2b + ab^2 + a^3b^3 =$ _____
7. $14 + 42p - 7 =$ _____
8. $1000x^3 - x = x($ _____ - _____ $)$
9. $5m - 10mn - 15 =$ _____ $(m - 2mn - 3)$
10. $2\pi r^2 + 2\pi rh =$ _____
11. $ay^2 + ab + 3a =$ _____
12. $12x^2 - 4xy =$ _____
13. $4ac + c = c($ _____ + _____ $)$
14. $-5x^2 - 10z^2 =$ _____
15. $4a + 16b =$ _____

Copyright © 1984 by Allyn and Bacon, Inc. Reproduction of this material is restricted to use with *A Guidebook for Teaching Algebra,* by Terry A. Goodman, John Bernard, Martin P. Cohen, and Joanne E. Meldon.

MULTIPLYING VS. FACTORING

Directions: *Multiply the following and record your answer on the line.*

1. $(x + 2)(x + 3)$ 1. _____ ( )( )
2. $(x - 2)(x + 2)$ 2. _____ ( )( )
3. $(x - 4)(x - 4)$ 3. _____ ( )( )
4. $(x - 2)(x + 3)$ 4. _____ ( )( )
5. $(x - 5)(x + 1)$ 5. _____ ( )( )
6. $(x + 7)(x + 7)$ 6. _____ ( )( )
7. $(x - 2)(x + 1)$ 7. _____ ( )( )
8. $(x - 3)(x + 4)$ 8. _____ ( )( )
9. $(x - 5)(x - 2)$ 9. _____ ( )( )
10. $(x - 3)(x + 2)$ 10. _____ ( )( )
11. $(x + 4)(x + 1)$ 11. _____ ( )( )
12. $(x + 5)(x + 5)$ 12. _____ ( )( )
13. $(x - 5)(x + 2)$ 13. _____ ( )( )
14. $(x + 6)(x - 3)$ 14. _____ ( )( )
15. $(x + 8)(x - 8)$ 15. _____ ( )( )
16. $(2x + 1)(x - 3)$ 16. _____ ( )( )
17. $(3x - 2)(x - 1)$ 17. _____ ( )( )
18. $(2x + 1)(x + 3)$ 18. _____ ( )( )
19. $(3x - 4)(3x - 4)$ 19. _____ ( )( )
20. $(2x - 3)(2x + 3)$ 20. _____ ( )( )

Leave blank till
further notice.

Copyright © 1984 by Allyn and Bacon, Inc. Reproduction of this material is restricted to use with *A Guidebook for Teaching Algebra,* by Terry A. Goodman, John Bernard, Martin P. Cohen, and Joanne E. Meldon.

FACTORING POLYNOMIALS

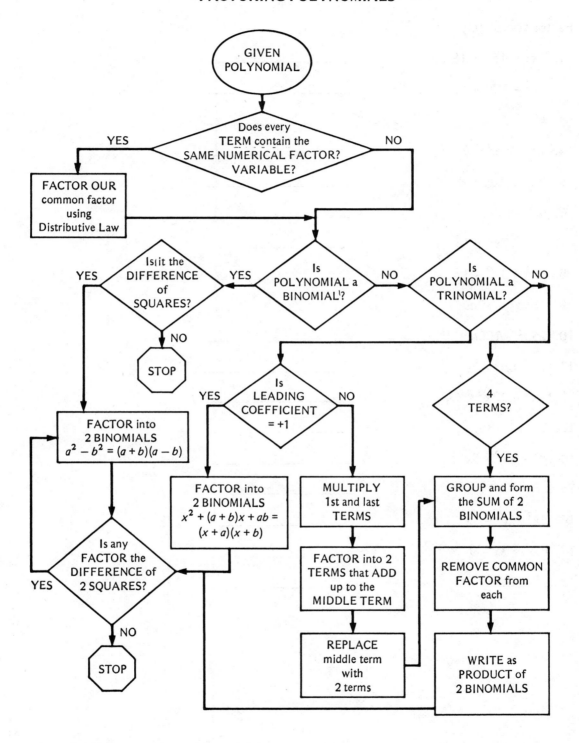

Copyright © 1984 by Allyn and Bacon, Inc. Reproduction of this material is restricted to use with *A Guidebook for Teaching Algebra*, by Terry A. Goodman, John Bernard, Martin P. Cohen, and Joanne E. Meldon.

FACTORING IN GENERAL

Factor completely:

1. $3x^2 + 15x + 18$ _____

2. $-x^2 - 12x - 11$ _____

3. $x^4 - y^4$ _____

4. $x^4 - 10x^2 + 9$ _____

5. $2x^2 + 10x + 8$ _____

6. $m^4 - 16$ _____

7. $x^4 - 17x^2 + 16$ _____

8. $6x^3 + 3x^2 - 3x$ _____

9. $18ab^2 - 50ac^2$ _____

10. $25a^2 - 100b^2$ _____

11. $p^5 + 6p^3 - 7p$ _____

12. $4x^4 - 32x^2 + 64$ _____

13. $9x^2y^2 - 36x^2$ _____

14. $x^3 - 4x^2 - 5x$ _____

15. $x^2 + 4x$ _____

16. $3x^3 - x^2 - 4x$ _____

17. $6x^2 + 3x - 9$ _____

18. $a^4 - 81b^4$ _____

Copyright © 1984 by Allyn and Bacon, Inc. Reproduction of this material is restricted to use with *A Guidebook for Teaching Algebra*, by Terry A. Goodman, John Bernard, Martin P. Cohen, and Joanne E. Meldon.

DIVIDING POLYNOMIALS

A. Find the first term in the dividend:

1. $x + 2\overline{)x^2 + 5x}$ $\square$

2. $2x + 3\overline{)6x^2 + 5x}$ $\square$

3. $4x - 1\overline{)8x^3 + 2x^2}$ $\square$

B. Multiply to find the missing row:

1. $x + 2\overline{)3x^2 + 4x + 5}$ $\dfrac{3x}{}$ $\square$

2. $x - 3\overline{)x^2 + 2x - 6}$ $\dfrac{x}{}$ $\square$

3. $2x + 5\overline{)6x^2 - 5x - 1}$ $\dfrac{3x}{}$ $\square$

C. Subtract to find the missing term:

1. $x + 3\overline{)x^2 - 2x - 7}$
   $\dfrac{x}{}$
   $x^2 + 3x$
   $\square - 7$

2. $x - 4\overline{)2x^2 - 5x - 2}$
   $\dfrac{2x}{}$
   $2x^2 - 8x$
   $\square - 2$

3. $2x - 3\overline{)6x^2 - 5x - 2}$
   $\dfrac{3x}{}$
   $6x^2 - 9x$
   $\square - 2$

D. Do the following division problems:

1. $x + 5\overline{)x^2 + 5x + 6}$

3. $2x + 3\overline{)8x^2 - 2x - 3}$

2. $x - 4\overline{)x^2 + 2x - 12}$

4. $x + 3\overline{)x^2 - x - 12}$

Copyright © 1984 by Allyn and Bacon, Inc. Reproduction of this material is restricted to use with *A Guidebook for Teaching Algebra*, by Terry A. Goodman, John Bernard, Martin P. Cohen, and Joanne E. Meldon.

The quizzes for Reproduction Pages 74–76 are numbered in order of increasing difficulty. After running off a sufficient number of each Reproduction Page (one per student), separate the four quizzes on each page by using a paper cutter. Sort into twelve piles (Quiz I, Quiz II, . . . , Quiz XII) and use one set each day.

SAMPLE QUIZZES

QUIZ I

NAME _____

Multiply:

1. $2 \cdot 3x$ _____

2. $6x \cdot 4$ _____

3. $3(x + 4)$ _____

4. $(2x - 3)x$ _____

5. $(x - 3)(x + 5)$ _____

6. $(x - 4)^2$ _____

Factor:

7. $2x - 4$ _____

8. $3ax - a$ _____

9. $x^2 - 9$ _____

10. $x^2 - 5x - 24$ _____

11. $4x^2 - 12$ _____

12. $x^2 - 12x + 36$ _____

QUIZ II

NAME _____

Multiply:

1. $2x \cdot 3x$ _____

2. $(4x)5$ _____

3. $2(x - 1)$ _____

4. $(x - 4)x$ _____

5. $(x + 7)(x - 4)$ _____

6. $(x + 3)^2$ _____

Factor:

7. $x^2 + 4x$ _____

8. $6a - 3$ _____

9. $9 - m^2$ _____

10. $x^2 + 2x + 1$ _____

11. $x^2 - x - 12$ _____

12. $2ax^2 - 2x$ _____

QUIZ III

NAME _____

Multiply:

1. $x \cdot 2x$ _____

2. $(4b)(3a)$ _____

3. $3(4x - 2)$ _____

4. $(2x + 3)x$ _____

5. $(x - 5)(x - 2)$ _____

6. $(x - 7)^2$ _____

Factor:

7. $x^2 - 4x$ _____

8. $x^2 - 4$ _____

9. $x^2 - 4x - 12$ _____

10. $x^2 + 4x + 12$ _____

11. $3a - 6ab$ _____

12. $a^2 - b^2$ _____

QUIZ IV

NAME _____

Multiply:

1. $a \cdot 4$ _____

2. $b \cdot 3b$ _____

3. $4(2x - 3)$ _____

4. $(x - 4)(x - 1)$ _____

5. $-(3x + 4)$ _____

6. $(2x + 3)^2$ _____

Factor:

7. $3ax - 3a$ _____

8. $x^2 - 36$ _____

9. $x^2 + 5x + 6$ _____

10. $x^2 - 5x - 6$ _____

11. $x^2 - 25x$ _____

12. $x^2 - 25$ _____

Copyright © 1984 by Allyn and Bacon, Inc. Reproduction of this material is restricted to use with *A Guidebook for Teaching Algebra*, by Terry A. Goodman, John Bernard, Martin P. Cohen, and Joanne E. Meldon.

SAMPLE QUIZZES

QUIZ V

NAME _____

Multiply:

1. $x \cdot x$ _____
2. $2a(4b)$ _____
3. $-3(r - 2)$ _____
4. $(2a + b)a$ _____
5. $(x - 7)(x + 6)$ _____
6. $(x + 1)^2$ _____

Factor:

7. $a^2 - 16$ _____
8. $x^2 + x$ _____
9. $x^2 - 6x + 9$ _____
10. $x^2 + 5x - 14$ _____
11. $6ab - 6b$ _____
12. $x^2 + 5xy + y^2$ _____

QUIZ VI

NAME _____

Multiply:

1. $3b \cdot 4a$ _____
2. $-(2x + 4)$ _____
3. $(3a - b)2a$ _____
4. $(x - 3)(x - 5)$ _____
5. $(4 - a)(8 + a)$ _____
6. $(3 - x)^2$ _____

Factor:

7. $x^2 - 2x$ _____
8. $x^2 - 2x + 1$ _____
9. $x^2 - 1$ _____
10. $x^2 - 5x - 6$ _____
11. $3r^2 - 3r$ _____
12. $a^2 + 3ab - 10b^2$ _____

QUIZ VII

NAME _____

Multiply:

1. $(-3x)(-2)$ _____
2. $-6 \cdot 3a$ _____
3. $-2(4a - 3)$ _____
4. $(5r + 2)2r$ _____
5. $(x - 7)(x + 7)$ _____
6. $(6 + x)^2$ _____

Factor:

7. $x^2 - 5x + 4$ _____
8. $64 - x^2$ _____
9. $64 - 8x^2$ _____
10. $36 + 13a + a^2$ _____
11. $8x^2 + 8x$ _____
12. $x^2 - x - 56$ _____

QUIZ VIII

NAME _____

Multiply:

1. $(-3b)(2a)$ _____
2. $3x(2x - 1)$ _____
3. $(x - 4)^2$ _____
4. $(x - 7)(x - 1)$ _____
5. $(2x + 3)(2x - 3)$ _____
6. $(2x + 1)^2$ _____

Factor:

7. $4x - 36$ _____
8. $4x^2 - 1$ _____
9. $x^2 + x - 12$ _____
10. $r^2 - 8r - 9$ _____
11. $3x^2 + 3x$ _____
12. $a^2 - 4ab + 4b^2$ _____

Copyright © 1984 by Allyn and Bacon, Inc. Reproduction of this material is restricted to use with *A Guidebook for Teaching Algebra*, by Terry A. Goodman, John Bernard, Martin P. Cohen, and Joanne E. Meldon.

SAMPLE QUIZZES

QUIZ IX

NAME _____

Multiply:

1. $x \cdot x$ _____
2. $(x - 1)^2$ _____
3. $x(4 - 3x)$ _____
4. $(x - 9)(x - 2)$ _____
5. $(a - b)(a - 3b)$ _____
6. $(d - 1)(d - 1)$ _____

Factor:

7. $6x - 9x^2$ _____
8. $x^2 - 9x + 20$ _____
9. $a^2b^2 - ab - 6$ _____
10. $3x^2 - 9$ _____
11. $x^2 - 36$ _____
12. $4x^2 + 4x + 1$ _____

QUIZ X

NAME _____

Multiply:

1. $(3a)(2a)$ _____
2. $(x - 2)(-3x)$ _____
3. $(x + 5)(x - 5)$ _____
4. $(x + 3)^2$ _____
5. $(r + 2s)(r - 5s)$ _____
6. $(2m + 3)(2m + 3)$ _____

Factor:

7. $x^2 - 4y^2$ _____
8. $4ab + 4b$ _____
9. $x^2y^2 + xy - 30$ _____
10. $x^2 + 2x - 24$ _____
11. $12 - 2x^2$ _____
12. $1 - 5x + 4x^2$ _____

QUIZ XI

NAME _____

Multiply:

1. $(-4a)3$ _____
2. $-(2 - 3a)$ _____
3. $(4x - 3)^2$ _____
4. $(x + 4)(x - 5)$ _____
5. $(m - 3n)(m + n)$ _____
6. $(x - y)(x + y)$ _____

Factor:

7. $x^2y^2 - 49$ _____
8. $x^2 - 4x$ _____
9. $x^2 - 2x + 1$ _____
10. $2x^2 - 2x$ _____
11. $9x^2 - 6x + 1$ _____
12. $9 - 4x^2$ _____

QUIZ XII

NAME _____

Multiply:

1. $4x(3x^2)$ _____
2. $-x(-3 + x)$ _____
3. $(2a - 3)(4a - 5)$ _____
4. $(x - 3)(x - 3)$ _____
5. $(4 - 3x)(2 + x)$ _____
6. $(2a - 3b)^2$ _____

Factor:

7. $x^2 + 6x + 9$ _____
8. $1 + 8a + 16a^2$ _____
9. $8x - x^2$ _____
10. $2r^2 + 2r$ _____
11. $36a^2 - 25b^2$ _____
12. $12a^2b - 6ab$ _____

Copyright © 1984 by Allyn and Bacon, Inc. Reproduction of this material is restricted to use with *A Guidebook for Teaching Algebra*, by Terry A. Goodman, John Bernard, Martin P. Cohen, and Joanne E. Meldon.

245

EVALUATING RATIONAL EXPRESSIONS

A. Find the values of each rational expression below when $x = 1, 2, 3$.

	Given	Value of the Given When		
		$x = 1$	$x = 2$	$x = 3$
1.	$\dfrac{x-2}{x}$			
2.	$\dfrac{4}{x+2}$			
3.	$\dfrac{x+2}{x-3}$			
4.	$\dfrac{x^2+5x+6}{x^2-9}$			
5.	$\dfrac{x^2-4}{(x+2)^2}$			
6.	$\dfrac{x^2}{2x-3}$			
7.	$\dfrac{x+9}{x-9}$			
8.	$\dfrac{x-6}{6-x}$			
9.	$\dfrac{3x+2x-4}{4-5x}$			
10.	$\dfrac{x^2-4}{(x-2)^2}$			

B. For each problem above, state the value(s) of the variable which must be excluded when working with that expression.

1. _____   6. _____
2. _____   7. _____
3. _____   8. _____
4. _____   9. _____
5. _____   10. _____

Copyright © 1984 by Allyn and Bacon, Inc. Reproduction of this material is restricted to use with *A Guidebook for Teaching Algebra,* by Terry A. Goodman, John Bernard, Martin P. Cohen, and Joanne E. Meldon.

HOW TO SIMPLIFY RATIONAL EXPRESSIONS

Algorithm	Example
STEP I: Draw parentheses around any polynomial that appears in the numerator or denominator	
STEP II: Find the prime factors of the numerator and/or denominator (use FLOW CHART FOR FACTORING POLYNOMIALS)	
STEP III: Insert factors of 1, if needed. (The numerator and denominator must have the same number of factors.)	
STEP IV: Using the commutative law, line up "forms of one"	
STEP V: Apply the law $\dfrac{a \cdot b}{c \cdot d} = \dfrac{a}{c} \cdot \dfrac{b}{d}$	
STEP VI: Use the fact that $1 \cdot a = a$ and find the answer	
STEP VII: Check your answer by substituting a value(s) for the variable(s) involved in the given problem and in your answer	

Copyright © 1984 by Allyn and Bacon, Inc. Reproduction of this material is restricted to use with *A Guidebook for Teaching Algebra,* by Terry A. Goodman, John Bernard, Martin F Cohen, and Joanne E. Meldon.

247

SIMPLIFYING RATIONAL EXPRESSIONS

Directions: *Simplify each of the following by following the six-step algorithm in your notebook. If a step is not needed in the problem you are working on, darken the corresponding rectangle.*

STEPS	$\dfrac{3x}{6}$	$\dfrac{3x^2}{6x}$	$\dfrac{x^2-5x+6}{x^2-7x+6}$	$\dfrac{2x}{4x-8}$
I				
II				
III				
IV				
V				
VI				

STEPS	$\dfrac{a^2-9}{a-3}$	$\dfrac{x^2-16}{3x+12}$	$\dfrac{a^2+a-12}{4a-12}$	$\dfrac{r-3}{r^2-4-6}$
I				
II				
III				
IV				
V				
VI				

Copyright © 1984 by Allyn and Bacon, Inc. Reproduction of this material is restricted to use with *A Guidebook for Teaching Algebra,* by Terry A. Goodman, John Bernard, Martin P. Cohen, and Joanne E. Meldon.

MULTIPLYING RATIONAL EXPRESSIONS

Algorithm	Example
STEP I: Put ( ) around any polynomial appearing in the problem	
STEP II: Apply the rule $\frac{a}{b} \cdot \frac{c}{d} = \frac{a \cdot c}{b \cdot d}$, forming a single fraction [THE MULTIPLICATION HAS BEEN REDUCED TO A "SIMPLIFYING" ONE]	
STEP III: Find the prime factors of each monomial and polynomial given [USE FLOW CHART FOR POLYNOMIALS]	
STEP IV: Use the commutative law to line up identical factors	
STEP V: Identify "forms of one"	
STEP VI: Multiply the remaining factors in the numerator and denominator	
STEP VII: Check the results by substituting a value(s) for the variable(s) involved	

Copyright © 1984 by Allyn and Bacon, Inc. Reproduction of this material is restricted to use with *A Guidebook for Teaching Algebra*, by Terry A. Goodman, John Bernard, Martin P. Cohen, and Joanne E. Meldon.

MULTIPLYING AND REDUCING RATIONAL EXPRESSIONS

A. Using the algorithm, multiply the following. Darken each space corresponding to a step that is not needed.

STEPS	$\dfrac{5}{a} \cdot \dfrac{a^2}{15}$	$\dfrac{x+3}{5} \cdot \dfrac{10}{3+x}$	$\dfrac{m+5}{10m} \cdot \dfrac{5m}{(m+5)^2}$	$\dfrac{4x}{x^2-4} \cdot \dfrac{6x+12}{18x^2}$	$\dfrac{4x+3y}{8x} \cdot \dfrac{2x-4y}{x^2-4y^2}$
I					
II					
III					
IV					
V					
VI					

B. The following set of exercises contains many mistakes made by Pat (who foolishly thought that "cancelling" was allowed). Each of his answers is incorrect. Determine which rational expressions can be simplified and find what the answers should be.

1. $\dfrac{4x+2}{2} = 4x + 1$ _____

2. $\dfrac{a-2}{2-a} = \dfrac{0}{0}$ _____

3. $\dfrac{3(a+b)}{x+(a+b)} = \dfrac{3}{x+1}$ _____

4. $\dfrac{a+b}{c(a+b)} = c$ _____

5. $\dfrac{a+b}{x+y} \cdot \dfrac{y+x}{b+a} = 0$ _____

6. $\dfrac{x^2-y^2}{x-y} = x - y$ _____

7. $\dfrac{a+2}{(a+2)(a+2)} = a + 2$ _____

8. $\dfrac{x^2-9}{y^2-9} = \dfrac{x^2}{y^2}$ _____

9. $\dfrac{x^2+5x-36}{x^2-5x+4} = 9$ _____

10. $\dfrac{x}{x+y} = \dfrac{1}{x+y}$ _____

Copyright © 1984 by Allyn and Bacon, Inc. Reproduction of this material is restricted to use with *A Guidebook for Teaching Algebra*, by Terry A. Goodman, John Bernard, Martin P. Cohen, and Joanne E. Meldon.

RECIPROCALS: DIVIDING RATIONAL EXPRESSIONS

A. Complete the following chart. Verify that your answer is correct by using the rule
$a \cdot \dfrac{1}{a} = 1 \ldots a \neq 0$

a	$\dfrac{1}{a}$	$a \cdot \dfrac{1}{a}$
$-3x$		$= 1$
$-x + 4$		$= 1$
$-(x + 4)$		$= 1$
$\dfrac{4x}{x + 5}$		$= 1$
$\dfrac{1}{(x - 2)^2}$		$= 1$

B. Write each of the following as a multiplication problem. Then find the answer following the algorithm for multiplying rational expressions.

1. $\dfrac{3}{ay} \div \dfrac{a}{3}$

2. $\dfrac{3x^2 y}{7a} \div 15xy$

3. $\dfrac{3a + 9}{5x + 10} \div \dfrac{6}{25}$

4. $\dfrac{x^2 - y^2}{8x} \div \dfrac{3x - 3y}{2x}$

5. $\dfrac{2x - 2}{x^2 - 9} \div \dfrac{4x - 4}{x + 3}$

6. $\dfrac{x^2 + 4x - 12}{x^2 + 9x + 18} \div \dfrac{3x + 12}{x^2 - 4}$

Copyright © 1984 by Allyn and Bacon, Inc. Reproduction of this material is restricted to use with *A Guidebook for Teaching Algebra,* by Terry A. Goodman, John Bernard, Martin P. Cohen, and Joanne E. Meldon.

SIMPLIFYING COMPLEX FRACTIONS

Algorithm	Example
1. Insert parentheses around any polynomial appearing in the fraction	
2. Determine the *LCD* of all the fractions that appear within the fraction	
3. Multiply by the form of one: $\dfrac{LCD}{LCD}$ ALL FRACTIONS WITHIN THE FRACTION WILL BE GONE AT THIS POINT!	
4. Reduce the answer, if possible	
5. Check your answer	

Now Simplify These:

1. $\dfrac{\frac{x-y}{a}}{\frac{y-x}{a}}$	2. $\dfrac{1+\frac{1}{a}}{a-\frac{1}{a}}$	3. $\dfrac{2+\frac{x}{y}}{4-\frac{x^2}{y^2}}$	4. $\dfrac{\frac{1}{a}-\frac{1}{b}}{1-\frac{b}{a}}$
5. $\dfrac{\frac{7}{2}-\frac{2}{3}}{\frac{5}{4}+1}$	6. $\dfrac{\frac{x-16}{x-25}}{\frac{x+4}{x+5}}$	7. $\dfrac{\frac{y+3}{5}}{\frac{y^2-9}{10}}$	8. $\dfrac{\frac{c}{3}-\frac{3}{c}}{\frac{c}{3}-2+\frac{3}{c}}$

Copyright © 1984 by Allyn and Bacon, Inc. Reproduction of this material is restricted to use with *A Guidebook for Teaching Algebra,* by Terry A. Goodman, John Bernard, Martin P. Cohen, and Joanne E. Meldon.

ADDING RATIONAL EXPRESSIONS WITH THE SAME DENOMINATOR

Algorithm

STEP I: Insert ( ) around any polynomial

STEP II: Write each fraction as the product of

Numerator $\cdot$ $\dfrac{1}{\text{Denominator}}$

STEP III: Use the distributive law to factor

$\dfrac{1}{\text{Denominator}}$ out of each term

STEP IV: Simplify what is inside ( ), if possible

STEP V: Write the product in fraction form

STEP VI: Reduce the answer, if possible

STEP VII: Check your answer

I. $\dfrac{3}{(x+5)} + \dfrac{(x+2)}{(x+5)} = ?$

II. $3 \cdot \dfrac{1}{x+5} + (x+2) \cdot \dfrac{1}{x+5}$

III. $(3 + x + 2) \cdot \dfrac{1}{x+5}$

IV. $(x+5) \cdot \dfrac{1}{x+5}$

V. $\dfrac{x+5}{x+5}$

VI. 1

STEPS	1. $\dfrac{x}{3} + \dfrac{1}{3}$	2. $\dfrac{3}{x} + \dfrac{2}{x}$	3. $\dfrac{2}{x+2} + \dfrac{x}{x+2}$
STEP I			
STEP II			
STEP III			
STEP IV			
STEP V			
STEP VI			

Copyright © 1984 by Allyn and Bacon, Inc. Reproduction of this material is restricted to use with *A Guidebook for Teaching Algebra,* by Terry A. Goodman, John Bernard, Martin P. Cohen, and Joanne E. Meldon.

STEPS	4. $\dfrac{x+4}{2x} + \dfrac{x+6}{2x}$	5. $\dfrac{5}{3a} + \dfrac{3a-8}{3a}$	6. $\dfrac{z^2-2}{z+5} + \dfrac{27}{z+5}$
STEP I			
STEP II			
STEP III			
STEP IV			
STEP V			
STEP VI			

Copyright © 1984 by Allyn and Bacon, Inc. Reproduction of this material is restricted to use with *A Guidebook for Teaching Algebra,* by Terry A. Goodman, John Bernard, Martin P. Cohen, and Joanne E. Meldon.

PREREQUISITES FOR ADDITION OF RATIONAL EXPRESSIONS

A. Find the *prime factors* of

1. 6	4. $2x + 14$	7. $x^2 + 6x - 27$
2. $3x$	5. $b^2 + 3b$	8. $x^2 - x - 2$
3. a^2	6. $x^2 - 9$	9. $a^2 - 6x + 9$

B. Find the *least common multiple* of

1. $2x$ and $6x$

2. 8 and 18

3. 2 and $2a - 6$

4. $x + 3$ and $x - 3$

5. $a^2 - 9$ and $3 + a$

6. $b^2 + 2b + 1$ and $b^2 - 1$

C. Find the *form of one* that will convert each pair of fractions to *like fractions* (fractions having the same denominator)

1. $\square \cdot \dfrac{2}{3}$ and $\dfrac{4}{15}$

2. $\square \cdot \dfrac{3}{2x}$ and $\dfrac{7}{6x}$

3. $\square \cdot \dfrac{a}{2}$ and $\dfrac{3}{2a + 10}$

4. $\square \cdot \dfrac{1}{x - 3}$ and $\dfrac{x}{x^2 - 9}$

5. $\square \cdot \dfrac{3}{d + 2}$ and $\dfrac{d + 2}{d^2 + 4x + 4}$

6. $\square \cdot \dfrac{}{z - 7}$ and $\dfrac{}{7 - z}$

7. $\square \cdot \dfrac{3}{x}$ and $\dfrac{x}{2} \cdot \square$

8. $\square \cdot \dfrac{3}{4}$ and $\dfrac{5}{7} \cdot \square$

9. $\square \cdot \dfrac{a}{a - 2}$ and $\dfrac{3}{a + 2} \cdot \square$

10. $\square \cdot \dfrac{5}{6x}$ and $\dfrac{1}{2x^2}$

11. $\square \cdot \dfrac{b}{b + 2}$ and $\dfrac{b - 3}{b} \cdot \square$

12. $\square \cdot \dfrac{x + 3}{x^2 - 9}$ and $\dfrac{5}{3x - 9} \cdot \square$

Copyright © 1984 by Allyn and Bacon, Inc. Reproduction of this material is restricted to use with *A Guidebook for Teaching Algebra,* by Terry A. Goodman, John Bernard, Martin P. Cohen, and Joanne E. Meldon.

ADDITION OF RATIONAL EXPRESSIONS

Directions: *Add the given fractions and simplify the sum, if possible.*

Given	Using: $\dfrac{a}{c} + \dfrac{b}{c} = \dfrac{a+b}{c}$	Using: $\dfrac{a}{b} + \dfrac{c}{d} = \dfrac{ad+bc}{ad}$
1. $\dfrac{x}{2} + \dfrac{3x}{5}$		
2. $\dfrac{4r+3}{5r} + \dfrac{7}{10r}$		
3. $\dfrac{3b}{b-5} + \dfrac{2}{b+9}$		
4. $\dfrac{3y-1}{y^2-y} + \dfrac{1}{2y}$		
5. $\dfrac{3a+2b}{3b} + \dfrac{-a-2b}{6b}$		
6. $\dfrac{6a-3}{a^2-5a+6} + \dfrac{5}{a-3}$		

Copyright © 1984 by Allyn and Bacon, Inc. Reproduction of this material is restricted to use with *A Guidebook for Teaching Algebra,* by Terry A. Goodman, John Bernard, Martin P. Cohen, and Joanne E. Meldon.

ADDING RATIONAL EXPRESSIONS

1. $\dfrac{2}{9a} + \dfrac{11}{6a}$

=

2. $\dfrac{x+3}{x-5} + \dfrac{x-5}{x+3}$

=

3. $3x + \dfrac{x^2+2}{x}$

=

2. $\dfrac{9r}{4r-20} + \dfrac{9r}{6r-30}$

=

5. $\dfrac{2x+5}{5x-4} + \dfrac{9-3x}{4-5x}$

=

6. $\dfrac{3m}{2m-3} + \dfrac{2m}{3m-2}$

=

7. $\dfrac{2x+3}{2} + (x-4)$

=

8. $\dfrac{2a}{a^2-16} + \dfrac{4-a}{a^2-16}$

=

9. $\dfrac{3b+2}{3b+6} + \dfrac{b-2}{b^2-4}$

=

Copyright © 1984 by Allyn and Bacon, Inc. Reproduction of this material is restricted to use with *A Guidebook for Teaching Algebra*, by Terry A. Goodman, John Bernard, Martin P. Cohen, and Joanne E. Meldon.

OPPOSITES: SUBTRACTION OF RATIONAL EXPRESSIONS

A. Complete the following chart.

Given Number (a)	Its Opposite ($-a$)	Check: $a + (-a) = 0$
2		
x		
$-\dfrac{1}{2}$		
$(x - 3)$		
$\dfrac{x}{3}$		
$\dfrac{3}{x - 4}$		
$\dfrac{x - 2}{3x}$		
$\dfrac{2x - 3}{2x + 3}$		
$\dfrac{2(x - 3)}{x + 1}$		
$\left(-\dfrac{1}{x} + 2\right)$		

B. Change each subtraction problem to the equivalent addition problem.

1. $\dfrac{x + 2}{3} - \dfrac{2}{3}$ $= \dfrac{x + 2}{3} + \dfrac{\square}{3}$	2. $\dfrac{b}{b + 1} - \dfrac{1}{b + 1}$ $=$	3. $\dfrac{3a + 2b}{3b} - \dfrac{a + 2b}{6a}$ $=$

Copyright © 1984 by Allyn and Bacon, Inc. Reproduction of this material is restricted to use with *A Guidebook for Teaching Algebra*, by Terry A. Goodman, John Bernard, Martin P. Cohen, and Joanne E. Meldon.

4. $\dfrac{2x-1}{4} - \dfrac{x-1}{8}$

=

5. $\dfrac{4}{3r} - \dfrac{r+2}{r}$

=

6. $\dfrac{3x-2}{4x} - \dfrac{3x+1}{6x}$

=

7. $\dfrac{2z}{z-1} - \dfrac{3z}{z+1}$

=

8. $\dfrac{5a}{a^2-9} - \dfrac{4}{a+3}$

=

9. $\dfrac{y-5}{4y} - \dfrac{3y-1}{y}$

=

10. $\dfrac{2}{m-2} - \dfrac{2}{2-m}$

=

11. $\dfrac{x-2}{3x} - \dfrac{1-2x}{5x}$

=

12. $4x - \dfrac{2x-5}{3}$

=

Copyright © 1984 by Allyn and Bacon, Inc. Reproduction of this material is restricted to use with *A Guidebook for Teaching Algebra*, by Terry A. Goodman, John Bernard, Martin P. Cohen, and Joanne E. Meldon.

OPERATIONS WITH RATIONAL EXPRESSIONS

Reducing Fractions	Multiplying Fractions	Dividing Fractions
1. $\dfrac{4x}{6x}$	1. $\dfrac{6a}{17b} \cdot \dfrac{34ab}{a}$	1. $\dfrac{2a}{5b} \div \dfrac{3a}{5}$
2. $\dfrac{3}{3x-6}$	2. $\dfrac{6x+18}{x} \cdot \dfrac{3x}{5x+10}$	2. $\dfrac{6x+1}{27} \div \dfrac{6x+1}{9}$
3. $\dfrac{x^2-4}{x+2}$	3. $\dfrac{2t+16}{4t} \cdot \dfrac{10t^2}{3t+24}$	3. $\dfrac{a^2-4}{3a} \div \dfrac{a+2}{1}$
4. $\dfrac{2x+10}{x^2-25}$	4. $\dfrac{y-5}{8y-4} \cdot \dfrac{10y-5}{6y-30}$	4. $\dfrac{b+2}{b^2-9} \div \dfrac{1}{a-3}$
5. $\dfrac{a^2-9}{a^2-a-6}$	5. $\dfrac{3x-6}{4x+8} \cdot \dfrac{x+2}{x-2}$	5. $\dfrac{5}{a^2-9} \div \dfrac{5a-10}{a-3}$
H-1. $\dfrac{2x^2-32}{12x-48}$	H-1. $\dfrac{a^2+b^2}{a^2-b^2} \cdot \dfrac{a-b}{a+b}$	H-1. $\dfrac{y^2-36}{y^2+12y+36} \div \dfrac{5y-30}{y^3+6y^2}$
H-2. $\dfrac{2a^3+a^2-3a}{6a^3+5a^2-6a}$	H-2. $\dfrac{x^2-6x-7}{x^2+x} \cdot \dfrac{x^2-x}{3x-21}$	H-2. $\dfrac{x^2-4}{x^2-5x+6} \div \dfrac{x^3+3x^2+2y}{x^2-2x-3}$

Adding Like Fractions	Adding Unlike Fractions	Subtracting Like Fractions
1. $\dfrac{m+2}{m} + \dfrac{3}{m}$	1. $\dfrac{x}{y} + \dfrac{2x}{3y}$	1. $\dfrac{4}{a^2-4} - \dfrac{a^2}{a^2-4}$
2. $\dfrac{x}{x^2-1} + \dfrac{1}{x^2-1}$	2. $\dfrac{m+2}{3} + \dfrac{m-1}{6}$	2. $\dfrac{3x}{2x-6} - \dfrac{3x}{2x-6}$
3. $\dfrac{a^2}{a^2-4} + \dfrac{-4}{a^2-4}$	3. $\dfrac{3}{a^2+a} + \dfrac{3}{a+1}$	3. $\dfrac{5a+3}{2a+3} - \dfrac{a-3}{2a+3}$
4. $\dfrac{3r+2}{r+2} + \dfrac{r+6}{r+2}$	4. $\dfrac{3}{a+2} + \dfrac{a}{a^2+4a+4}$	4. $\dfrac{x^2+2x}{x-4} - \dfrac{x^2+8}{x-4}$
5. $\dfrac{m^2+m}{m+3} + \dfrac{3-m^2}{m+3}$	5. $\dfrac{x+1}{x-5} + \dfrac{x}{2x-10}$	5. $\dfrac{5n^2-6n}{n-3} - \dfrac{4n^2-9}{n+3}$
H-1. $\dfrac{x^2-2x}{x-4} + \dfrac{16-6x}{x-4}$	H-1. $\dfrac{-18}{x^2-9} + \dfrac{3}{x-3}$	H-1. $\dfrac{x}{(x-y)} - \dfrac{xy}{(x-y)^2}$
H-2. $\dfrac{2x^2-7}{2x^2-8} + \dfrac{2x-5}{2x^2-8}$	H-2. $\dfrac{a}{a^2-16} + \dfrac{2}{3a-12}$	H-2. $\dfrac{7n^2}{m^2-n^2} - \dfrac{2n^2-5m^2}{m^2-n^2}$

Copyright © 1984 by Allyn and Bacon, Inc. Reproduction of this material is restricted to use with *A Guidebook for Teaching Algebra*, by Terry A. Goodman, John Bernard, Martin P. Cohen, and Joanne E. Meldon.

Subtracting Unlike Fractions

1. $\dfrac{a}{b} - \dfrac{b}{a}$

2. $\dfrac{x-3}{6} - \dfrac{x-1}{10}$

3. $\dfrac{5}{x-1} - \dfrac{5}{x^2-x}$

4. $\dfrac{5m+6}{3m+9} - \dfrac{m}{m+3}$

5. $\dfrac{4x}{x^2-16} - \dfrac{2}{x+4}$

H-1. $\dfrac{3}{7-x} - \dfrac{4}{x-7}$

H-2. $\dfrac{n}{n^2-9} - \dfrac{1}{2n-6}$

Complex Fractions

1. $\dfrac{\dfrac{y+3}{5}}{\dfrac{y^2-9}{10}}$

2. $\dfrac{\dfrac{x^2-y^2}{12}}{\dfrac{x+y}{4}}$

3. $\dfrac{\dfrac{6}{x^2-1}}{\dfrac{3}{x+1}}$

4. $\dfrac{\dfrac{x-y}{xy}}{\dfrac{y-x}{xy}}$

5. $\dfrac{\dfrac{m+2}{x}}{\dfrac{m^2-4}{x^2}}$

H-1. $\dfrac{\dfrac{c}{d} - \dfrac{d}{c}}{\dfrac{c}{d} + \dfrac{d}{c} + 2}$

H-2. $\dfrac{\dfrac{2y-2z}{y-z}}{\dfrac{y-2}{y+2}}$

Potluck

1. $a - \dfrac{3a}{a-2}$

2. $\dfrac{4}{x-2} + \dfrac{3}{2-x}$

3. $\dfrac{2}{x} + \dfrac{3}{y} + \dfrac{4}{z}$

4. $\dfrac{4n}{n-5} - n$

5. $\dfrac{12a^2}{a^2+3a} \div \dfrac{2a}{a^2+6a+9}$

H-1. $\dfrac{a^2-5a+19}{a^2-3a-4} - \dfrac{3}{a-4}$

H-2. $\dfrac{4}{x^2-4} - \dfrac{x}{4-x^2}$

Copyright © 1984 by Allyn and Bacon, Inc. Reproduction of this material is restricted to use with *A Guidebook for Teaching Algebra,* by Terry A. Goodman, John Bernard, Martin P. Cohen, and Joanne E. Meldon.

PREREQUISITES FOR SOLVING FRACTIONAL EQUATIONS

A. Find the *LCD* of:

1. 2 and 9

2. 6 and 9 and 12

3. $3x$ and $6x$

4. x^2 and $3x$

5. $(x + 2)$ and $(x - 3)$

6. $(x - 2)$ and $(x^2 - 2)$

7. $(2x - 6)$ and $(3 - x)$

8. $(x^2 + 3x)$ and $(2x^2 - 18)$

B. Find the following products:

1. $3\left(\dfrac{1}{3}\right)$

2. $2\left(\dfrac{5}{2}\right)$

3. $x\left(\dfrac{1}{x}\right)$

4. $6\left(\dfrac{x}{2}\right)$

5. $6x\left(\dfrac{3}{x}\right)$

6. $(x + 2)\left(\dfrac{4}{x + 2}\right)$

7. $[(x - 2)(x + 3)]\left(\dfrac{4}{x + 3}\right)$

8. $[x(x - 4)]\left(\dfrac{x + 2}{x}\right)$

C. Multiply the following:

1. $5(2x - 3)$

2. $a\left(\dfrac{1}{a} + 4\right)$

3. $2\left(\dfrac{m}{2} + 3\right)$

4. $6\left(\dfrac{x}{6} - 1\right)$

5. $2x\left(\dfrac{x}{2} - \dfrac{3}{x}\right)$

6. $6x\left(1 - \dfrac{x}{3} + \dfrac{2}{x}\right)$

7. $(x + 3)\left(\dfrac{4}{x + 3} + 2\right)$

8. $(x^2 - 25)\left(\dfrac{2}{x - 5} - \dfrac{x}{x + 5}\right)$

D. Write as a fraction:

1. $\dfrac{1}{3}m$

2. $\dfrac{2}{5}x$

3. $\dfrac{x}{2} \cdot x$

4. $\dfrac{x - 2}{3} \cdot x$

Copyright © 1984 by Allyn and Bacon, Inc. Reproduction of this material is restricted to use with *A Guidebook for Teaching Algebra*, by Terry A. Goodman, John Bernard, Martin P. Cohen, and Joanne E. Meldon.

LCD BINGO

I	K	N	O	W
		F R E E		

*1. $3x$

*2. $6x$

*3. $6x^2$

4. $3x + 6$

*5. $2x - 4$

6. $4x - 8$

*7. $x^2 + 2x$

8. $x^2 + 4x + 4$

*9. $x^2 - 4$

*10. $4 - x^2$

*11. $x^2 - 4x + 4$

12. $2x + 4$

13. $x^2 + 5x + 6$

14. $x^2 + x - 6$

15. $x^2 + x - 6$

16. $x^2 + 4x$

―――――――
*Should be used twice.

Copyright © 1984 by Allyn and Bacon, Inc. Reproduction of this material is restricted to use with *A Guidebook for Teaching Algebra,* by Terry A. Goodman, John Bernard, Martin P. Cohen, and Joanne E. Meldon.

263

ALGORITHM FOR SOLVING FRACTIONAL EQUATIONS

Steps	Example	Problem
I. Express any term containing a rational coefficient as a single fraction		
II. Insert parentheses ( ) around any polynomial that appears in a fraction		
III. Change all minus signs between fractions to plus signs and REPLACE THE FOLLOWING NUMERATOR WITH ITS OPPOSITE		
IV. Determine the *LCD* of the function within the equation		
V. Multiply every term on both sides by the *LCD*		
VI. Solve the resulting equation		
VII. Check the answer		

Copyright © 1984 by Allyn and Bacon, Inc. Reproduction of this material is restricted to use with *A Guidebook for Teaching Algebra,* by Terry A. Goodman, John Bernard, Martin P. Cohen, and Joanne E. Meldon.

SOLVING EQUATIONS WITH RATIONAL COEFFICIENTS

Solve the following:

1. $\dfrac{a}{3} + \dfrac{a}{4} = \dfrac{7}{2}$

2. $\dfrac{x}{5} + \dfrac{x}{4} = \dfrac{9}{2}$

3. $\dfrac{2}{3}x + 1 = \dfrac{1}{2}x$

4. $\dfrac{3x - 2}{6} - \dfrac{2x + 5}{4} = 1$

5. $3 - \dfrac{3a}{2} - \dfrac{8 - 4a}{7} = 0$

6. $\dfrac{4b + 3}{6} = \dfrac{1}{2} + \dfrac{4}{9}b - \dfrac{1}{9}$

7. $\dfrac{1}{2}x + \dfrac{1}{3}y = 2$

$\dfrac{1}{3}x + \dfrac{1}{9}y = 1$

8. $\dfrac{a}{4} - \dfrac{b}{6} = 0$

$\dfrac{3}{8}a + \dfrac{5}{12}b = -4$

GRAPH 7.

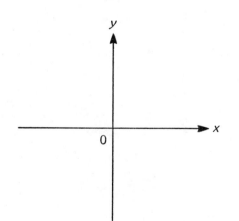

GRAPH 8.

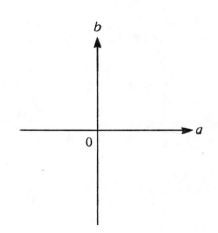

Copyright © 1984 by Allyn and Bacon, Inc. Reproduction of this material is restricted to use with *A Guidebook for Teaching Algebra*, by Terry A. Goodman, John Bernard, Martin P. Cohen, and Joanne E. Meldon.

SOLVING FRACTIONAL EQUATIONS

Solve the following equations (State the restriction on the variable)

1. $\dfrac{3}{c} - \dfrac{2}{3c} = \dfrac{14}{3}$ $\lfloor c \neq$ 2. $\dfrac{1}{2} + \dfrac{1}{x} = \dfrac{2}{x}$ $\lfloor x \neq$

3. $\dfrac{3a - 1}{5a - 4} = \dfrac{2}{3}$ $\lfloor a \neq$ 4. $\dfrac{m}{m - 1} + 3 = \dfrac{1}{m - 1} - 1$ $\lfloor m \neq$

5. $\dfrac{x - 5}{x - 4} = \dfrac{3x}{3x + 1}$ $\lfloor x \neq$ 6. $\dfrac{8}{t + 2} + \dfrac{8}{t - 2} = 3 - \dfrac{3t^2}{t^2 - 4}$ $\lfloor t \neq$

7. $\dfrac{x}{x + 4} - \dfrac{4}{x - 4} = \dfrac{x^2 + 16}{x^2 - 16}$ $\lfloor x \neq$ 8. $\dfrac{2r - 1}{r - 1} = \dfrac{2r}{r + 1}$ $\lfloor r \neq$

Copyright © 1984 by Allyn and Bacon, Inc. Reproduction of this material is restricted to use with *A Guidebook for Teaching Algebra*, by Terry A. Goodman, John Bernard, Martin P. Cohen, and Joanne E. Meldon.

WORKING WITH PROPORTIONS

Directions: *Combine the side indicated into a single fraction. Then solve the resulting proportion by cross-multiplying.*

1. $4 + \dfrac{2}{x} = \dfrac{12}{x}$

$\underline{\quad} x \neq \underline{\qquad}$

2. $\dfrac{3}{y} - 2 = \dfrac{3}{y}$

$\underline{\quad} y \neq \underline{\qquad}$

3. $\dfrac{5m}{m+1} = 5 - \dfrac{2}{m}$

$\underline{\quad} m \neq \underline{\qquad}$

4. $2 - \dfrac{3}{x} = \dfrac{2x}{x+1}$

$\underline{\quad} x \neq \underline{\qquad}$

5. $3 + \dfrac{2-3m}{m+3} = \dfrac{8}{m-3}$

$\underline{\quad} m \neq \underline{\qquad}$

6. $\dfrac{4}{a} + \dfrac{3}{2a} = \dfrac{11}{2}$

$\underline{\quad} a \neq \underline{\qquad}$

Copyright © 1984 by Allyn and Bacon, Inc. Reproduction of this material is restricted to use with *A Guidebook for Teaching Algebra,* by Terry A. Goodman, John Bernard, Martin P. Cohen, and Joanne E. Meldon.

ORDERED PAIRS

A. GAS-GUZZLER Motor Company is producing its new car, the Torpedo. The list of interior colors for this car is *I* = {red, blue, white, green} and the exterior colors *E* = {red, white, blue}.

1. List all of the ordered pairs formed by listing an interior color first and an exterior color second. Use this table to help you make the list.

		Interior			
		red	blue	white	green
Exterior	red	(red, red)			
	white		(blue, white)		
	blue				

B. The UNIVERSAL RENT-ALL COMPANY rents lawn mowers for $3.50 per hour.

1. Complete this table relating hours rented to rental cost.

Hours rented	Total cost
1	3.50
2	
	10.50
4	

2. List the ordered pairs formed above.

(1,3.50), (,   ), (,   ), (,   )

3. Can you state a rule (equation) relating hours used to cost?

$y = ($ $) \cdot x$

where y is the cost for x hours used?

Copyright © 1984 by Allyn and Bacon, Inc. Reproduction of this material is restricted to use with *A Guidebook for Teaching Algebra*, by Terry A. Goodman, John Bernard, Martin P. Cohen, and Joanne E. Meldon.

EQUATIONS AND ORDERED PAIRS

A. Determine which of the followed ordered pairs belong to the truth set of the given equation.

$y = x - 4$				
(1,2) $y = x - 4$ $2 = \underline{1 - 4}$ ② ⊝③ No	(3,−1) $y = x - 4$ $-1 = \underline{3 - 4}$ ⊝① ⊝① Yes	(−2,−6)	(0,4)	(7,3)
$y = 3x$				
(2,6)	(1,31)	(0,3)	(4,12)	(−2,−6)
$y = 2x + 5$				
(0,25)	(1,7)	(3,11)	(−1,−3)	(−3,1)
$y = \frac{x}{2} - 3$				
(0,−1)	(4,−1)	(6,6)	(8,1)	(−10,−8)

Copyright © 1984 by Allyn and Bacon, Inc. Reproduction of this material is restricted to use with *A Guidebook for Teaching Algebra,* by Terry A. Goodman, John Bernard, Martin P. Cohen, and Joanne E. Meldon.

B. Complete the chart that corresponds to each set of ordered pairs; then "guess" the relationship between x and y.

1. $\{(1,3), (2,6), (4,12), (8,24)\}$

x				
y				

Relationship: $y = 3x$

2. $\{(1,1), (2,4), (3,9), (4,16)\}$

x				
y				

Relationship:

3. $\{(1,5), (2,7), (3,9), (4,11)\}$

x				
y				

Relationship:

4. $\{(0,-5), (2,-4), (4,-3), (6,-2)\}$

x				
y				

Relationship:

Copyright © 1984 by Allyn and Bacon, Inc. Reproduction of this material is restricted to use with *A Guidebook for Teaching Algebra*, by Terry A. Goodman, John Bernard, Martin P. Cohen, and Joanne E. Meldon.

RELATIONS AND ORDERED PAIRS

A. Consider the following relation:

$S = \{(1,2), (2,4), (3,5), (3,6), (4,7), (4,3)\}$

1. List all the first components as a set

   $D = \{1, 2, \text{_____}\}$

2. List all the second components as a set

   $R = \{2, 4, \text{_____}\}$

B. Let $T_1 = \{(1,2), (2,5), (3,7), (5,6)\}$ and

   $T_2 = \{(2,7), (1,5), (3,6), (5,2), (2,6)\}$

   be relations and let D and R be defined as above. Then for T_1,

   $D = \text{_____}$

   $R = \text{_____}$

   and for T_2,

   $D = \text{_____}$

   $R = \text{_____}$

   What do you notice about these sets?

C. Let $y = 3x$ define a relation.

1. List some ordered pairs formed by this relation. (Use only whole numbers.)

   $(0,0), (1,3), \text{_____}$

2. What do you think D (the set of first components) would be here?

   $D = \text{_____}$

3. How about R (the set of second components)?

   $R = \text{_____}$

Copyright © 1984 by Allyn and Bacon, Inc. Reproduction of this material is restricted to use with *A Guidebook for Teaching Algebra*, by Terry A. Goodman, John Bernard, Martin P. Cohen, and Joanne E. Meldon.

DOMAIN AND RANGE

Directions: *For each of the following relations, find the range given the domain.*

1. $y = 2x$ $D = \{0, 1, 2, \ldots, 10\}$

   $R =$ _____

2. $y = 3x + 1$ $D = \{\text{whole numbers}\}$

   $R =$ _____

3. $y = 3x + 1$ $D = \{\text{even whole numbers}\}$

   $R =$ _____

4. $y = \dfrac{1}{x}$ $D = \{\text{counting numbers}\}$

   $R =$ _____

   In (4), could the domain be the set of whole numbers? Why or why not?

5. $y = \sqrt{x}$ $D = \{\text{whole numbers}\}$

   $R =$ _____

   In (5), could the domain be the set of integers? Why or why not?

6. $y = \dfrac{x - 3}{x^2 - 9}$ $D = \{1, 2, 4, 5\}$

   $R =$ _____

   In (6), could 3 be an element of the domain? Why or why not?

7. $y = |x - 3|$ $D = \{\text{integers}\}$

   $R =$ _____

Copyright © 1984 by Allyn and Bacon, Inc. Reproduction of this material is restricted to use with *A Guidebook for Teaching Algebra,* by Terry A. Goodman, John Bernard, Martin P. Cohen, and Joanne E. Meldon.

RELATIONS AND FUNCTIONS

A. Let's go back to our example about the automobiles. Remember, I = {red, blue, white, green} (the interior colors) and E = {red, white, blue} (the exterior colors).
To shorten our writing let's agree that

    red   = 1
    blue = 2
    white = 3
    green = 4

Then,
I = {1,2,3,4}   and E = {1,3,2}.

1. List all the ordered pairs (possible color combinations) using the above code.
(1,1), (1,3), (1,2), (2,1) _____

2. How many different combinations can you get if you insist on the interior color red (1)? List them.

_____

Notice that there are several different combinations (ordered pairs) with the same first component.

B. Recall the equation y = (3.50)x relating hours rented to rental fee.

1. Let the domain D = {1,2,3,4,5}. List the ordered pairs formed using this domain.
(1,3.50), (2,7.00), _____

2. How many different ordered pairs can you get for the domain element 4?

_____

Notice that for this relation every domain element (first component) is matched with *only 1* range element (second component). Such a relation is called a *function*. Which of the above examples is a function?

_____

C. Circle each relation below that is a function.

Example:
$y = 2x + 3$ Domain = {whole numbers}
Solution: Make a table

x	$2x + 3$
0	3
1	5
2	7
3	9

etc.

For each x value how many different y values do we get? That's right! One.
So, $y = 2x + 3$ is a function.

Copyright © 1984 by Allyn and Bacon, Inc. Reproduction of this material is restricted to use with *A Guidebook for Teaching Algebra*, by Terry A. Goodman, John Bernard, Martin P. Cohen, and Joanne E. Meldon.

1. R_1 = {(1,3), (4,2), (1,5), (2,6), (3,3)}
   Look at the first components!!
2. $y = 3x + 4$
3. $y = x^2$
4. R_2 = {(1,3), (2,7), (3,6), (4,6), (5,6), (7,6)}
5. $x = |y|$ This is a little more difficult. Look at the table

x	y
0	0
1	1
1	–1
2	2
2	–2

Copyright © 1984 by Allyn and Bacon, Inc. Reproduction of this material is restricted to use with *A Guidebook for Teaching Algebra*, by Terry A. Goodman, John Bernard, Martin P. Cohen, and Joanne E. Meldon.

VALUES OF $F(X)$

A. Complete the following table for $y = 2x + 3$

x	2x + 3
0	3
1	
2	
-3	
5	
-4	

1. To find $2x + 3$ we must know _____ .
2. In other words, the value for $2x + 3$ is dependent upon the value for _____ _____ .

3. Is $y = 2x + 3$ a function? _____ .
   y is a function of _____ .
4. When $x = 6$, we know that $y = 15$. We can express this by saying that $f(6) = 15$. This means that for the function f, a domain value of 6 gives a range value of _____ _____ .

B. Fill in the following for $f(x) = 2x + 3$

x	$f(x) = 2x + 3$
0	3
-1	
2	
-3	
4	

Copyright © 1984 by Allyn and Bacon, Inc. Reproduction of this material is restricted to use with *A Guidebook for Teaching Algebra,* by Terry A. Goodman, John Bernard, Martin P. Cohen, and Joanne E. Meldon.

C. Do each of the following:
  1. $f(x) = 3x - 2$ $f(2)\ =$ _____ ; $f(3)\ =$ _____
  2. $f(x) = x^2 + 1$ $f(-1) =$ _____ ; $f(7)\ =$ _____
  3. $f(x) = (x - 1)(x + 2)$ $f(1)\ =$ _____ ; $f(-2) =$ _____

D. Suppose $f(1) = 3$
                 $f(2) = 4$
                 $f(4) = 6$
  Then $f(x) =$ _____ .

E. Complete these:
  1. $f(1) = -1, f(3) = 1, f(-1) = -3, f(x) =$ _____
  2. $f(0) = 1, \ \ f(3) = 7, f(-2) = -1, f(x) =$ _____
  3. $f(0) = 0, \ \ f(2) = 4, f(-3) = 9, f(x) =$ _____

F. Challenge:
  If $f(x) = 3x^2 - 1$, find
  1. $f(-1) =$ _____
  2. $f(a) =$ _____
  3. $f(b + 1) =$ _____

Copyright © 1984 by Allyn and Bacon, Inc. Reproduction of this material is restricted to use with *A Guidebook for Teaching Algebra*, by Terry A. Goodman, John Bernard, Martin P. Cohen, and Joanne E. Meldon.

FUNCTION MACHINES

Directions: *List the output of each of the following function machines. Complete the rule or draw the machine if not given.*

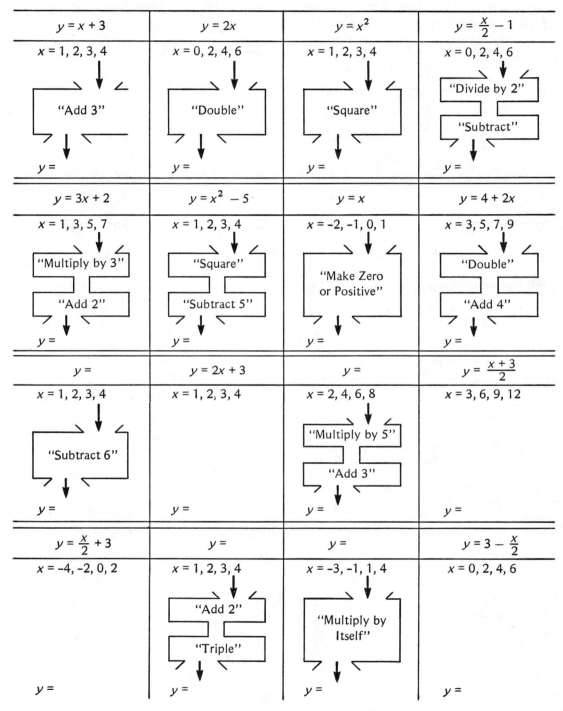

Copyright © 1984 by Allyn and Bacon, Inc. Reproduction of this material is restricted to use with *A Guidebook for Teaching Algebra*, by Terry A. Goodman, John Bernard, Martin P. Cohen, and Joanne E. Meldon.

DOMAINS AND RANGE

Instruction to teacher: *The following is a game to be played by 2 teams. The teams will be answering questions involving the concepts of domain and range of functions. There will be three types of equations: 1 point, 2 points, 3 points (1—easiest to 3—most difficult). On its turn a team may choose a 1, 2, or 3 point question.*

Questions 1, 4, 7 etc., are 1 point, 2, 5, 8, etc., are 2 points, and 3, 6, 9, etc., are three point questions.

Find the range for each of the following:

1. $f(x) = 2x$ Domain = {1,2,3,4}   Range = _____

2. $f(x) = \dfrac{2}{x-1}$ Domain = {3,6,9,12}   Range = _____

3. $f(x) = \dfrac{2}{x-1}$ Domain = $\{x \mid x \in W$ and $x \neq 1\}$ Range = _____

4. $f(x) = 3x - 2$ Domain = {2,4,6,8,...}   Range = _____

5. $f(x) = \dfrac{3}{x-2}$ Domain = {2,4,6,8,...}   Range = _____

6. $f(x) = +\sqrt{x-4}$ Domain = $\{x \mid x \in W$ and $x > 4\}$ Range = _____

Find the restrictions in the domain of each of the following functions, assuming $x \in I$:

7. $f(x) = 3x + 2$

8. $f(x) = +\sqrt{x-3}$

9. $f(x) = \dfrac{x-4}{(x+2)(x-1)}$

10. $f(x) = +\sqrt{x}$

11. $f(x) = \dfrac{x}{x-2}$

12. $f(x) = +\sqrt{\dfrac{2}{x-3}}$

Find the domain for each of the following:

13. $f(x) = 3x$ Range = {0,3,9,12}   Domain = _____

14. $f(x) = \dfrac{2}{x-1}$ Range = $\{y \mid y \in R$ and $y < 1\}$ Domain = _____

15. $f(x) = \dfrac{+\sqrt{x+1}}{x-3}$ Range = $\{y \mid y \in R$ and $y \leqslant 0\}$ Domain = _____

16. $f(x) = 2x - 1$ Range = {3,7,11,.....}   Domain = _____

17. $f(x) = x^2 - 2$ Range = $\{y \mid y < 0$ and $y \in R\}$ Domain = _____

18. $f(x) = x^3$ Range = $\{y \mid y \in R$ and $-9 < y < 0\}$ Domain = _____

Copyright © 1984 by Allyn and Bacon, Inc. Reproduction of this material is restricted to use with *A Guidebook for Teaching Algebra,* by Terry A. Goodman, John Bernard, Martin P. Cohen, and Joanne E. Meldon.

GRAPHING FUNCTIONS

Directions: *Complete the following tables of values. Plot the ordered pairs and draw a "smooth" curve (or line) connecting them from left to right.*

1. $y = 2x - 3$

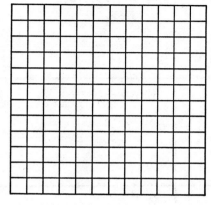

x	-3	-2	-1	0	1	2	3
y							

2. $y = x^2 - 6x + 9$

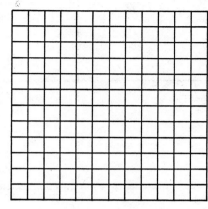

x	+1	2	3	4	5
y					

3. $y = |x + 3|$

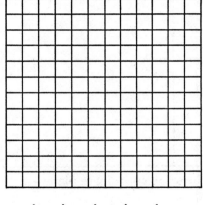

x	-5	-4	-3	-2	-1
y					

4. $y = \dfrac{4}{x}$

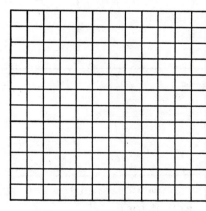

x	$\frac{1}{2}$	1	2	4	8	16
y						

Copyright © 1984 by Allyn and Bacon, Inc. Reproduction of this material is restricted to use with *A Guidebook for Teaching Algebra*, by Terry A. Goodman, John Bernard, Martin P. Cohen, and Joanne E. Meldon.

LINEAR FUNCTIONS

Instructions: *(1) Find the slopes of the following linear functions (equations) and (2) Graph each function on a coordinate plane.*

1. $y = 2x - 8$	2. $3x - 2y = 6$	3. $4x - 2y = 8$
4. $2x - y = 4$	5. $y = 4(x - 1)$	6. $y = \frac{1}{2}(x + 6)$
7. $-2x - y = 3$	8. $x = 3$	9. $y = 5$
10. $y = |x|$	11. $y = x^2 + 1$	12. $xy = 10$
13. $\frac{x}{3} - 4y = 1$	14. $4x - \frac{6}{y} = 2$	15. $x = 0$

Are all of the above linear functions? Graph 3 and 4 on the same coordinate plane—what do you notice? Repeat for 6 and 7.

Copyright © 1984 by Allyn and Bacon, Inc. Reproduction of this material is restricted to use with *A Guidebook for Teaching Algebra,* by Terry A. Goodman, John Bernard, Martin P. Cohen, and Joanne E. Meldon.

SLOPES AND LINES

A. Graph all of the following on the same set of axes.

   1. $y = \frac{1}{3}x$

   2. $y = \frac{1}{2}x$

   3. $y = 1x$
   4. $y = 2x$
   5. $y = 3x$

   What happens to the graph when m (the slope) gets larger?

   _____

B. Graph each of the following pairs on the same set of axes.
   1. $y = mx$ for $m = -1, +1$
   2. $y = mx$ for $m = -2, +2$

   3. $y = mx$ for $m = -\frac{1}{2}, +\frac{1}{2}$

   When m is positive the graph of $y = mx$ _____.
   When m is negative the graph of $y = mx$ _____.

C. Graph each of the following on the same set of axes.
   1. $y = x$ 3. $y = x + 2$
   2. $y = x + 1$ 4. $y = x + 3$

   What happens to the graph of $y = x + b$ as b gets larger?

   _____

D. Graph each of the following pairs on the same set of axes.
   1. $y = x + 1$ 2. $y = x + 2$
      $y = x + (-1)$ $y = x + (-2)$

   When b is positive, what happens to the graph of $y = x + b$?

   _____

   When b is negative, what happens to the graph of $y = x + b$?

   _____

Copyright © 1984 by Allyn and Bacon, Inc. Reproduction of this material is restricted to use with *A Guidebook for Teaching Algebra,* by Terry A. Goodman, John Bernard, Martin P. Cohen, and Joanne E. Meldon.

THE INVERSE OF A FUNCTION

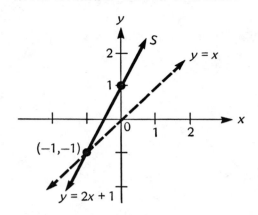

Consider $s = \{(x, y) : y = 2x + 1\}$. Reflect this line through the line $y = x$. The images of $(-1,-1)$ and $(0,1)$ are $(-1,-1)$ and $(1,0)$, respectively. Therefore, the image of s will be determined by the points $(-1,-1)$ and $(1,0)$. Hence, the image of $s = \left\{ (s, y) : y = \frac{1}{2}x - \frac{1}{2} \right\}$. The slope of the image of s is the reciprocal of the slope of s.

1. What are the images of $t = (x, y) : y = \frac{1}{2}x$,

$$u = (x, y) : y = x + 3,$$
$$v = (x, y) : y = -3x + 2.$$

Remember, reflected over $y = x$.

2. Reflect lines t, u, and v through the x-axis and y-axis. What conclusions can you draw?

Copyright © 1984 by Allyn and Bacon, Inc. Reproduction of this material is restricted to use with *A Guidebook for Teaching Algebra*, by Terry A. Goodman, John Bernard, Martin P. Cohen, and Joanne E. Meldon.

PARALLEL AND PERPENDICULAR LINES

Directions: *Complete the following.*

A. Graph on the same set of axes:

$$y = \frac{3}{4}x \quad \text{and} \quad y = -\frac{4}{3}x$$

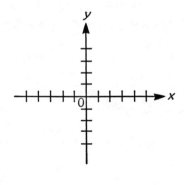

Complete:

x	y
0	
④	

x	y
0	
③	

Let $B = (4, \underline{})$ Let $B' = (3, \underline{})$
Label $A = (4,0)$ and $A' = (3,0)$

1. How long is $\overline{OB}$? _____
2. How long is $\overline{OB'}$? _____
3. What kind of triangle is AOB? _____
4. What kind of triangle is $A'OB'$? _____
5. $m(\angle AOB) + m(\angle A'OB') =$ _____
6. How are lines $\overleftrightarrow{OB}$ and $\overleftrightarrow{OB'}$ related? _____

B. Graph on the same set of axes:

$$y = 2x + 1 \quad \text{and} \quad y = 2x - 3$$

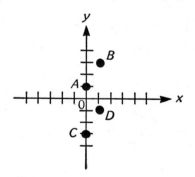

	x	y
$A = $	0	
$B = $	1	

	x	y
$C = $	0	
$D = $	1	

1. How long is AC? _____ BD? _____
2. What kind of figure is $ABCD$? _____
3. How are lines $\overleftrightarrow{AB}$ and $\overleftrightarrow{CD}$ related? _____

Copyright © 1984 by Allyn and Bacon, Inc. Reproduction of this material is restricted to use with *A Guidebook for Teaching Algebra*, by Terry A. Goodman, John Bernard, Martin P. Cohen, and Joanne E. Meldon.

SOLVING SYSTEMS

Directions: *Solve each system by the "ratio and proportion" method. Check your solution by graphing each system on the graph paper provided by your teacher.*

1. $\begin{cases} x + y = 2 \\ x - y = 6 \end{cases}$

2. $\begin{cases} x + y = 5 \\ 4x + 4y = 20 \end{cases}$

3. $\begin{cases} x + 2 = \frac{1}{2}(y + 1) \\ 5(x + 1) = 3(y - 2) \end{cases}$

4. $\begin{cases} 3x - y = 0 \\ 4x - 2y = 0 \end{cases}$

5. $\begin{cases} x + y = -3 \\ x + y = 1 \end{cases}$

Copyright © 1984 by Allyn and Bacon, Inc. Reproduction of this material is restricted to use with *A Guidebook for Teaching Algebra,* by Terry A. Goodman, John Bernard, Martin P. Cohen, and Joanne E. Meldon.

GRAPHS OF VARIABLES

Directions: *Graph each of the following equations. State whether the graph represents a direct or an inverse variation.*

1. $y = 3x$

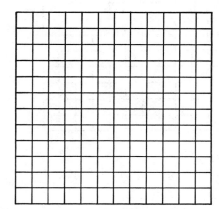

2. $c = \frac{1}{3}d$

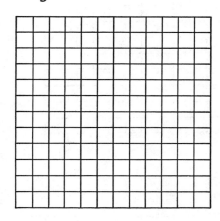

3. $xy = 6$

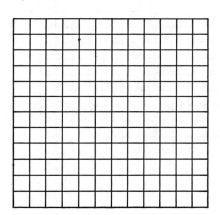

4. $c = 2\pi r$

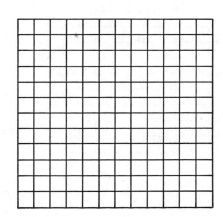

Copyright © 1984 by Allyn and Bacon, Inc. Reproduction of this material is restricted to use with *A Guidebook for Teaching Algebra,* by Terry A. Goodman, John Bernard, Martin P. Cohen, and Joanne E. Meldon.

5. $y = x + 5$

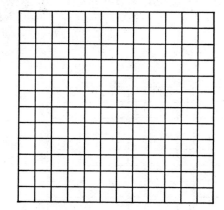

6. $\dfrac{x}{y} = 3$

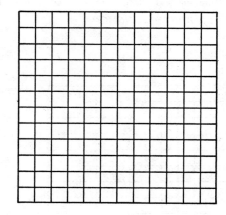

7. $\dfrac{3}{y} = x$

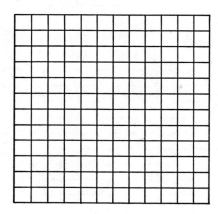

8. $\dfrac{x}{4} = \dfrac{3}{y}$

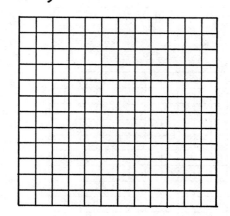

Copyright © 1984 by Allyn and Bacon, Inc. Reproduction of this material is restricted to use with *A Guidebook for Teaching Algebra*, by Terry A. Goodman, John Bernard, Martin P. Cohen, and Joanne E. Meldon.

CHOOSING PROPER OPERATIONS

For each of the following, first decide which operations, and in what order, should be used. Then follow your plan to compute the solution. Be prepared to discuss why you used those processes.

1. Cindy has 310 U.S. and 573 foreign stamps in her collection. How many stamps altogether?
   Operation(s):   Solution:

2. Jill has five blouses, each of which looks nice with any one of three pairs of slacks she also owns. With these, how many different outfits can she form?
   Operation(s):   Solution:

3. One of the star basketball players scored 29 points in last night's game, 7 as free throws. How many other baskets (goals) did he make from the floor?
   Operation(s):   Solution:

4. Mr. Carr used 19 gallons of gasoline to travel 418 miles.
   a. What was his gasoline mileage for the trip?
   b. At $1.33 per gallon, how much did the gasoline for the trip cost?
   c. On the average, how far will his car go on one dollar's worth of gasoline?
   Operation(s):   Solution:

5. If Jim has $2.55 altogether in nickels and quarters, and if he has seven quarters, how many nickels does he have?
   Operation(s):   Solution:

6. Mrs. Estes invested $1500 in a one-year savings certificate paying 12% for interest. How much money will she receive if she cashes in the certificate at the end of the one-year term?
   Operation(s):   Solution:

7. If mowing at a steady pace, Dale does two-thirds of the lawn in $1\frac{1}{2}$ hours, how long will it take to do the entire job?
   Operation(s):   Solution:

Copyright © 1984 by Allyn and Bacon, Inc. Reproduction of this material is restricted to use with *A Guidebook for Teaching Algebra*, by Terry A. Goodman, John Bernard, Martin P. Cohen, and Joanne E. Meldon.

8. Referring to the investment in problem 5, if interest payments are made only at the end of each year and each is left in her account to accumulate with her original deposit, how many years will it take for her money to earn at least $500 for Mrs. Estes?
   Operation(s):   Solution:

9. A round puddle three meters in diameter is situated in a grassy field six meters by nine meters. What is the area of the grassy part (shaded in the figure) of the field?
   Operation(s):

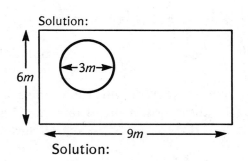

Solution:

Solution:

10. What is Billy's average for the following bowling scores—142, 137, 140, 143, 138, and 152?
    Operation(s):   Solution:

Copyright © 1984 by Allyn and Bacon, Inc. Reproduction of this material is restricted to use with *A Guidebook for Teaching Algebra,* by Terry A. Goodman, John Bernard, Martin P. Cohen, and Joanne E. Meldon.

EQUATIONS AS MODELS

Matching exercises: *You are given a list of 16 equations (some formulae) from which to choose. Read and analyze each story problem to determine which of the equations might serve as models for the problem. (There might be more than one, but there will always be at least one.) Indicate your choices by placing its corresponding number in the blank preceding the story problem.*

Equations

1. $5n + 70 = 110$
2. $r \cdot t = d$
3. $a \cdot b = c$
4. $5n = 22 + 3n$
5. $5a - 22 = 3a$
6. $x + 3(11) + x = 451$
7. $n + 3(n + 11) = 451$
8. $5x + 22 = 110 - 3x$

9. $P = 2(l + w)$
10. $a \cdot b + c = d$
11. $110 = 22w$
12. $22t = 110$
13. $110 = \frac{1}{3}(122 + 103 + x)$
14. $A = l \cdot w$
15. $\frac{122 + 103 + x}{3} = 110$
16. $7(22) + r(22) = 5(22 + 22)$

Story Problems

1. _____ When Lesley took 22 from five times her age, she got three times her age. How old is she?
2. _____ At 22 km/hr, how long does it take to go 110 km?
3. _____ A certain rectangle has an area of 110 square centimeters. If its length is 22 cm, how wide is it?
4. _____ Sara has some nickels plus 70 cents in dimes for a total of $1.10. How many nickels does she have?
5. _____ Twenty-two more than five times a certain number is the same as 110 minus three times the number. What is its value?
6. _____ Gail has just finished bowling 122 and 103 for her first two games. How much does she need to get on her next game to average at least 110 for the series?
7. _____ Mr. Jogger has just run his first 22 minutes at an average of 7 km/hr. How fast does he need to jog the next 22 minutes to average 5 km/hr for the entire trip?
8. _____ Cindy has some domestic stamps and three times even more than that number of foreign stamps in her collection of 451 stamps. How many of each kind does she have?

Copyright © 1984 by Allyn and Bacon, Inc. Reproduction of this material is restricted to use with *A Guidebook for Teaching Algebra,* by Terry A. Goodman, John Bernard, Martin P. Cohen, and Joanne E. Meldon.

USING THE SUBSTITUTION PRINCIPLE

Practice using the substitution principle as you solve each of the following systems of equations.

1. $F = \frac{9}{5}C + 32$

   $F = -40$

   Find C

2. $A = lw, P = 2(l + w)$

   $A = 60, w = 5$

   Find P and l

3. $5a + 10b = 255$

   $a = 26 - 1$

   Find a and b

4. $x + 3y = 451$

   $y - x = 11$

   Find x and y

5. $x + y + z = 12$

   $y = \frac{1}{3}(x + z)$

   $z = (x + 1)$

   Find x, y, and z

Copyright © 1984 by Allyn and Bacon, Inc. Reproduction of this material is restricted to use with *A Guidebook for Teaching Algebra*, by Terry A. Goodman, John Bernard, Martin P. Cohen, and Joanne E. Meldon.

USING THE ALGEBRAIC METHOD

Practice using the algebraic method (translate, solve, interpret) as you solve each of the following problems.

1. Tim is four years older than Robin. The sum of their ages is 28. How old is each?

2. There are 5 more students in Kenny's history class than in his biology class. If the biology class was double its size, there would be 17 more students in biology compared to history. How many students are currently in each of Kenny's two classes?

3. Traveling by car with his parents on a vacation trip, math whiz decided to count the trucks going in the opposite-bound lane of the interstate highway. After seeing 17 of of them, some trailer-tractors ("eighteen wheelers") and some pickups (4 wheels each) he noted that altogether those trucks have 236 tires rolling on the pavement! How many of each type of truck had he seen?

4. Mary bought some large envelopes costing 4 cents each and some stamps costing 18 cents each from the post office for a total of $2.36. If there were 17 individual items, how many envelopes did she buy?

5. Working with her calculator, Jenny found that four times two less than her age was the same as three times two more than her age. How old is she?

6. Checking back after a lengthy bicycle trip, "Wheeler" noted that averaging two kilometers per hour faster, the trip would have only taken 3 hours. Averaging 2 kilometers per hour less, the trip would have taken 4 hours. How far did he travel, how long did it take, and what was his average speed for the trip?

7. Rhoda has a fixed amount of money and wants to buy a certain number of party favors (nominal gifts). If they cost 25¢ each, the number she can buy is 7 less than what she needs. If they cost 10¢ each, she can get 20 more than what she needs. How many items is she needing to buy?

8. Ted has 17 coins, some dimes, and the others quarters. Their total value is $3.50. How many of each type of coin does he have?

Copyright © 1984 by Allyn and Bacon, Inc. Reproduction of this material is restricted to use with *A Guidebook for Teaching Algebra*, by Terry A. Goodman, John Bernard, Martin P. Cohen, and Joanne E. Meldon.

USING FORMULAE

Practice using formulae to solve problems. When an unfamiliar formula is part of the algebraic model, you are given a *hint* containing the formula and specific information about the way to measure the quantities envalued. Otherwise, you are given to your own resourcefulness to provide such information.

1. How much current is drained from a 12 volt battery overcoming a resistance of 5 Ohms?

   Hint: $E = \dfrac{I}{R}$ where E is the voltage measured in volts, I is the current measured in Amperes, and R is the resistance measured in Ohms.

2. Determine the current and resistance of a 225 watt light bulb operating on a 120 volt circuit.
   Hint: $P = I^2R$ where P is the power measured in watts, I is the current measured in Amperes, and R is the resistance measured in Ohms. See also the hint to problem 1.

3. What are the dimensions of a rectangle with an area of 60 square centimeters whose perimeter is 34 centimeters?
   (We note that the formulae for number 3 are fairly common and are therefore left for the students to access on his own.)

4. Find out for what temperature is the Fahrenheit reading twice the Celsius.
   Hint: $F = \dfrac{9}{5}C + 32$, F degrees Fahrenheit, and C degrees Celsius or Centigrade.

5. Find the selling price of an item that cost $4500 if the dealer computes the margin as 30% of his cost.
   Hint: $S = C + M$, where S is selling price, C is cost, M is margin, and all are measured in the same monetary unit, say dollars in this case.

*6. Referring to number 5, (a) What is the dealer's gain or actual profit if overhead expenses constitute 60% of the margin, and (b) Express this answer as a rate of percent relative to the cost.
   Hint: $G = M - E$, where G is gain, M is margin or markup, E is overhead or operating expenses, and all are measured in the same monetary units.

---

*Note: Nested within the larger problem is a subtask using

(Percentage) = (rate of percent) · (base).

Depending on the students, it may help to prepare them with a review of the uses for this principle.

Copyright © 1984 by Allyn and Bacon, Inc. Reproduction of this material is restricted to use with *A Guidebook for Teaching Algebra,* by Terry A. Goodman, John Bernard, Martin P. Cohen, and Joanne E. Meldon.

USING THE BALANCE PRINCIPLE

Practice using the Balance Principle for Levers while doing the following problems using the algebraic method.

1. If a 6 gram mass (proportional to weight as a set location on the earth) is placed 3 units from the fulcrum on the right side of a lever, at what location should a 2 gram mass be placed if the lever is to balance?

2. (Optional) Where might a 3 pound weight and a 5 pound weight be placed at opposite distances from the fulcrum if the lever is to balance? Having found one solution, find another, and another. Express a relationship for the 3 pound distance in terms of the 5 pound distance. (Hint: a table and a systematic approach might help.)

3. Mr. Bill weighs 180 pounds, Jimmy weighs 90 pounds, and Mary weighs 60 pounds. Jimmy is sitting 4 feet from the center on a teeter-totter (seesaw) opposite to Mr. Bill, $2\frac{1}{2}$ feet from the pivot point on the other side. Where should Mary be seated if they are to balance?

4. Ignoring the weight of the lever, how far from the fulcrum would you need to apply 90 pounds of force to raise a 720 pound piano 2 feet on the other side? (Are you heavy enough to do it?)

5. A man wishes to balance a pole with 3 buckets containing water over his shoulder. Each bucket weighs 2 pounds. The bucket 3 feet behind him has 8 pounds of water in it, the one 3 feet in front has 5 pounds of water. If the third bucket is to be 2 feet in front of him, how much water should be in it?

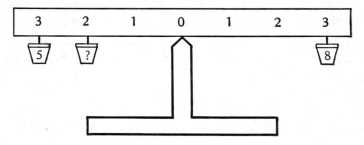

6. A 9-gram mass is placed 4 units to the right of the fulcrum on a lever. Suppose for the counter balance on the left we want the number of grams of weight to be equal to the number of units of distance. How much weight should be used and where should it be located?

7. Find a counter balance like that in number 6 when both an 8-pound weight and a 4-pound weight are suspended at distances of 5 inches and 15 inches respectively.

8. Check that a 5-gram mass at 5 cm will balance both a 3-gram mass at 3 cm and a 4-gram mass at 4 cm. Staying with integers as above, we will call the "three at three and four at four" a sum of squares decomposition of the "five at five," or more simply "five." See if you can produce a sum of squares decomposition for 13. (What principle in geometry is this like?)

Copyright © 1984 by Allyn and Bacon, Inc. Reproduction of this material is restricted to use with *A Guidebook for Teaching Algebra*, by Terry A. Goodman, John Bernard, Martin P. Cohen, and Joanne E. Meldon.

SOLVING PROBLEMS

Some of the following problems will seem routine, others will seem novel or unusual. Work to solve each using the algebraic method noting explicit versus implicit or hidden information and irrelevant or inconsistent information.

1. Find two consecutive odd integers such that three times the smaller is four less than twice the larger.

2. Jimmy has $7.45 in coins, some nickels, some dimes, and the rest quarters. There are five more nickels than dimes and twice as many quarters as dimes. How many coins does he have?

3. Thinking back to the problem about Mr. Prince, student tickets cost $3 and adult tickets were $5. How many adults and how many students would have been in the group if it had cost him $20 to treat?

4. Refer to problem number 3 for prices. What is the largest number of guests he could treat for $23?

5. Moe, Larry, and Curly were paid $435 cash from their vacuum-cleaner selling job. This was the accumulation from their combined efforts and their $15 commission for each unit sold. Moe took charge of dividing up the money saying, "I'll handle this." To Larry he said, "Let's see, you sold twice as many as I did, so that's $15x$ dollars for you and $15(2x)$ dollars for me." To Curly, "Hmm, you sold one more than Larry so that's $15x + 1$ dollars for you, but then I better take the other 14 dollars so it comes out even." "OK, we've got

$$(15x) + (15(2x) + 14) + (15x + 1) = 435$$

and once we find x we can figure out how much we each should get," How much did each receive?

Copyright © 1984 by Allyn and Bacon, Inc. Reproduction of this material is restricted to use with *A Guidebook for Teaching Algebra*, by Terry A. Goodman, John Bernard, Martin P. Cohen, and Joanne E. Meldon.

RECOGNIZING QUADRATIC EQUATIONS

Instructions: *Determine which of the equations below are quadratic. Rewrite those equations which are quadratic in the equivalent form* $ax^2 + bx + c = 0$, $a \neq 0$, *and solve for x.*

1. $\dfrac{x^2 - 1}{2} = 4$

2. $x + x^2 = 72$

3. $(x + 1)(x - 1) = 0$

4. $x^2 + 3x = x^2 + x$

5. $x^3 + x^2 + x = 0$

6. $x(x^2 + 1) = 2x$

7. $2x(x - 1) = 4 - 2x$

8. $2 - x^2 = 1$

9. $(2x + 1)(x - 3) = 0$

10. $4x^2 - 9 = 0$

11. $\dfrac{2x^2 + 1}{3} = \dfrac{1}{3}$

12. $x + 6 = 9$

Copyright © 1984 by Allyn and Bacon, Inc. Reproduction of this material is restricted to use with *A Guidebook for Teaching Algebra,* by Terry A. Goodman, John Bernard, Martin P. Cohen, and Joanne E. Meldon.

FACTORING POLYNOMIAL EXPRESSIONS

Instructions: *Factor completely the following polynomial expressions into a product of linear factors.*

1. $x^2 + x - 6$

2. $12y^2 + 17y + 6$

3. $b^2 - 5b$

4. $x^2 + 6x + 9$

5. $y^2 - 16$

6. $12x^2 + 2x - 2$

7. $y^4 - 10y^2 + 9$

8. $a^3 - 4a$

9. $3y^2 + 16y - 35$

10. $4t^2 + 14t - 30$

Copyright © 1984 by Allyn and Bacon, Inc. Reproduction of this material is restricted to use with *A Guidebook for Teaching Algebra,* by Terry A. Goodman, John Bernard, Martin P. Cohen, and Joanne E. Meldon.

SOLVING QUADRATIC EQUATIONS BY FACTORING

Instructions: *Use the five-step method to solve the following quadratic equations by factoring.*

1. $x(x + 2) = -1$

2. $6x + 9x^2 = 1$

3. $15x(x - 1) = 14 - 4x$

4. $b^2 - 4 = 0$

5. $p^4 - 13p^2 + 36 = 0$

6. $\frac{3}{4}(x^2 - 2) = x$

7. $(z + 4)^2 = 36$

8. $\frac{x}{x + 1} - \frac{9}{x + 3} = 0$

9. $(b + 1)(b + 2) = 4$

10. $200 = -2a^2 + 40a$

Copyright © 1984 by Allyn and Bacon, Inc. Reproduction of this material is restricted to use with *A Guidebook for Teaching Algebra,* by Terry A. Goodman, John Bernard, Martin P. Cohen, and Joanne E. Meldon.

SOLVING EQUATIONS OF THE FORM $(x + k)^2 = c$

Use the method of solving equations of the form $x^2 = a$ to do the following.

1. $(x + 3)^2 = 9$

2. $(y - 4)^2 = 25$

3. $6 = (a - 3)^2$

4. $(4 + e)^2 = 8$

5. $(10 - b)^2 + 5 = 9$

Add a term to each of the following binomials to change it to a perfect-square trinomial. Then factor it.

1. $x^2 - 4x + \underline{\quad} = (x - \underline{\quad})^2$

2. $y^2 + 5y + \underline{\quad} = (y + \underline{\quad})^2$

3. $4a^2 + 20a + \underline{\quad} = (2a + \underline{\quad})^2$

4. $x^2 - 6x + \underline{\quad} = (x - \underline{\quad})^2$

Copyright © 1984 by Allyn and Bacon, Inc. Reproduction of this material is restricted to use with *A Guidebook for Teaching Algebra,* by Terry A. Goodman, John Bernard, Martin P. Cohen, and Joanne E. Meldon.

SOLVING QUADRATIC EQUATIONS BY COMPLETING THE SQUARE

Instructions: *Solve each of the following by the method of completing the square.*

1. $x^2 - 7x + 12 = 0$

2. $3x^2 + 18 = 9x$

3. $x^2 - x = 1$

4. $2x(x + 1) = 1$

5. $x^2 - 1 = \frac{4}{3}x$

6. $3p = \frac{p + 2}{p - 1}$

7. $1 + 2y = 4y^2$

8. $(x - 2)(x - 4) = 24$

9. $(x - 3)^2 = 49^2$

10. $n - \frac{1}{2} = \frac{3}{n}$

Copyright © 1984 by Allyn and Bacon, Inc. Reproduction of this material is restricted to use with *A Guidebook for Teaching Algebra*, by Terry A. Goodman, John Bernard, Martin P. Cohen, and Joanne E. Meldon.

USING THE DISCRIMINANT

Instructions: *Fill in the spaces provided.*

Equation	Discriminant $b^2 - 4ac$	Number of real roots	Nature of roots rational or irrational
1. $x^2 = 4x$			
2. $2x = x^2 + 3$			
3. $x^2 + 3 = 5x^2 - 6$			
4. $4x^2 + 8x = -4$			
5. $3y^2 + 7y + 2 = 0$			
6. $2y^2 + 11 = -2y$			

Copyright © 1984 by Allyn and Bacon, Inc. Reproduction of this material is restricted to use with *A Guidebook for Teaching Algebra,* by Terry A. Goodman, John Bernard, Martin P. Cohen, and Joanne E. Meldon.

SOLVING QUADRATIC EQUATIONS USING THE QUADRATIC FORMULA

Solve each of the following problems using the quadratic formula. Check your solutions.

1. $y^2 - 2y = 0$

2. $x^2 = 9$

3. $3x^2 - 4x = -1$

4. $p^2 = p + 1$

5. $(x - 3)(x + 2) = 1$

6. $-3x = x^2 + 2$

Write a quadratic equation in the form $ax^2 + bx + c = 0$ whose roots are:

1. $6, -2$

2. $\dfrac{1}{2}, \dfrac{1}{2}$

3. $0, -5$

4. $\sqrt{5}, \sqrt{20}$

5. no real roots

Copyright © 1984 by Allyn and Bacon, Inc. Reproduction of this material is restricted to use with *A Guidebook for Teaching Algebra,* by Terry A. Goodman, John Bernard, Martin P. Cohen, and Joanne E. Meldon.

GRAPHING LINEAR AND QUADRATIC EQUATIONS

Instructions: *Find the solution(s) of each equation and graph its corresponding function. Use point-plotting.*

1. $y = x^2$; $x^2 = 0$

2. $y = (x - 1)^2$; $(x - 1)^2 = 0$

3. $y = 2x^2 + 3x + 1$; $2x^2 + 3x + 1 = 0$

4. $y = 3x - 12$; $3x - 12 = 0$

5. $y = 4x + 8$; $4x + 8 = 0$

6. $y = x^2 + 3$; $x^2 + 3 = 0$

7. $y = (x + 2)^2 - 5$; $(x + 2)^2 - 5 = 0$

8. $y = \dfrac{x + 3}{6}$; $\dfrac{x + 3}{6} = 0$

9. $y = 2(x + 2)^2$; $2(x + 2)^2 = 0$

10. $y = 3(x - 1)^2 - 27$; $3(x - 1)^2 - 27 = 0$

Copyright © 1984 by Allyn and Bacon, Inc. Reproduction of this material is restricted to use with *A Guidebook for Teaching Algebra,* by Terry A. Goodman, John Bernard, Martin P. Cohen, and Joanne E. Meldon.

RELATIONSHIP BETWEEN THE GRAPH AND THE DISCRIMINANT

Instructions: *Fill in the spaces provided.*

Function	Number of times graph crosses x-axis 0, 1, or 2	Discriminant $b^2 - 4ac$	Number of real roots
1. $y = x^2 + 2x - 3$	2	16	2
2. $y = (x + 2)^2$			
3. $y = x^2 + 2x$			
4. $y = x^2 - x - 1$			
5. $y = x^2 - 10$			
6. $y = -x^2 + 2x + 3$			
7. $y = \frac{1}{2}x^2 + 5$			
8. $y = x^2$			
9. $y = 4x + x^2$			
10. $y = -2 + x + 2x^2$			

Copyright © 1984 by Allyn and Bacon, Inc. Reproduction of this material is restricted to use with *A Guidebook for Teaching Algebra*, by Terry A. Goodman, John Bernard, Martin P. Cohen, and Joanne E. Meldon.

FINDING THE VERTEX AND AXIS OF SYMMETRY

Instructions: *Identify the vertex and axis of symmetry for each parabola shown on the grids below.*

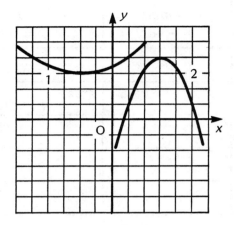

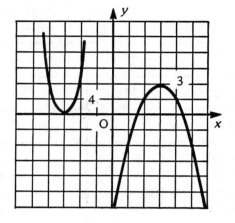

1. $V = ($, $)$ axis: $x =$
2. $V = ($, $)$ axis:

3. $V = ($, $)$ axis:
4. $V = ($, $)$ axis:

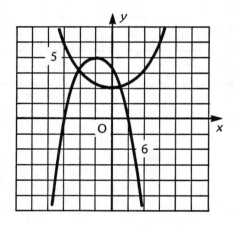

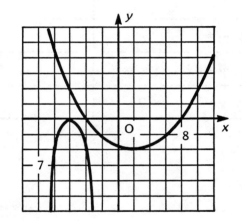

5. $V = ($, $)$ axis:
6. $V = ($, $)$ axis:

7. $V = ($, $)$ axis:
8. $V = ($, $)$ axis:

Copyright © 1984 by Allyn and Bacon, Inc. Reproduction of this material is restricted to use with *A Guidebook for Teaching Algebra*, by Terry A. Goodman, John Bernard, Martin P. Cohen, and Joanne E. Meldon.

GRAPHING QUADRATIC FUNCTIONS OF THE FORM $a(x - h)^2 + k$

Instructions: *For each of the following, (a) graph the function, (b) find the vertex, and (c) find the equation of the axis of symmetry.*

1. $y = (x - 2)^2$

2. $y = x^2 + 3$

3. $y = (x + 3)^2 + 2$

4. $y = x^2 - 4$

5. $y = (x - 3)^2 - 4$

6. $y = (x + 1)^2$

7. $y = x^2 - 3$

8. $y = (x + 2)^2 - 5$

9. $y = 2(x - 1)^2 + 1$

10. $y = \frac{1}{2}(x + 1)^2$

11. $y = x^2 + 2x + 1$

12. $y = x^2 + 2x - 3$

13. $y = x^2 + 9$

14. $y = 2x^2 + 3x - 14$

15. $y = 3x^2 + 6x$

Copyright © 1984 by Allyn and Bacon, Inc. Reproduction of this material is restricted to use with *A Guidebook for Teaching Algebra*, by Terry A. Goodman, John Bernard, Martin P. Cohen, and Joanne E. Meldon.

$$y = a(x - h)^2 + k, \ a < 0$$

Instructions: *For each of the following, find the "steps" and graph the function.*

1. $y = (x - 3)^2$

2. $y = -x^2 + 4$

3. $y = (x + 2)^2 - 5$

4. $y = -x^2$

5. $y = x^2 - 4$

6. $y = -(x + 2)^2$

7. $y = x^2 - 6x + 9$

8. $y = -(x - 4)^2 + 3$

Copyright © 1984 by Allyn and Bacon, Inc. Reproduction of this material is restricted to use with *A Guidebook for Teaching Algebra*, by Terry A. Goodman, John Bernard, Martin P. Cohen, and Joanne E. Meldon.

REPRODUCTION PAGE 130

THE ROLE OF a IN $y = a(x - h)^2 + k$

Instructions: *Graph the following functions.*

1. $y = x^2$

2. $y = 4x^2 - 3$

3. $y = -2(x - 3)^2$

4. $y = 8(x + 5)^2 - 3$

5. $y = -x^2 + 3$

6. $y = (x - 2)^2 + 1$

7. $y = \frac{1}{2}(x + 5)^2 - 2$

8. $y = -\frac{1}{4}x^2 + 6$

Copyright © 1984 by Allyn and Bacon, Inc. Reproduction of this material is restricted to use with *A Guidebook for Teaching Algebra*, by Terry A. Goodman, John Bernard, Martin P. Cohen, and Joanne E. Meldon.

APPENDIX **D**

Microcomputer Activities

This section includes selected microcomputer activities that can be used to supplement the material and activities found in this *Guidebook*. These microcomputer activities have been divided into three categories: (1) copies of programs to be used, (2) descriptions of programs that can be found in other sources, and (3) microcomputer student research problems. There is also a listing of relevant computer resources.

Where appropriate, it is indicated for which chapter(s) a given activity is most useful. We have attempted to selected activities that could be used to supplement more than one algebra concept.

Algebra Microcomputer Programs

For each of the programs there will be a brief description. At the end of this section will be a listing of each program, written for Apple II Plus.

1. *WIPEOUT.* In this game, the player chooses a start number (less than 90). The computer then presents an array of the numbers 1 through the number chosen. The player then begins to select numbers from the list. When the player chooses a number he gets for his score that number plus all the factors of the number that are in the list. Play continues until the player can no longer find a number that has any factors remaining in the list. The computer then reports the player's total score and the record score for that start number. Could be used with Chapters 2 and 8.

2. *LARGEST PRODUCT.* In this game, the computer generates random one-digit numbers. The player must place the numbers (one at a time) in a 2 digit by 2 digit multiplication problem so as to get the largest possible product. Could be used with Chapters 2 and 8.

3. *MEAN.* In this game, the computer generates numbers from an imaginary spinner. The player is to collect five numbers whose mean is as close as possible to a goal mean. For each of five rounds, the player may either take the first number that is

"spun" or ask the computer to "spin" again. If he asks for another spin, he must keep the second number as one of his five. Could be used with Chapters 2, 7, and 8.

4. *MEDIAN.* Similar to MEAN except the object is to collect five numbers whose median is as close as possible to a goal median. Could be used with Chapters 2, 7, and 8.

5. *GUESS MY RULE.* In this game, a player chooses one of three levels of difficulty. The computer selects a rule that will be used to generate output values for input values given by the player. For example, if the rule is "add 5," the computer will give an output of 9 when the player inputs 4. The goal for the player is to discover what rule the computer is using. The "rules" range from simple linear relationships to one involving quadratic and cubic terms. Could be used with Chapters 4, 5, 7, 8, and 9.

6. *ESTIMATE.* In this program students are given a goal interval and a starting number. They are to use successive multiplications to obtain an answer in the goal interval. Could be used with Chapters 2 and 8.

7. *MYSTERY BLOCK.* In this game, students must ask questions in order to discover a "mystery block." This mystery block comes from a collection of blocks that have three attributes—size, shape, and color. Could be used with Chapter 8.

WIPEOUT

```
130    HOME
140    NORMAL
150    SPEED= 125
160    REM
170    REM  ********************
180    REM      INSTRUCTIONS
190    REM  ********************
200    REM
210    PRINT "YOU ARE GOING TO PLAY A GAME CALLED"
220    FLASH : PRINT : PRINT : PRINT : HTAB (16): PRINT "WIPEOUT"
230    NORMAL
240    VTAB (12): PRINT "DO YOU WANT TO SEE THE INSTRUCTIONS?"
250    PRINT "(Y/N)"
260    INPUT C$
270    IF C$ = "Y" OR C$ = "N" THEN 310
280    PRINT : PRINT "YOU MUST ENTER 'Y' OR 'N' ."
290    PRINT "PLEASE TRY AGAIN."
300    GOTO 260
310    IF C$ = "N" THEN 350
320    PRINT : PRINT "YOUR JOB WILL BE TO CHOOSE NUMBERS FROM A LIST.  YOU W
       ANT TO CHOOSE A NUMBER   THAT HAS FACTORS IN THE LIST.  AS A      SCO
       RE, YOU WILL RECEIVE THE NUMBER YOU  CHOOSE PLUS ALL THE FACTORS OF T
       HAT      NUMBER."
330    PRINT : PRINT "FOR EXAMPLE, IF YOU CHOOSE 20 YOU WILL   GET 20+10+5+4+
       2 ADDED TO YOUR SCORE.    THESE NUMBERS WILL THEN BE ELIMINATED   FRO
       M THE LIST."
340    PRINT : PRINT "YOU MAY ONLY CHOOSE A NUMBER THAT HAS   FACTORS REMAIN
       ING IN THE LIST.  WHEN YOU CAN NO LONGER MAKE CHOICES, YOUR SCORE WIL
       L BE TOTALED.  THE 'COMPUTER' WILL    GET WHAT IS LEFT PLUS THE 1."
350    CLEAR
360    PRINT : PRINT "WHAT IS THE LARGEST NUMBER YOU WANT"
370    PRINT "IN YOUR LIST?"
380    PRINT : PRINT "YOU MAY CHOOSE ANY MULTIPLE OF 10 THAT"
390    PRINT "IS LESS THAN OR EQUAL TO 90."
400    REM
410    REM  **********************
420    REM  SELECT A START NUMBER
430    REM  ********************
```

```
440   REM
450   SPEED= 255
460   DIM A$(100)
470   INPUT N$:N =  VAL (N$): HOME
475   ONERR  GOTO 1540
480   IF  ASC (N$) < 48 OR  ASC (N$) > 57 THEN 1540
490   IF N > 90 THEN 510
500   GOTO 550
510   PRINT "REMEMBER, YOU MUST CHOOSE A NUMBER LESS"
520   PRINT "THAN OR EQUAL TO 90.  PLEASE MAKE"
530   PRINT "ANOTHER SELECTION."
540   GOTO 470
550 S = N / 10
560   IF S =  INT (S) THEN 610
570   PRINT : PRINT "REMEMBER, THE NUMBER MUST BE A MULTIPLE"
580   PRINT "OF 10"
590   GOTO 350
600   REM
610   REM  ***********************
620   REM    PRINTS ORIGINAL LIST
630   REM  ***********************
640   REM
650   FOR I = 1 TO N
660 A$(I) =  STR$ (I)
670 Z = 3
680   IF I > 9 THEN Z = 2
690   IF I > 99 THEN Z = 1
700 R = (I - 1) / 10
710   IF R =  INT ((I - 1) / 10) THEN  PRINT
720   PRINT  SPC( Z);A$(I);
730   NEXT I
740   PRINT : PRINT
750   PRINT "IF YOU ARE READY TO STOP, PRESS THE '1' KEY.  IF YOU WANT TO C
      ONTINUE, CHOOSE A NUMBER IN THE LIST.  YOU WILL GET THAT   NUMBER PLU
      S ITS FACTORS IN THE LIST."
760   INPUT S$:S =  VAL (S$)
765   ONERR  GOTO 1570
770   IF  ASC (S$) < 48 OR  ASC (S$) > 57 THEN 1570
780   IF S > N THEN 800
790   GOTO 830
800   PRINT : PRINT "YOU MAY NOT CHOOSE A NUMBER GREATER THAN"
810   PRINT N;".  PLEASE MAKE ANOTHER SELECTION."
820   GOTO 760
830   IF S = 1 THEN 1190
840   REM
850   REM  ***********************
860   REM  CHECKS FOR FACTORS OF
870   REM  S AND PRINTS A NEW
880   REM  LIST
890   REM  ***********************
900   REM
910   FOR J = 2 TO S
920 K = S / ( VAL (A$(J)))
930   IF K <  > INT (S / ( VAL (A$(J)))) THEN 970
940 M = M +  VAL (A$(J))
950 A$(J) =  STR$ (N + 1)
960 F = F + 1
970   NEXT J
980   IF F = 1 THEN 1140
990   HOME
1000   PRINT
1010   FOR L = 1 TO N
1020   IF  VAL (A$(L)) = N + 1 THEN 1040
1030 Z = 3: GOTO 1050
1040 A$(L) = "":Z = 4
1050   IF  VAL (A$(L)) > 9 THEN Z = 2
1060   IF  VAL (A$(L)) > 99 THEN Z = 1
1070 P = (L - 1) / 10
1080   IF P =  INT ((L - 1) / 10) THEN  PRINT
1090   PRINT  SPC( Z);A$(L);
1100   IF  VAL (A$(L)) = 0 THEN A$(L) =  STR$ (N + 1)
```

```
1110   NEXT L
1120 F = 0
1130   GOTO 740
1140   PRINT
1150 A$(S) =  STR$ (S)
1160   PRINT "SORRY!!  THERE ARE NO FACTORS OF  ";S;"     LEFT IN THE LIST.
       "
1170 M = M -  VAL (A$(S))
1180   GOTO 1120
1190   HOME
1200   PRINT "YOUR SUM IS  ";M
1210 T = ((N * (N + 1)) / 2) - M
1220   PRINT : PRINT : PRINT "THE COMPUTER'S TOTAL IS   ";T
1230   REM  ***********************
1240   REM    TEXT FILE CREATED TO
1250   REM    KEEP RECORD SCORES
1260   REM  ***********************
1270 DD$ =  CHR$ (4)
1280   PRINT DD$;"OPEN RECORD SCORE,L100"
1290   PRINT DD$;"READ RECORD SCORE,R";N
1300   INPUT R
1310   IF R > M THEN 1350
1320 R = M
1330   PRINT DD$;"WRITE RECORD SCORE,R";N
1340   PRINT R
1350   PRINT DD$;"CLOSE RECORD SCORE"
1360   VTAB (9): PRINT "*******************************************"
1370   VTAB (12): PRINT "START NUMBER       YOUR SCORE       RECORD"
1380   PRINT  SPC( 4);N; SPC( 15);M; SPC( 12);R
1390   VTAB (17): PRINT "*******************************************"
1400   PRINT : PRINT : PRINT "DO YOU WANT TO PLAY AGAIN?  (Y/N)"
1410   INPUT B$
1420   IF B$ = "N" THEN 1450
1430   HOME
1440   GOTO 240
1450   PRINT : PRINT
1460   FLASH
1470   HTAB (20): PRINT "THANKS FOR PLAYING!!"
1480   NORMAL
1490   FOR K = 1 TO 3000
1500   NEXT K
1510 D$ =  CHR$ (4)
1520   PRINT D$;"RUN HELLO"
1530   NORMAL
1540   PRINT : PRINT "REMEMBER, YOU MUST ENTER A NUMBER."
1550   PRINT "PLEASE TRY AGAIN."
1560   GOTO 470
1570   PRINT : PRINT "REMEMBER, YOU MUST ENTER A NUMBER."
1580   PRINT "PLEASE TRY AGAIN."
1590   GOTO 760
```

LARGEST PRODUCT

```
120   DIM A$(5): DIM B(5): DIM C(5)
130 A$(1) = " "
140 A$(2) = " "
150 A$(3) = " "
160 A$(4) = " "
170 T = 1
180 I = 1
190 J = 1
200   HOME
210   REM
220   REM  *********************
230   REM    GAME INSTRUCTIONS
240   REM  *********************
250   REM
260   PRINT "YOU ARE GOING TO PLAY A GAME.  LOOK AT   THE FOLLOWING FIGURE."
```

```
270    FOR K = 1 TO 3000
280    NEXT K
290    GOSUB 310
300    GOTO 520
310    HOME
320    REM
330    REM   **********************
340    REM     DISPLAY OF PROBLEM
350    REM   **********************
360    REM
370    PRINT "         *****    *****"
380    PRINT "         *   *    *   *"
390    PRINT "         * ";A$(1);" *    * ";A$(2);" *"
400    PRINT "         *   *    *   *"
410    PRINT "         *****    *****
420    PRINT
430    PRINT
440    PRINT "         *****    *****"
450    PRINT " X   X   *   *    *   *"
460    PRINT "  X X    * ";A$(3);" *    * ";A$(4);" *"
470    PRINT "   X     *   *    *   *"
480    PRINT "  X X    *****    *****"
490    PRINT " X   X   "
500    PRINT " ----------------------------"
510    RETURN
520    PRINT
530    PRINT
540    IF I > 1 THEN 1030
550    REM
560    REM   **********************
570    REM      MORE INSTRUCTIONS
580    REM   **********************
590    REM
600    PRINT
610    PRINT "YOU ARE GOING TO FILL IN THE BOXES WITH FOUR NUMBERS (0-9).
       THE COMPUTER WILL TELL YOU WHAT THE NUMBERS ARE."
620    PRINT
630    PRINT "PRESS ";: INVERSE : PRINT "RETURN";: NORMAL : PRINT " WHEN YOU
       ARE READY TO GO ON"
640    INPUT D$
650    GOSUB 310
660    PRINT
670    PRINT
680    PRINT "WHEN THE COMPUTER TELLS YOU A NUMBER"
690    PRINT "YOU MUST DECIDE WHICH BOX TO PUT IT IN."
700    PRINT "THE GOAL IS TO FILL IN THE BOXES SO"
710    PRINT "AS TO GET THE LARGEST POSSIBLE PRODUCT."
720    PRINT
730    PRINT "PRESS ";: INVERSE : PRINT "RETURN";: NORMAL : PRINT " WHEN YOU
       ARE READY TO GO ON"
740    INPUT C$
750    GOSUB 310
760    PRINT : PRINT
770    PRINT "ARE YOU READY?  GOOD LUCK!!"
780    PRINT "PRESS ";: INVERSE : PRINT "RETURN";: NORMAL : PRINT " WHEN YOU
       ARE READY TO GO ON"
790    INPUT D$
800    GOSUB 310
810    PRINT : PRINT
820    REM
830    REM   **********************
840    REM     RANDOM DIGIT GIVEN
850    REM   **********************
860    REM
870    Z =  INT ( RND (1) * 10)
880    Y = Z + 1
890    B(T) = Z
900    T = T + 1
910    PRINT "YOUR NUMBER IS  ";Z;" .  IN WHICH BOX DO"
920    PRINT "YOU WANT TO PLACE THIS NUMBER?  USE THE"
```

```
930    PRINT "FOLLOWING TO SHOW YOUR CHOICE."
940    PRINT
950    PRINT "UPPER LEFT- 1          UPPER RIGHT- 2"
960    PRINT "LOWER LEFT- 3          LOWER RIGHT- 4"
970    INPUT U
980 P$ = "0123456789"
990 T$ =  LEFT$ (P$,Y)
1000 A$(U) =  RIGHT$ (T$,1)
1010 I = I + 1
1020   GOSUB 310
1030   PRINT
1040   PRINT
1050   PRINT "HERE'S WHAT YOU HAVE SO FAR."
1060   PRINT
1070   PRINT "PRESS ";: INVERSE : PRINT "RETURN";: NORMAL : PRINT " WHEN YO
       U ARE READY TO GO ON"
1080   INPUT Z$
1090   HOME
1100   IF J = 4 THEN 1140
1110 I = 1
1120 J = J + 1
1130   GOTO 800
1140   PRINT
1150   PRINT
1160   PRINT
1170 C(1) =  VAL (A$(1)):C(2) =  VAL (A$(2)):C(3) =  VAL (A$(3)):C(4) =   VAL
     (A$(4))
1180 K = ((10 * C(1)) + C(2)) * ((10 * C(3)) + C(4))
1190   PRINT "YOUR PRODUCT IS  ";: INVERSE : PRINT K
1200   NORMAL
1210 F = 0
1220   GOTO 1310
1230   REM
1240   REM   ********************
1250   REM    ORDERS THE DIGITS
1260   REM   AND COMPUTES THE
1270   REM   LARGEST POSSIBLE
1280   REM   PRODUCT
1290   REM   ********************
1300   REM
1310 C(1) =  VAL (A$(1)):C(2) =  VAL (A$(2)):C(3) =  VAL (A$(3)):C(4) =   VAL
     (A$(4))
1320 F = 0
1330   FOR I = 1 TO 3
1340   IF C(I) <  = C(I + 1) THEN 1390
1350 T = C(I)
1360 C(I) = C(I + 1)
1370 C(I + 1) = T
1380 F = 1
1390   NEXT I
1400   IF F = 1 THEN 1320
1410 P = (10 * C(4) + C(1)) * (10 * C(3) + C(2))
1420   IF K = P THEN 1610
1430   PRINT
1440   PRINT
1450   PRINT "THE LARGEST POSSIBLE PRODUCT USING YOUR FOUR NUMBERS IS  ";: FLAS
       : PRINT P
1460   NORMAL
1470   PRINT : PRINT : PRINT :
1480   PRINT "REMEMBER, YOUR FOUR NUMBERS WERE   "
1490   PRINT
1500   PRINT  TAB( 6);B(1); TAB( 15);B(2); TAB( 24);B(3); TAB( 33);B(4)
1510   PRINT : PRINT
1520   PRINT "WOULD YOU LIKE TO PLAY AGAIN?   Y/N"
1530   INPUT M$
1540   IF M$ = "Y" THEN 130
1550   HOME
1560   PRINT "THANKS FOR PLAYING!!"
1570   FOR K = 1 TO 3000
```

```
1580   NEXT K
1590  D$ =  CHR$ (4)
1600   PRINT D$;"RUN HELLO"
1610   PRINT
1620   PRINT
1630   PRINT "CONGRATULATIONS!!  YOUR PRODUCT IS THE   LARGEST POSSIBLE PROD
       UCT USING YOUR FOUR NUMBERS."
1640   GOTO 1470
```

THE MEAN GAME

```
 80   REM
 90   REM    ************************
100   REM         THE MEAN GAME
110   REM    ************************
120   REM
130   HOME : CLEAR
140   DIM A(6)
150   REM
160   REM    ************************
170   REM   CHOOSE A GOAL MEAN
180   REM    ************************
190   REM
200  W =   INT ( RND (1) * 21) + 10
210   HTAB (13): PRINT "THE MEAN GAME"
220   PRINT : PRINT "DO YOU WANT TO SEE THE INSTRUCTIONS?"
230   PRINT "(Y/N)"
240   INPUT Z$
250   IF Z$ = "N" THEN 490
260   REM
270   REM    ************************
280   REM    GAME INSTRUCTIONS
290   REM    ************************
300   REM
310   PRINT "YOU ARE GOING TO PLAY A GAME.  YOU WILL COLLECT FIVE NUMBERS."
320   PRINT : PRINT
330   PRINT "YOU WANT THE MEAN OF YOUR FIVE NUMBERS   TO BE AS CLOSE TO   ";
      W;"  AS POSSIBLE."
340   PRINT : PRINT : PRINT "REMEMBER, THE MEAN OF A SET OF NUMBERS"
350   PRINT "IS FOUND BY ADDING THE NUMBERS AND"
360   PRINT "DIVIDING BY THE NUMBER OF SCORES"
370   PRINT "YOU HAVE.  IF YOU HAVE THE SET"
380   PRINT "3,5,6,9,7  THE MEAN WILL BE"
390   PRINT : PRINT "(3+5+6+9+7)/5 OR 30/5 = 6"
400   PRINT : PRINT
410   PRINT : PRINT "PRESS 'RETURN' WHEN YOU WANT TO GO ON.": INPUT D$
415   HOME
420   PRINT "YOU WILL COLLECT YOUR NUMBERS FROM A"
430   PRINT "SPINNER WITH NUMBERS  0-40.  THE"
440   PRINT "COMPUTER WILL TELL YOU THE RESULTS"
450   PRINT "EACH SPIN."
460   PRINT : PRINT
470   PRINT "FOR EACH OF FIVE ROUNDS, YOU MAY TAKE    THE FIRST SPIN.  IF Y
      OU CHOOSE TO SPIN    AGAIN, YOU MUST TAKE THE SECOND SPIN."
480   PRINT
490   PRINT "YOUR GOAL IS A MEAN OF   ";W
500   PRINT "PRESS 'RETURN' WHEN YOU WANT TO START."
510   INPUT F$: HOME
520  J = 1
530  I = 1
540   REM
550   REM    ************************
560   REM    START OF FIVE SPINS
570   REM    ************************
580   REM
590   FOR N = 1 TO 5
600  X =   INT ( RND (1) * 41)
```

```
610    PRINT "YOUR FIRST SPIN IS ";X
620    PRINT
630    PRINT "DO YOU WANT TO SPIN AGAIN?  Y/N"
640    PRINT : PRINT "(REMEMBER, YOUR GOAL IS A MEAN OF  ";W;"  )"
650    INPUT A$
660    IF A$ = "Y" THEN 840
670  A(I) = X
680    PRINT
690    PRINT
700    HOME
710    PRINT "YOUR NUMBERS SO FAR ARE"
720    FOR I = 1 TO J
740    PRINT A(I)
750    NEXT I
760    IF N = 5 THEN 820
770    PRINT
780    PRINT
790    PRINT
800    PRINT "YOU ARE READY FOR THE NEXT ROUND"
810  J = J + 1
820    NEXT N
830    GOTO 1090
840  Y =  INT ( RND (1) * 41)
850    PRINT
860    PRINT
870    HOME
880    REM
890    REM  ***********************
900    REM   SECOND SPIN ON A TURN
910    REM  ***********************
920    REM
930    PRINT "YOUR SECOND SPIN IS  ";Y
950    PRINT
960  A(I) = Y
970    PRINT "YOUR NUMBERS SO FAR ARE"
980    FOR I = 1 TO J
1000   PRINT A(I)
1010   NEXT I
1020   IF N = 5 THEN 1080
1030   PRINT
1040   PRINT
1050   PRINT
1060   PRINT "YOU ARE READY FOR THE NEXT ROUND"
1070 J = J + 1
1080   NEXT N
1090 Z = (A(1) + A(2) + A(3) + A(4) + A(5)) / 5
1100   PRINT : PRINT
1105   PRINT "----------------------------------------"
1110   PRINT "YOUR MEAN IS  ";Z
1120   PRINT : PRINT : PRINT "THE GOAL MEAN WAS  ";W
1130   IF  ABS (Z - W) < 4 THEN 1230
1140   PRINT
1150   PRINT
1160   PRINT "YOU WEREN'T TOO CLOSE THAT TIME."
1170   PRINT
1180   PRINT
1190   PRINT "DO YOU WANT TO PLAY AGAIN? Y/N"
1200   INPUT B$
1210   IF B$ = "Y" THEN 130
1220   GOTO 1270
1230   PRINT : PRINT "YOU DID VERY WELL THAT TIME!!!"
1240   PRINT
1250   PRINT
1260   GOTO 1190
1270   HOME
1280   PRINT "THANKS FOR PLAYING"
1290   FOR K = 1 TO 3000
1300   NEXT K
1310 D$ =  CHR$ (4)
1320   PRINT D$;"RUN HELLO"
```

THE MEDIAN GAME

```
80   REM    ***********************
90   REM        THE MEDIAN GAME
100   REM    ***********************
110   HOME : CLEAR
120   DIM A(6)
130   REM
140   REM    ***********************
150   REM    RANDOM GOAL MEDIAN
160   REM    ***********************
170   REM
180   W =  INT ( RND (1) * 21) + 10
190   HTAB (12): PRINT "THE MEDIAN GAME"
200   PRINT : PRINT : PRINT "DO YOU WANT TO SEE THE INSTRUCTIONS?"
210   PRINT "(Y/N)"
220   INPUT Z$
230   IF Z$ = "N" THEN 490
240   REM
250   REM    *********************
260   REM    GAME INSTRUCTIONS
270   REM    *********************
280   REM
290   PRINT "YOU ARE GOING TO PLAY A GAME.   YOU WILL COLLECT FIVE NUMBERS."

300   PRINT
310   PRINT "YOU WANT THE MEDIAN OF YOUR FIVE NUMBERS TO BE AS CLOSE TO  ";
      W;"  AS POSSIBLE."
320   PRINT : PRINT : PRINT "REMEMBER THAT THE MEDIAN OF A LIST"
330   PRINT "OF NUMBERS IS THE MIDDLE NUMBER WHEN"
340   PRINT "THE NUMBERS ARE LISTED IN ORDER."
350   PRINT "IN THIS LIST, 15 IS THE MEDIAN."
360   PRINT : PRINT "5, 9, 15, 20, 26"
370   PRINT : PRINT "PRESS 'RETURN' WHEN YOU WANT TO GO ON."
380   INPUT D$
385   HOME
390   PRINT "YOU WILL COLLECT YOUR NUMBERS FROM A"
400   PRINT "SPINNER WITH NUMBERS  0-40.   THE"
410   PRINT "COMPUTER WILL TELL YOU THE RESULTS"
420   PRINT "OF EACH SPIN."
430   INPUT E$: HOME
440   PRINT "FOR EACH OF FIVE ROUNDS YOU MAY TAKE THE"
450   PRINT "FIRST SPIN OR YOU MAY CHOOSE TO SPIN"
460   PRINT "AGAIN.   IF  YOU CHOOSE TO SPIN AGAIN,"
470   PRINT "YOU MUST TAKE THE SECOND SPIN AS YOUR"
480   PRINT "NUMBER FOR THAT ROUND."
490   PRINT
500   PRINT "YOUR GOAL IS A MEDIAN OF  ";W
510   PRINT : PRINT "PRESS 'RETURN' WHEN YOU WANT TO START."
520   INPUT F$: HOME
530   J = 1
540   I = 1
550   REM
560   REM    *********************
570   REM    START OF FIVE SPINS
580   REM    *********************
590   REM
600   FOR N = 1 TO 5
610   X =  INT ( RND (1) * 41)
620   PRINT "YOUR FIRST SPIN IS   ";X
630   PRINT
640   PRINT "DO YOU WANT TO SPIN AGAIN?    Y/N"
650   PRINT : PRINT "(REMEMBER, YOUR GOAL IS A MEDIAN OF   ";W;")"
660   INPUT A$
670   IF A$ = "Y" THEN 830
680   A(I) = X
690   HOME
700   PRINT "YOUR NUMBERS SO FAR ARE"
710   FOR I = 1 TO J
730   PRINT A(I)
740   NEXT I
```

```
750    IF N = 5 THEN 810
760    PRINT
770    PRINT
780    PRINT
790    PRINT "YOU ARE READY FOR THE NEXT  ROUND."
800  J = J + 1
810    NEXT N
820    GOTO 1060
830  Y =   INT ( RND (1) * 41 )
840    HOME
850    REM
860    REM   **********************
870    REM   SECOND SPIN ON A TURN
880    REM   **********************
890    REM
900    PRINT "YOUR SECOND SPIN IS  ";Y
910    PRINT
920    PRINT
930  A( I ) = Y
940    PRINT "YOUR NUMBERS SO FAR ARE"
950    FOR I = 1 TO J
970    PRINT A( I )
980    NEXT I
990    IF N = 5 THEN 1050
1000   PRINT
1010   PRINT
1020   PRINT
1030   PRINT "YOU ARE READY FOR THE NEXT  ROUND."
1040 J = J + 1
1050   NEXT N
1060 F = 0
1070   GOTO 1140
1080 F = 0
1090   REM
1100   REM   **********************
1110   REM    ORDERS THE NUMBERS
1120   REM   **********************
1130   REM
1140   FOR I = 1 TO 4
1150   IF A( I ) <  = A( I + 1 ) THEN 1200
1160 T = A( I )
1170 A( I ) = A( I + 1 )
1180 A( I + 1 ) = T
1190 F = 1
1200   NEXT I
1210   IF F = 1 THEN 1080
1220   PRINT : PRINT
1225   PRINT "----------------------------------------"
1230   PRINT "YOUR MEDIAN IS  ";A(3)
1240   PRINT : PRINT : PRINT "THE GOAL MEDIAN WAS   ";W
1250   IF  ABS (W - A(3)) <  = 5 THEN 1350
1260   PRINT
1270   PRINT
1280   PRINT "YOU WEREN'T TOO CLOSE THAT TIME."
1290   PRINT
1300   PRINT
1310   PRINT "DO YOU WANT TO PLAY AGAIN?  Y/N"
1320   INPUT B$
1330   IF B$ = "Y" THEN 110
1340   GOTO 1390
1350   PRINT : PRINT "YOU DID VERY WELL THAT TIME!!!"
1360   PRINT
1370   PRINT
1380   GOTO 1310
1390   HOME
1400   PRINT "THANKS FOR PLAYING!!"
1410   FOR K = 1 TO 3000
1420   NEXT K
1430 D$ =   CHR$ (4)
1440   PRINT D$;"RUN HELLO"
```

GUESS MY RULE

```
80    REM    *********************
90    REM     GUESS MY RULE
100   REM    *********************
110   REM
120   HOME
130   SPEED= 100
140   DIM X(50)
150   DIM Y(50)
160   PRINT "YOU ARE GOING TO PLAY 'GUESS MY RULE'."
170   PRINT : PRINT "DO YOU WANT TO SEE THE INSTRUCTIONS?     (Y/N)"
180   INPUT J$
190   IF J$ = "N" THEN 480
200   REM
210   REM    *********************
220   REM     INSTRUCTIONS
230   REM    *********************
240   REM
250   PRINT : PRINT "IN THIS GAME, YOU WILL SELECT A NUMBER."
260   PRINT : PRINT "THE COMPUTER WILL TAKE YOUR NUMBER AND"
270   PRINT "USE A RULE TO PRODUCE ANOTHER NUMBER."
280   PRINT : PRINT "YOUR TASK WILL BE TO DISCOVER WHAT RULE"
290   PRINT "THE COMPUTER IS USING."
300   PRINT : PRINT "FOR EXAMPLE, LET'S SUPPOSE THE RULE IS  'ADD 5' "
310   PRINT : PRINT "IF YOU CHOOSE 3, THEN THE COMPUTER"
320   PRINT "WILL 'ADD 5' AND REPORT AN ANSWER OF 8."
330   FOR M = 1 TO 4000
340   NEXT M
350   HOME
360   REM
370   REM    *********************
380   REM     SAMPLE PROBLEM
390   REM    *********************
400   REM
410   PRINT "HERE IS WHAT A TABLE WOULD LOOK LIKE FOR THIS RULE."
420   PRINT : PRINT : PRINT "     INPUT     OUTPUT"
430   PRINT "--------------------"
440   PRINT "       3          8"
450   PRINT "       5         10"
460   PRINT "       7         12"
470   PRINT "      18         23"
480   PRINT : PRINT : PRINT "NOW, CHOOSE A LEVEL OF DIFFICULTY."
490   SPEED= 200
500   REM
510   REM    *********************
520   REM    R- NUMBER OF GUESSES
530   REM     STUDENT MAKES IF HE
540   REM     THINKS HE KNOWS THE
550   REM     RULE
560   REM    K,K1,K2 ARE NUMBER OF
570   REM     INPUTS MADE BY
580   REM     STUDENT AT BEGINNER,
590   REM     ADVANCED, AND EXPERT
600   REM     LEVELS, RESPECTIVELY
610   REM    *********************
620   REM
630 R = 0
640 K = 0:K1 = 0:K2 = 0
650   PRINT : PRINT "BEGINNER- 1"
660   PRINT "ADVANCED- 2"
670   PRINT "EXPERT- 3"
680   INPUT LEV
690   S =  INT ( RND (1) * 3) + 1
700   IF LEV = 1 THEN 750
710   IF LEV = 2 THEN 2550
720   GOTO 3240
730   REM
740   REM    *********************
750   REM   BEGINNER LEVEL
760   REM
```

```
770   REM   A- RANDOM COEFFICIENT
780   REM   *********************
790   REM
800  A =   INT ( RND (1) * 7) + 1
810   GOSUB 830
820   GOTO 890
830   PRINT "YOU WILL CHOOSE A NUMBER AS YOUR INPUT"
840   PRINT "THE COMPUTER WILL GIVE YOU THE OUTPUT"
850   PRINT : PRINT "YOU CAN CHOOSE TEN NUMBERS IF NECESSARY"
860   PRINT : PRINT "PRESS 'RETURN' WHEN YOU WANT TO START."
870   INPUT A$
880   RETURN
890   HOME
900  R = 0
910   FOR I = 1 TO 10
920   PRINT "WHAT NUMBER DO YOU WANT TO ENTER?"
930   INPUT X(I)
940  K = K + 1
950   REM
960   REM   *********************
970   REM   VALUE OF S DETERMINES
980   REM   RULE COMPUTER CHOOSES
990   REM   AT BEGINNER LEVEL
1000   REM   *********************
1010   REM
1020   IF S = 1 THEN 1990
1030   IF S = 2 THEN 2010
1040   GOTO 2030
1050   GOSUB 1140
1060   GOTO 1210
1070   REM
1080   REM   *********************
1090   REM   PRINTS STUDENT INPUT
1100   REM   AND CORRESPONDING
1110   REM   OUTPUT
1120   REM   *********************
1130   REM
1140   PRINT : PRINT : PRINT "INPUT       OUTPUT"
1150   PRINT "-----------------"
1160   FOR J = 1 TO I
1170   PRINT "  ";X(J);"            ";Y(J)
1180   NEXT J
1190   PRINT : PRINT : PRINT "HERE'S WHAT YOU HAVE SO FAR."
1200   RETURN
1210   PRINT : PRINT "IF YOU THINK YOU KNOW THE RULE, PRESS Y."
1220   INPUT B$
1230   IF B$ = "Y" THEN 1330
1240   HOME
1250   NEXT I
1260   HOME
1270   PRINT "THAT IS TEN TRIES."
1280   PRINT "DO YOU WANT TO TRY THIS ONE AGAIN?"
1290   PRINT "(Y/N)"
1300   INPUT C$
1310   IF C$ = "Y" THEN 890
1320   ON S GOTO 3970,4060,4080
1330   GOSUB 1350
1340   GOTO 1510
1350   HOME
1360   REM
1370   REM   *********************
1380   REM   TEST TO SEE IF PLAYER
1390   REM   HAS DISCOVERED THE
1400   REM   RULE
1410   REM   *********************
1420   REM
1430   PRINT "TO SEE IF YOU HAVE DISCOVERED THE RULE"
1440   PRINT "THE COMPUTER WILL GIVE YOU A NUMBER"
1450   PRINT "AND YOU MUST TELL WHAT THE OUTCOME"
1460   PRINT "WILL BE, USING THE RULE."
```

```
1470   PRINT : PRINT "YOU MUST ANSWER CORRECTLY THREE IN A ROW"
1480   PRINT : PRINT : PRINT "PRESS 'RETURN' WHEN YOU WANT TO GO ON."
1490   INPUT Z$
1500   RETURN
1510   HOME
1520   REM
1530   REM   **********************
1540   REM   T- RANDOM INPUT VALUE
1550   REM   P- PLAYER'S RESPONSE
1560   REM     FOR CORRESPONDING
1570   REM       OUTPUT
1580   REM   **********************
1590 T =  INT ( RND (1) * 20) + 10
1600   PRINT "IF  ";T;"  IS THE INPUT, THE OUTPUT IS?"
1610   INPUT P
1620 R = R + 1
1630   IF S = 1 THEN 2050
1640   IF S = 2 THEN 2070
1650   GOTO 2090
1660   REM
1670   REM   **********************
1680   REM   TEST PLAYER'S OUTPUT
1690   REM   AGAINST TRUE OUTPUT
1700   REM   **********************
1710   REM
1720   IF P <  > Y THEN 1840
1730   PRINT : PRINT "THAT IS CORRECT!!"
1740   IF R = 3 THEN 1770
1750   PRINT : PRINT
1760   GOTO 1590
1770   PRINT : PRINT : PRINT "THAT IS GREAT!  YOU FOUND THE RULE"
1780   PRINT "IN  ";K;"  TRIES!!"
1790   PRINT : PRINT "DO YOU WANT TO PLAY AGAIN?  (Y/N)"
1800   INPUT E$
1810   IF E$ = "N" THEN 4010
1820   HOME
1830   GOTO 480
1840   PRINT : PRINT "SORRY, THAT IS INCORRECT."
1850   PRINT : PRINT "DO YOU WANT TO KEEP WORKING ON"
1860   PRINT "THIS RULE?  (Y/N)"
1870   INPUT F$
1880   IF F$ = "Y" THEN 890
1890   PRINT : PRINT "DO YOU WANT TO TRY ANOTHER ONE?  (Y/N)"
1900   INPUT G$
1910   IF G$ = "N" THEN 870
1920   HOME
1930   GOTO 480
1940   REM
1950   REM   **********************
1960   REM   BEGINNER LEVEL RULES
1970   REM   **********************
1980   REM
1990 Y(I) = X(I) * A
2000   GOTO 1050
2010 Y(I) = X(I) - A
2020   GOTO 1050
2030 Y(I) = X(I) + A
2040   GOTO 1050
2050 Y = T * A
2060   GOTO 1720
2070 Y = T - A
2080   GOTO 1720
2090 Y = T + A
2100   GOTO 1720
2110   REM
2120   REM   **********************
2130   REM   ADVANCED LEVEL RULES
2140   REM   **********************
2150   REM
2160 Y(I) = A * X(I) + B
```

```
2170   GOTO 2750
2180 Y(I) = A * X(I) - B
2190   GOTO 2750
2200 C = A * B
2210 Y(I) = ((X(I) + A) * C) / B
2220   GOTO 2750
2230 Y = A * T + B
2240   GOTO 3030
2250 Y = A * T - B
2260   GOTO 3030
2270 Y = ((T + A) * C) / B
2280   GOTO 3030
2290   REM
2300   REM   *********************
2310   REM   EXPERT LEVEL RULES
2320   REM   *********************
2330   REM
2340 Y(I) = A * (X(I) * X(I)) + (B * X(I))
2350   GOTO 3510
2360 Y(I) = (X(I) * X(I) * X(I)) - (B * X(I) * X(I))
2370   GOTO 3510
2380 Y(I) = ((A * X(I)) * (A * X(I)) * (A * X(I))) + (B * X(I) * X(I))
2390   GOTO 3510
2400 Y = (A * T * T) + (B * T)
2410   GOTO 3790
2420 Y = (T * T * T) - (B * T * T)
2430   GOTO 3790
2440 Y = ((A * T) * (A * T) * (A * T)) + (B * T * T)
2450   GOTO 3790
2460 Y = A * T - B
2470   GOTO 3030
2480   REM
2490   REM   *********************
2500   REM   ADVANCED LEVEL
2510   REM    A AND B ARE RANDOM
2520   REM    COEFFICIENTS
2530   REM   *********************
2540   REM
2550   REM   ADVANCED LEVEL
2560 A =   INT ( RND (1) * 8) + 1
2570 B =   INT ( RND (1) * 8) + 1
2580   GOSUB 830
2590   HOME
2600 R = 0
2610   FOR I = 1 TO 10
2620   PRINT "WHAT NUMBER DO YOU WANT TO ENTER?"
2630   INPUT X(I)
2640 K1 = K1 + 1
2650   REM
2660   REM   *********************
2670   REM   S CHOOSES TYPE OF
2680   REM    RULE AT ADVANCED
2690   REM    LEVEL
2700   REM   *********************
2710   REM
2720   IF S = 1 THEN 2160
2730   IF S = 2 THEN 2180
2740   GOTO 2200
2750   GOSUB 1140
2760   PRINT : PRINT "IF YOU THINK YOU KNOW THE RULE, PRESS Y."
2770   INPUT I$
2780   IF I$ = "Y" THEN 2880
2790   HOME
2800   NEXT I
2810   HOME
2820   PRINT "THAT IS TEN TRIES."
2830   PRINT "DO YOU WANT TO TRY THIS ONE AGAIN?"
2840   PRINT "(Y/N)"
2850   INPUT J$
2860   IF J$ = "Y" THEN 2590
```

```
2870    ON S GOTO 4100,4120,4140
2880    GOSUB 1350
2890    HOME
2900    REM
2910    REM    *********************
2920    REM    T- RANDOM INPUT
2930    REM    P- PLAYER'S OUTPUT
2940    REM    *********************
2950    REM
2960 T =    INT ( RND (1) * 20) + 10
2970    PRINT "IF  ";T;"  IS THE INPUT, THE OUTPUT IS?"
2980    INPUT P
2990 R = R + 1
3000    IF S = 1 THEN 2230
3010    IF S = 2 THEN 2250
3020    GOTO 2270
3030    IF P < > Y THEN 3150
3040    PRINT : PRINT "THAT IS CORRECT!!"
3050    PRINT : PRINT
3060    IF R = 3 THEN 3080
3070    GOTO 2960
3080    PRINT "THAT IS GREAT!   YOU FOUND THE RULE"
3090    PRINT "IN  ";K1;"   TRIES!!"
3100    PRINT : PRINT "DO YOU WANT TO PLAY AGAIN?  (Y/N)"
3110    INPUT M$
3120    IF M$ = "N" THEN 4010
3130    HOME
3140    GOTO 480
3150    PRINT : PRINT "SORRY, THAT IS INCORRECT."
3160    PRINT : PRINT "DO YOU WANT TO KEEP WORKING ON THIS RULE?  (Y/N)"
3170    INPUT N$
3180    IF N$ = "Y" THEN 2590
3190    PRINT : PRINT "DO YOU WANT TO TRY ANOTHER ONE?  (Y/N)"
3200    INPUT P$
3210    IF P$ = "N" THEN 870
3220    HOME
3230    GOTO 480
3240    REM
3250    REM    *********************
3260    REM    EXPERT LEVEL
3270    REM     A AND B ARE RANDOM
3280    REM      COEFFICIENTS
3290    REM    *********************
3300    REM
3320 A =    INT ( RND (1) * 5) + 1
3330 B =    INT ( RND (1) * 5) + 1
3340    GOSUB 830
3350    HOME
3360 R = 0
3370    FOR I = 1 TO 10
3380    PRINT "WHAT NUMBER DO YOU WANT TO ENTER?"
3390    INPUT X(I)
3400    HOME
3410    K2 = K2 + 1
3420    REM
3430    REM    *********************
3440    REM    S CHOOSES TYPE OF
3450    REM     RULE AT EXPERT LEVEL
3460    REM    *********************
3470    REM
3480    IF S = 1 THEN 2340
3490    IF S = 2 THEN 2360
3500    GOTO 2380
3510    GOSUB 1140
3520    PRINT : PRINT "IF YOU THINK YOU KNOW THE RULE, PRESS Y."
3530    INPUT S$
3540    IF S$ = "Y" THEN 3640
3550    HOME
3560    NEXT I
3570    HOME
```

```
3580    PRINT "THAT IS TEN TRIES."
3590    PRINT "DO YOU WANT TO TRY THIS ONE AGAIN?"
3600    PRINT "(Y/N)"
3610    INPUT T$
3620    IF T$ = "Y" THEN 3350
3630    ON S GOTO 4160,4180,4200
3640    GOSUB 1350
3650    HOME
3660    REM
3670    REM    *********************
3680    REM    T- RANDOM INPUT
3690    REM    P- PLAYER'S OUTPUT
3700    REM    *********************
3710    REM
3720 T =  INT ( RND (1) * 20) + 10
3730    PRINT "IF  ";T;"   IS THE INPUT, THE OUTPUT IS?"
3740    INPUT P
3750 R = R + 1
3760    IF S = 1 THEN 2400
3770    IF S = 2 THEN 2420
3780    GOTO 2440
3790    IF P <  > Y THEN 3910
3800    PRINT : PRINT "THAT IS CORRECT!!"
3810    PRINT : PRINT
3820    IF R = 3 THEN 3840
3830    GOTO 3720
3840    PRINT "THAT IS GREAT!  YOU FOUND THE RULE"
3850    PRINT "IN  ";K2;"  TRIES!!"
3860    PRINT : PRINT "DO YOU WANT TO PLAY AGAIN?  (Y/N)"
3870    INPUT V$
3880    IF V$ = "N" THEN 4010
3890    HOME
3900    GOTO 480
3910    PRINT : PRINT "SORRY, THAT IS INCORRECT."
3920    PRINT : PRINT "DO YOU WANT TO KEEP WORKING ON THIS RULE?  (Y/N)"
3930    INPUT W$
3940    IF W$ = "Y" THEN 3350
3950    GOTO 3980
3960    GOTO 480
3970    PRINT : PRINT "THE RULE WAS  Y = X * ";A
3980    PRINT : PRINT "DO YOU WANT TO TRY ANOTHER ONE? (Y/N)"
3990    INPUT D$
4000    IF D$ = "Y" THEN 480
4010    PRINT : PRINT "THANKS FOR PLAYING!!"
4015    SPEED= 255
4020    FOR K = 1 TO 3000
4030    NEXT K
4040 D$ =  CHR$ (4)
4050    PRINT D$;"RUN HELLO"
4060    PRINT : PRINT "THE RULE WAS  Y = X - ";A
4070    GOTO 3980
4080    PRINT : PRINT "THE RULE WAS  Y = X + ";A
4090    GOTO 3980
4100    PRINT : PRINT "THE RULE WAS  Y = ";A;" * X + ";B
4110    GOTO 3980
4120    PRINT : PRINT "THE RULE WAS  Y = ";A;" * X - ";B
4130    GOTO 3980
4140    PRINT : PRINT "THE RULE WAS  Y = ((X + ";A;") * ";C;")/";B
4150    GOTO 3980
4160    PRINT : PRINT "THE RULE WAS  Y = ";A;" * (X↑2) + (";B;" * X)"
4170    GOTO 3980
4180    PRINT : PRINT "THE RULE WAS  Y = (X↑3) - (";B;" * (X↑2))"
4190    GOTO 3980
4200    PRINT : PRINT "THE RULE WAS"
4210    PRINT "Y = ((";A;" * X) ↑ 3) + (";B;" * (X ↑ 2))"
4220    GOTO 3980
```

ESTIMATE

```
0 N1 =  INT (6000 *  RND (1)) + 1000
1 N2 = ( INT (5 *  RND (1)) + 1) * 100
2 N3 = N1 + N2
3 T1 =  INT (N1 / 1000):T2 =  INT (N3 / 1000)
4 R1 = N1 - (1000 * T1):R2 = N3 - (1000 * T2)
5 H1 =  INT (R1 / 100):H2 =  INT (R2 / 100)
6 S1 = R1 - (100 * H1):S2 = R2 - (100 * H2)
7 Q1 =  INT (S1 / 10):Q2 =  INT (S2 / 10)
8 U1 = S1 - (10 * Q1):U2 = S2 - (10 * Q2)
9 N =  INT (70 *  RND (1)) + 11
10 C = 0: HOME
12  GOSUB 20
14  GOTO 70
20  PRINT "------------------*-*-------------------"
30  POKE 1170,48 + T1: POKE 1172,48 + T2
40  POKE 1298,48 + H1: POKE 1300,48 + H2
50  POKE 1426,48 + Q1: POKE 1428,48 + Q2
60  POKE 1554,48 + U1: POKE 1556,48 + U2
65  RETURN
70  VTAB (12): PRINT "LOOK AT THE LINE SHOWN ABOVE."
100  FOR I = 1 TO 2000: NEXT I
110  PRINT : PRINT : PRINT "USING THE START NUMBER ";N;" AND"
120  PRINT "SUCCESSIVE MULTIPLICATION, YOU ARE TO"
130  PRINT "OBTAIN A NUMBER IN THIS RANGE."
135  PRINT : PRINT  SPC( 14)N1;" - ";N3
137  PRINT : PRINT : PRINT "DO YOU WANT TO SEE AN EXAMPLE? (Y/N)"
138  GET A$
140  IF A$ = "N" THEN 250
150  HOME
155  SPEED= 100
160  PRINT "EXAMPLE:    START         RANGE"
170  PRINT " `          -----         -----"
180  PRINT "             12           5000-5500"
190  PRINT : PRINT
200  PRINT "  1. 12 X 400 = 4800      TOO SMALL"
210  PRINT "  2. 4800 X 1.2 = 5760    TOO LARGE"
220  PRINT "  3. 5760 X 0.95 = 5472   WE DID IT"
230  PRINT  SPC( 25)"IN THREE STEPS!"
235  SPEED= 255
240  PRINT : PRINT : PRINT "PRESS 'RETURN' WHEN YOU WANT TO GO ON."
245  GET A$
250  HOME : GOSUB 20
260  VTAB (12): PRINT "YOU WILL BE ASKED TO TELL THE COMPUTER"
270  PRINT "YOUR ESTIMATE EACH TIME AND IT WILL"
280  PRINT "SHOW YOU WHERE YOUR RESULT IS ON THE"
290  PRINT "LINE ABOVE."
300  PRINT : PRINT : PRINT "PRESS 'RETURN' WHEN YOU ARE READY"
305  PRINT "TO START."
310  GET A$
315  HOME
325  GOSUB 20
330  VTAB (12): PRINT N;" X "
335  POKE 1458,127: POKE 1459,127
340  PRINT : PRINT : PRINT "WHAT NUMBER DO YOU WANT TO MULTIPLY"
342  PRINT : PRINT  SPC( 15)N;"   BY?"
350  INPUT X
351  IF X = 0 THEN 353
352  GOTO 355
353  PRINT : PRINT : PRINT "YOU DON'T WANT TO USE  0  DO YOU!!": PRINT : PRIN
     "WHY DON'T YOU PICK ANOTHER NUMBER."
354  GOTO 350
355 C = C + 1
360  P = X * N
380  HOME
390  GOSUB 20
400  VTAB (12): PRINT N;" X ";X;" = ";P
410  IF P > N3 THEN 495
420  IF P > N1 THEN 600
425  GOSUB 1000
```

```
430   PRINT : PRINT "THIS PRODUCT IS TOO SMALL."
440   PRINT : PRINT "YOU WILL NEED TO MAKE ANOTHER ESTIMATE."
445   PRINT : PRINT "THE FLASHING  ";C;"  MEANS YOU HAVE MADE  ";C
447   PRINT "ESTIMATES SO FAR."
450   PRINT : PRINT "PRESS 'RETURN' WHEN YOU WANT TO GO ON."
460   GET A$
465  N = P
470   HOME : GOTO 325
495   GOSUB 1000
500   PRINT : PRINT "THIS PRODUCT IS TOO LARGE."
510   PRINT : PRINT "YOU WILL NEED TO MAKE ANOTHER ESTIMATE."
515   PRINT : PRINT "THE FLASHING  ";C;"  MEANS YOU HAVE MADE  ";C
517   PRINT "ESTIMATES SO FAR."
520   PRINT : PRINT "PRESS 'RETURN' WHEN YOU WANT TO GO ON."
530   GET A$
540  N = P
550   HOME : GOTO 325
600  U = 19
603   GOSUB 1020
605   PRINT : PRINT "YOU DID IT!!!"
610   PRINT : PRINT : PRINT "IT TOOK YOU  ";C;"  TRIES!!"
620   PRINT : PRINT : PRINT "DO YOU WANT TO PLAY AGAIN? (Y/N)"
630   INPUT B$
640   IF B$ = "Y" THEN 0
650   PRINT : PRINT "THANK YOU"
652   FOR J = 1 TO 2000: NEXT J
654  D$ =  CHR$ (4)
656   PRINT D$;"RUN HELLO"
660   END
1000 L = N2 / 2
1002 E1 = N1 - (18 * L)
1004 R = P - E1
1010 U =  INT (R / L)
1020   IF U > 39 THEN U = 39
1025   IF P < E1 THEN U = 0
1027   POKE 1024 + U,112 + C
1030   RETURN
```

MYSTERY BLOCK

```
2    HOME : VTAB (12)
4    INVERSE : HTAB (14): PRINT "MYSTERY BLOCK"
6    FOR K = 1 TO 3000: NEXT K
8    NORMAL : HOME
10   HOME :I = 0: CLEAR
20   SPEED= 125
30   DIM L$(30): DIM M$(30): DIM N$(30): DIM P$(30)
40   PRINT "DO YOU WANT TO SEE INSTRUCTIONS?  (Y/N)"
50   INPUT T$
60   IF T$ = "Y" THEN 80
70   GOTO 320
80   HOME : PRINT "YOU ARE GOING TO PLAY"
90   PRINT : PRINT "            THE MYSTERY BLOCK"
100   PRINT : PRINT "THE COMPUTER WILL CHOOSE A BLOCK THAT"
110   PRINT "HAS THREE FEATURES: SIZE,COLOR,SHAPE"
120   PRINT : PRINT : PRINT "THE LIST BELOW GIVES THE POSSIBLE"
130   PRINT "CHOICES FOR EACH BLOCK."
140   PRINT : PRINT : PRINT "SIZE- SMALL,LARGE"
150   PRINT "COLOR- RED,BLUE,YELLOW,GREEN"
160   PRINT "SHAPE- CIRCLE,SQUARE,TRIANGLE,DIAMOND"
170   FOR K = 1 TO 5000: NEXT K
180   HOME
190   PRINT "YOU WILL TRY TO IDENTIFY THE MYSTERY"
200   PRINT "BLOCK BY ASKING QUESTIONS OF THIS FORM"
210   PRINT : PRINT "IS IT LIKE THE (SIZE,COLOR,SHAPE) BLOCK?"
220   PRINT : PRINT : PRINT "THE COMPUTER WILL RESPOND WITH YES OR NO"
230   PRINT : PRINT "USING THIS INFORMATION,YOU ARE TO"
240   PRINT "IDENTIFY THE MYSTERY BLOCK IN AS FEW"
```

```
250   PRINT "GUESSES AS POSSIBLE"
260   FOR K = 1 TO 5000: NEXT K
270   HOME : SPEED= 255
280   PRINT "REMEMBER, YOUR GUESSES MUST COME FROM"
290   PRINT : PRINT "SIZE-'SMALL,LARGE"
300   PRINT "COLOR- RED,BLUE,YELLOW,GREEN"
310   PRINT "SHAPE- CIRCLE,SQUARE,TRIANGLE,DIAMOND"
320   SPEED= 255:X =  INT ( RND (1) * 2) + 1
330 Y =  INT ( RND (1) * 4) + 1
340 Z =  INT ( RND (1) * 4) + 1
350   ON X GOTO 380,390
360   ON Y GOTO 400,410,420,430
370   ON Z GOTO 440,450,460,470
380 X$ = "SMALL": GOTO 360
390 X$ = "LARGE": GOTO 360
400 Y$ = "RED": GOTO 370
410 Y$ = "BLUE": GOTO 370
420 Y$ = "YELLOW": GOTO 370
430 Y$ = "GREEN": GOTO 370
440 Z$ = "CIRCLE": GOTO 480
450 Z$ = "SQUARE": GOTO 480
460 Z$ = "TRIANGLE": GOTO 480
470 Z$ = "DIAMOND"
480   PRINT : PRINT "INPUT YOUR GUESS IN THE FORM"
490   PRINT "  SIZE,COLOR,SHAPE"
500   PRINT : PRINT "IS IT LIKE THE"
510   PRINT
520   INPUT A$,B$,C$
530   IF A$ = X$ THEN 590
540   IF B$ = Y$ THEN 590
550   IF C$ = Z$ THEN 590
560   PRINT : PRINT "NO, IT IS NOT"
570 D$ = "NO"
580   GOTO 610
590   PRINT : PRINT "YES, IT IS"
600 D$ = "YES"
610 I = I + 1
620 L$(I) = A$:M$(I) = B$:N$(I) = C$:P$(I) = D$
630   FOR K = 1 TO 3000: NEXT K
640   HOME
650   PRINT "HERE IS WHAT YOU HAVE SO FAR."
660   PRINT : PRINT "IS IT LIKE THE . . ."
670   PRINT
680   FOR J = 1 TO I
690   PRINT L$(J);",";M$(J);",";N$(J);"-  ";P$(J)
700   NEXT J
710   PRINT : PRINT : PRINT "DO YOU WANT TO GUESS WHAT BLOCK"
720   PRINT "IT IS?  (Y/N)"
730   INPUT F$
740   IF F$ = "Y" THEN 790
750   PRINT : PRINT "SIZE- SMALL,LARGE"
760   PRINT "COLOR- RED,BLUE,YELLOW,GREEN"
770   PRINT "SHAPE- CIRCLE,SQUARE,TRIANGLE,DIAMOND"
780   GOTO 480
790   HOME : PRINT "INPUT YOUR GUESS IN THE FORM"
800   PRINT "  SIZE,COLOR,SHAPE"
810   INPUT U$,V$,W$
820   IF U$ <  > X$ THEN 960
830   IF V$ <  > Y$ THEN 960
840   IF W$ <  > Z$ THEN 960
850   PRINT : PRINT "YOU ARE CORRECT!!"
860   PRINT : PRINT "IT TOOK YOU  ";I;"  GUESSES TO FIND THE"
870   PRINT "MYSTERY BLOCK"
880   PRINT : PRINT "DO YOU WANT TO PLAY AGAIN? (Y/N)"
890   INPUT T$
900   IF T$ = "Y" THEN 10
910   PRINT : PRINT "THANKS FOR PLAYING"
920   FOR K = 1 TO 3000: NEXT K
930   HOME
940 D$ =  CHR$ (4)
```

```
950   PRINT D$;"RUN HELLO"
960   PRINT : PRINT "SORRY, YOU ARE NOT CORRECT."
970   PRINT "PLEASE TRY AGAIN."
980   FOR K = 1 TO 3000: NEXT K
990   HOME : GOTO 480
```

Other Programs Available

1. *Computer Assisted Algebra Program.* Region XIII Service Center, Austin, Texas. Algebra I and II software consisting of twenty-six tutorial programs covering a wide range of algebra concepts.

2. *Algebra Drill and Practice I and II.* CONDUIT. This package covers most of the topics included in an elementary algebra course, as well as some prealgebra topics.

3. The Micro Center. A variety of software packages dealing with such topics as graphing, number properties, exponents, problem solving, and factoring. Programs available for APPLE, PET, TRS-80, and Atari.

4. Gamco Industries, Inc. A variety of software packages dealing with such topics as solving equations (one and two variables), graphing, inequalities, and problem solving. Programs available for APPLE, PET, and TRS-80.

5. Opportunities for Learning, Inc. Selected algebra software dealing with such topics as graphing, solving equations, quadratic equations, simultaneous equations, and word problems. Programs available for APPLE, PET, Atari, and TRS-80.

6. MECC Software prepared by teachers. Includes most of the topics found in an elementary algebra course.

7. Various microcomputer journals such as: *Classroom Computer News, Educational Computing,* and *The Computing Teacher.*

Student Research Problems

The following problems would be appropriate for students who have some programming experience in BASIC.

1. *GREATEST COMMON FACTOR.* If *A* and *B* are two integers, any number that divided evenly into *A* and *B* is called a common divisor. The largest number that divides evenly into *A* and *B* is called the greatest common factor (*GCF*). For instance, the *GCF* of 12 and 18 is 6. Write a program so that I can put in any two numbers. The computer will then print out the *GCF* of the two numbers. (Chapter 2)

2. *LEAST COMMON DENOMINATOR.* The set of multiples of 12 is 12, 24, 36, 48, 60, etc. The set of multiples of 18 is 18, 36, 54, 72, 108, etc. The *LCD* of 18 and

12 is 36. Write a program so that I can put in any two numbers. The computer will then print out the *LCD* of the two numbers. (Chapter 2)

3. *NUMBER DIVISIBLE BY 14.* The numbers 126 and 294 are divisible by 14. Write a program that will print out all the numbers between 100 and 500 that are evenly divisible by 14. (Chapter 2)

4. *PRIME FACTORS.* The prime factors of $24 = 2^3$ times 3; 638 = 2 times 11 times 29; 1447 = prime number. Write a program that will print out the prime factors of any number between 1 and 100 which I will put in. (Chapter 2)

5. *SAVING MONEY.* Susan Thriftway opens a Savings Account. Each day she deposits twice the amount as on the previous day. She puts $1 in on the first day, $2 on the second day, $4 on the 3rd day, etc. Write a program to determine how much Susan invests on the 10th day. (Chapters 7 and 8)

6. *POWERS AND ROOTS.* Write a program to list the integers from 1 to 10, their squares, their cubes, and their square roots in a table of nicely spaced columns. Label the columns appropriately. (Chapter 2)

7. *MULTIPLYING BINOMIALS.* Write a program that will multiply 2 binomials ($Mx + P$) and ($Nx + T$) when given any values of *M, P, N,* and *T.* The result must be printed in the form $Ax^2 + Bx + C.$ (Chapter 5)

8. *QUADRATIC EQUATION.* Write a program that will print out the roots of any quadratic equation ($ax^2 + bx + c$), given the 3 coefficients. (Chapter 9)

$$x = \frac{-b \pm \sqrt{b^2 - 4ac}}{2a}$$

9. *NUMBERS DIVISIBLE BY 3.* Write a program to print out all numbers between 1 and 100 which are divisible by 3. (Chapters 2 and 8)

10. *SUM OF NUMBERS.* Write a program to print the sum of the numbers 1 through the number I will be putting in. For example, if I put in the number 5, the computer would print out the value of 1 + 2 + 3 + 4 + 5. (Chapters 2 and 8)

11. *SUM OF ODD INTEGERS.* Write a program to determine the sum of the odd integers less than 100. (Chapters 2 and 8)

12. *EQUATION OF A LINE.* Write a program to determine the equation of a line that passes through 2 points. I want to input the two points and have the computer print out the equation of the line. (Chapter 4)

13. *SQUARE ROOTS, CUBE ROOTS.* Use the expression $x \uparrow \left(\frac{1}{2}\right)$ to indicate square root and $x \uparrow \left(\frac{1}{3}\right)$ to indicate cube root. For the integers 1 through 15 print a table of the integer, its square root, and its cube root. (Chapters 2 and 6)

14. *PERFECT SQUARE.* I want to be able to put in a positive number (*N*) and the computer will give me the product of the number and the next 3 numbers up from that number. For instance, if I put in the number 5, I want the computer to give me the product of 5 × 6 × 7 × 8. (The product plus 1 will always be a perfect square.) (Chapters 2 and 6)

15. *MONEY.* I want to be able to put in the amount of money I have. I then want the computer to tell me the equivalent amount in dimes, nickels, and pennies. (Chapter 8)

16. *TRAVELING TORTOISE.* Moving along a straight path, a tortoise traveled 1 yard in 1 minute. In the next minute he moved $\frac{1}{2}$ yard. Similarly, in each succeeding minute he traveled half as far as he had in the preceding minute. If the tortoise could keep moving for 5 minutes at the same rate, how far would he travel? Put answer in inches. (Chapters 7 and 8)

17. *ADDING FRACTIONS.* Write a program which will print out the sum of $\frac{1}{2} + \frac{1}{3} + \frac{1}{4} \ldots + \frac{1}{100}$. (Chapters 2 and 8)

18. A dog is chasing a rabbit. The rabbit takes three jumps in the same length of time the dog takes two jumps, but each rabbit jump covers only $\frac{1}{2}$ of the distance of a dog jump. The rabbit was 13 rabbit jumps ahead of the dog when the dog first spotted the rabbit and started after it. If both go in a straight line, how many more jumps will the rabbit take before the dog catches it? (Chapters 7 and 8)

19. Find two rational fractions the sum of whose cubes is 6. (Chapters 6 and 8)

20. The equation $X^3 + Y^3 + Z^3 = 3$ has solutions (1,1,1) and (4,4,-5). Determine as many additional *integer* solutions as you can. (Chapters 4 and 8)

APPENDIX **E**

Feedback Form

Your comments about this book will be very helpful to us in planning other books in the *Guidebook for Teaching* Series and in making revisions in *A Guidebook for Teaching Algebra*. Please tear out the form that appears on the following page and use it to let us know your reactions to *A Guidebook for Teaching Algebra*. The authors promise a personal reply. Mail the form to:

Drs. Terry A. Goodman, et al.
c/o Longwood Division
Allyn & Bacon, Inc.
7 Wells Avenue
Newton, Massachusetts 02159

Your school: _____

Address: _____

City and state: _____

Date: _____

QA159 .G85 1984   c.1
                                         100107 000
A Guidebook for teaching algeb

3 9310 00066291 4
GOSHEN COLLEGE-GOOD LIBRARY

Drs. Terry A. Goodman, John Bernard,
Martin P. Cohen, and Joanne Meldon
c/o Longwood Division
Allyn and Bacon, Inc.
7 Wells Avenue
Newton, Massachusetts 02159

Dear Authors:

My name is _____ and I wanted to tell you what I thought
of your book *A Guidebook for Teaching Algebra*. I liked certain things about the book,
including:

I do, however, feel that the book could be improved in the following ways:

There were some other things I wish the book had included, such as:

Here is something that happened in my class when I used an idea from your book:

Sincerely yours,

_____